geog.SG

standard grade geography

<catherine hurst><anna king><john edwards><chris stevens>
<jack mayhew><ollie bray><malcolm mcdonald>

OXFORD
UNIVERSITY PRESS

OXFORD
UNIVERSITY PRESS

Great Clarendon Street, Oxford OX2 6DP

Oxford University Press is a department of the University of Oxford.
It furthers the University's objective of excellence in research,
scholarship, and education by publishing worldwide in

Oxford   New York

Auckland Cape Town Dar es Salaam Hong Kong Karachi
Kuala Lumpur Madrid Melbourne Mexico City Nairobi
New Delhi Shanghai Taipei Toronto

With offices in

Argentina Austria Brazil Chile Czech Republic France Greece
Guatemala Hungary Italy Japan Poland Portugal Singapore
South Korea Switzerland Thailand Turkey Ukraine Vietnam

Oxford is a registered trade mark of Oxford University Press
in the UK and in certain other countries

© Oxford University Press

Authors: Catherine Hurst, Anna King, John Edwards, Chris Stevens,
Jack Mayhew, Ollie Bray, Malcolm McDonald

The moral rights of the author have been asserted

Database right Oxford University Press (maker)

First published 2007

British Library Cataloguing in Publication Data

Data available

ISBN: 978-0-19-913472-4

10 9 8 7 6 5 4 3 2 1

We would like to thank our editorial advisors Ollie Bray and Malcolm
McDonald.

Printed in Singapore by KHL Printing Co. Pte Ltd.

Acknowledgements

The publisher and authors would like to thank the following for permission to use
photographs and other copyright material:

p6 Mick Rock/Cephas Picture Library/Alamy; p8br Corbis/Oxford University Press;
p9t Max Stuart/Alamy, p9b Geophotos; p10t Geoscience Features Picture Library,
p10b PA/Empics; p11l&r Mike Page; p14l Still Pictures, p14tr Mark Edwards/Still
Pictures, p14br www.aerialphotography.com/Air Images Limited; p16 Still Pictures;
p19 John Farmar/Ecoscene; p21t www.aerialphotography.com/Air Images Limited,
p21b M-Sat Ltd/Science Photo Library; p22 Bridget Clyde/Stockshots/Alamy; p24 Bill
Varie/Corbis UK Ltd.; p28 Stone/Getty Images; p29t Stone/Getty Images, p29b
Geophotos; p31r John Cleare Mountain Camera; p33 Patrick Ward/Corbis UK Ltd.;
p34 Colin McPherson/Scottish Viewpoint; p35t Balliefurth Farm/Alastair MacLennan,
p35b Doug Houghton/Alamy; p36 P. Tomkins/VisitScotland/Scottish Viewpoint; p37
William McKelvie/Eye Ubiquitous/Corbis UK Ltd.; p38 Ruaridh Pringle/Scottish
Viewpoint; p39l David Gowans/Alamy, p39r Roger Antrobus/Corbis UK Ltd.; p40
Jason Politte/Alamy; p45c nagelestock.com/Alamy, p45b Ace Stock Limited/Alamy;
p46 Jeff Morgan/Alamy; p52 Anthony John West/Corbis UK Ltd.; p53t Phil
Noble/PA/Empics; p53b Ashley Cooper/Corbis UK Ltd.; p54 Bios Klein & Hubert/Still
Pictures; p59 David L. Moore/Alamy; p60l Owen Franken/Corbis UK Ltd., p60c Eitan
Simanor/Alamy, p60r Peter Adams Photography/Alamy; p61t Peter Adams
Photography/Alamy, p61b Buzz Pictures/Alamy; p62 Voltchev/UNEP/Still Pictures;
p63 A. Mountain/www.tropix.co.uk; p64 UNEP/Still Pictures; p65 Nikolas
Giakoumidis/AP/Empics; p66l&r Paisajes Españoles; p67 Panda Photo/Frank Lane
Picture Agency; p68 Bryan & Cherry Alexander; p69t Geophotos, p69c Kennan
Ward/Corbis UK Ltd., p69b Charles Mauzy/Corbis UK Ltd.; p70 John Gaps
III/AP/Empics; p71 Danny Lehman/Corbis UK Ltd.; p73t Mark Edwards/Still Pictures,
p73b Michael J. Doolittle/Still Pictures; p74 Peter Arnold/Still Pictures; p75 Sue
Cunningham/Worldwide Picture Library/Alamy; p76 Tim Davis/Corbis UK Ltd.; p80
Neil Rabinowitz/Corbis UK Ltd.; p82tl Michael S. Yamashita/Corbis UK Ltd., p82cl
Sergio Pitamitz/Corbis UK Ltd., p82bl E. Streichan/zefa/Corbis UK Ltd., p82tr
Aerofilms/Alamy, p82cr Sandro Vannini/Corbis UK Ltd., p82br The Travel Library/Rex

Features; p83t&b Mary Evans Picture Library, p83c Historical Picture Archive/Corbis
UK Ltd.; p84tc Richard T. Nowitz/Corbis UK Ltd., p84bc Awad Awad/AFP/Getty
Images, p84t Hanan Isachar/Corbis UK Ltd., p84b David Levenson/Getty Images; p88
Corbis UK Ltd.; p89 G. Boutin/zefa/Corbis UK Ltd.; p90tl Joe Pepler/Rex Features,
p90bl Powered by Light/Alan Spencer/Alamy, p90bc Alex Segre/Alamy, p90tr Scottish
Viewpoint, p90br Martin Bond/Photofusion Picture Library/Alamy; p91 The
Photolibrary Wales/Alamy; p93 Jason Hawkes/Corbis UK Ltd.; p94 Jonathan
Hordle/Rex Features; p95t&b Brindleyplace; p96 Duncan Hale-Sutton/Alamy; p97 tie
limited; p98t Skyscan Photolibrary/Alamy, p98b Christa Stadtler/Photofusion Picture
Library/Alamy; p99l&r Martin Bond/Photofusion Picture Library/Alamy; p100 Paul Zanre
Photography/Edinburgh Park/New Edinburgh Limited; p101t The Royal Bank of
Scotland Group, p101b Skyscan Photolibrary/Alamy; p102 Photonica/Getty Images;
p104l James Russell Cant/Sygma/Corbis UK Ltd., p104r Nigel Cattlin/Holt Studios
International Ltd/Alamy; p106t Ashley Cooper/Corbis UK Ltd., p106b Wayne
Hutchinson/Holt Studios International/Frank Lane Picture Agency; p107bl Holt Studios
International/Frank Lane Picture Agency, p107br geogphotos/Alamy, p107t Peter
Dean/Agripicture Images/Alamy; p108 www.face-online.org.uk/Farming And
Countryside Education; p109t Des Topping/Herdship Farm, p109b Nigel Cattlin/Holt
Studios International Ltd/Alamy; p112t Tesco Stores Limited, p112b Holt Studios
International/Frank Lane Picture Agency; p113l Justin Kase/Alamy, p113r Nigel
Cattlin/Holt Studios International Ltd/Alamy; p114t Herdship Farm, p114b Holt
Studios International/Frank Lane Picture Agency; p115 RSPCA Freedom Food; p116t
Patrick Ward/Corbis UK Ltd., p116b Adam Woolfitt/Corbis UK Ltd.; p117t Peter
Cairns/Worldwide Picture Library/Alamy, p117b Tyrrells Potato Chips Ltd; p118
Mark Edwards/Still Pictures; p120tl Marcel Mochet/AFP/Getty Images, p120bl Pictor
International/ImageState/Alamy, p120tr Kin Cheung/Reuters/Corbis UK Ltd., p120br
Bill Varie/Corbis UK Ltd.; p121l Armando Dadi/Rex Features, p121c Yun Suk-
bong/Reuters/Corbis UK Ltd., p121r Toyota (GB) PLC; p122 Toyota (GB) PLC; p124t
David Levenson/Alamy, p124b Jeff Morgan/Alamy; p125t Roberta
Osborne/iStockphoto, p125b Ted Spiegel/Corbis UK Ltd.; p126 Getty Images; p129
Robert Brook/Photofusion Picture Library/Alamy; p130 The Photolibrary
Wales/Alamy; p131 platz.eins - sport incentives; p132 Malcolm McDonald/Oxford
University Press; p133t Craig A. Hunter/Ecosse Regeneration Limited, p133b Alan
Doherty/Oxford University Press; p134 Stone/Getty Images; p137l Bill Ross/Corbis
UK Ltd., p137r David Keith Jones/Images of Africa Photobank/Alamy; p144t Konrad
Zelazowski/Alamy, p144b PA Photos/Empics; p148t Scott Nelson/Getty Images,
p148b Guillaume Bonn/Corbis UK Ltd.; p149t Marco Longari/AFP/Getty Images,
p149b Scott Nelson/Getty Images; p150 George Osodi/AP/Empics; p151 Horizon
International Images Limited/Alamy; p152 Brian A. Vikander/Corbis UK Ltd.; p153
Don Mason/Corbis UK Ltd.; p155 Mark Pearson/Alamy; p156
picturescolourlibrary.com/Alamy; p157 Kapoor Baldev/Sygma/Corbis UK Ltd.; p158
Dan White/Alamy; p160l Roberta Osborne/iStockphoto, p160r Kamal
Kishore/Reuters/Corbis UK Ltd.; p164t Nick Haslam/Alamy, p164b Ron Giling/Still
Pictures; p165 Jlp/Jose L. Pelaez/Corbis UK Ltd.; p166 Evan Schneider/United
Nations/AP/Empics; p168 Josef Hinterleitner/UNEP/Still Pictures; p171 Jorgen
Schytte/Still Pictures; p172l Charles O'Rear/Corbis UK Ltd., p172r China
Features/Sygma/Corbis UK Ltd.; p175t Steve Bent/Rex Features, p175b Sean
Adair/Reuters/Corbis UK Ltd.; p176 Don Mason/Corbis UK Ltd.; p178 Charlotte
Thege/Das Fotoarchiv/Still Pictures; p182 Danny Lehman/Corbis UK Ltd.; p183t Pat
Roque/AP/Empics, p183b www.fairtrade.org.uk/The Fairtrade Foundation; p184 Sipa
Press/Rex Features; p185l Keren Su/Corbis UK Ltd., p185r Kin Cheung/Reuters/Corbis
UK Ltd.; p186 Raveendran/AFP/Getty Images; p187 Dibyangshu Sarkar/AFP/Getty
Images; p188l Finbarr O'Reilly/Reuters/Corbis UK Ltd., p188r Maria R.
Campbell/UNEP/Still Pictures; p189 Ton Koene/Still Pictures; p190t Ron Gilling/Still
Pictures, p190b Isobel Perry/www.presentaid.org/Christian Aid Photo Library; p191t
Jim Young/Reuters/Corbis UK Ltd., p191b Radu Sigheti/Reuters/Corbis UK Ltd.; p192
flickr.com/Jos Verhoogen; p193t Practical Action, p193b Penny Tweedie/Alamy; p194
Guillen Photography/Alamy.

Illustrations are by:

Barking Dog: p 43b; Stefan Chabluk: p 20; Ordnance Survey Crown Copyright:
pp16, 17, 18, 19, 20, 32, 85; Q2A India: pp10,12b, 14t, 16, 18,19, 26t, 31, 34, 36, 42,
46, 47, 49br, 50, 51, 56, 60, 61, 62, 63, 64, 65, 67, 68, 70, 72, 73, 76, 77, 79, 90, 91,
92, 95, 96, 98, 100, 107, 108, 109, 110, 111,122, 123, 124, 125, 127, 128, 129, 130,
132, 138, 140, 141, 143, 146, 147, 148, 151r, 154, 156, 163, 165, 168, 169, 170, 174,
178, 179, 180, 181, 182, 184, 186:

Other illustrations © Oxford University Press.

On planet Earth

 nearly 70% of the surface is covered by saltwater

 about 33% is covered by the Pacific Ocean

 roughly 10% of the land is covered by glacial ice

 around 20% is covered by deserts

 and about 25% is mountainous.

It's the third planet from the Sun,
and it's home to over 6.5 billion people.

Contents

The physical environment

The human environment

The big picture

This chapter is about processes, rivers and the landscapes they create. These are the big ideas behind the chapter:

◆ There are lots of different processes which affect the landscape.

◆ The processes and changes affecting the landscape are connected.

◆ The drainage basin cycle is part of the water cycle.

◆ Rivers have energy which means they can erode and transport material. When a river doesn't have enough energy to transport its load it deposits it.

◆ A river changes from source to mouth. You'll find different landforms in the upper, middle and lower courses of a river.

Your goals for this chapter

By the end of this chapter you should be able to answer these questions:

◆ Name three processes which affect the landscape.

◆ Give an example of mass movement, and describe how the process works.

◆ How are the processes affecting the landscape connected?

◆ Can you draw and label a simple diagram of the water cycle?

◆ How does a river change from its source to its mouth?

◆ Name four ways rivers erode, and four ways they transport their load.

◆ How are these formed?
V-shaped valley, interlocking spurs, waterfalls, meanders, oxbow lake, floodplains, levées, estuaries, deltas

◆ Which river landforms can you recognise on OS maps?

◆ What do these terms mean?
source, mouth, river channel, tributaries, distributaries, watershed, drainage basin, floodplain, interception, surface run-off, infiltration, through-flow, percolation, groundwater flow

And then . . .

When you finish the chapter, come back here and see if you've met your goals!

Did you know?
The world's longest river is the Nile. It's 6670 km long.

Did you know?
The UK's longest river is the Severn. It's 354 km long.

Did you know?
Less than 1% of the world's water is in rivers. But rivers have helped shape our landscape.

Did you know?
◆ The River Amazon is the world's largest river – it carries the most water.
◆ Its mouth is over 400 km wide.

Your chapter starter

Look at the photo on page 6. It shows the Grand Canyon of the Verdon River, in France. It is Europe's widest and deepest gorge.
Is this near the river's source or mouth?
Where has the river come from? Where is it going?
How would you describe this landscape?
What processes are affecting this landscape?

Anyone seen my raft?

Landscapes and processes – introduction

In this unit you'll learn about different types of rock and weathering.

What are landscapes and processes?

Land – it's all around us. Some of it is natural, some of it's been built on and altered. The natural bit – unchanged by people – is the **physical landscape**. Land which has been changed by people makes up the **human landscape**.

There's lots of different **processes** (things going on) which affect the landscape. Things like weathering, erosion and so on. The processes affect the rock that the landscape is made up of.

> It's sedimentary my dear Watson.

Rock types

There are lots of different types of rocks. But they can be fitted into just three categories. These are **sedimentary, igneous, and metamorphic**.

Did you know?
Fossils of plants and animals can be found in some sedimentary rocks.

Sedimentary rocks are formed from things (sediments) that have fallen to the bottom of a lake or sea. These sediments could be sand, shells, or even skeletons! Limestone, chalk, clay and sandstone are examples of sedimentary rocks.

Metamorphic rocks have been heated or squashed (put under pressure) until they have changed to make a new type of rock. These rocks are usually very hard and don't get eroded or weathered very much.

Schists (in the photo) are formed from basalt (an igneous rock) or shale (a sedimentary rock) that has been pressurised. Marble is made from limestone that has been subjected to moderate heat and pressure.

Igneous rocks have come from magma – that's molten rock from under the Earth's crust. Igneous rocks are either from lava that erupted from a volcano (like basalt), or from magma that cooled inside the earth (like **granite** in the photo).

Rocks and weathering

Weathering is the process in which rocks are broken up into smaller pieces. It happens when they are exposed on the Earth's surface. Weathering happens *in situ* – that means it happens just where the rock is. There are three main kinds of weathering (and they can all happen at once – but *very slowly*).

▼ *Scree running on Cuillin Ridge in the Isle of Skye.*

1 Physical

Rocks break up because of stress.

◆ Rainwater trickles into joints or cracks in the rock. If the temperature drops below 0 °C the water freezes and expands, and the joints get wider. Eventually pieces of rock break off. This is called **freeze-thaw,** or **frost-shattering**. All the broken bits of rock form scree.

◆ In warm climates the outside layers of rock heat up in the day and expand. At night they cool down and contract. This makes the outside layers peel off, like an onion. So this is called **onion weathering**, or **exfoliation**.

2 Chemical

Rocks react with water and air. Chemical changes in the rocks make them rot.

◆ Limestone solution is an example of chemical weathering. Carbonic acid in rainwater reacts with rocks containing calcium carbonate – like limestone (the rock on the right is limestone). The limestone slowly dissolves and is removed by running water.

3 Biological

This happens when tree roots grow into cracks in a rock and widen them (see the photo on the right). Eventually bits of rock break off.

Activities

1 Make a large copy of the mind map on the right in your book. Add extra legs to complete it for all the information on rock types in this unit.
2 Make a table with these headings: Type of weathering, Example, What happens. Complete it using the information on this page.

Examples   How formed

Sedimentary

Rock types   Metamorphic

Mass movement and systems

In this unit you'll find out how the processes affecting the landscape are connected.

What is mass movement?

It's when all those weathered, broken up bits of rock move downhill. Why? Because of gravity. Mass movement happens all the time. It can be really, really slow – like soil creep. Or really fast – like mudflows and landslides.

Soil creep is so slow that it can be less than 1 cm in a whole year. It's just what it says – soil creeping downhill, usually on very gentle slopes. It causes terracettes (tiny terraces, like those pictured on the right), as well as making trees bend over, soil pile up behind walls and making fences break.

Mudflows and **landslides** happen much faster than soil creep. They often happen with no warning. Lots of heavy rain can make the top layers of soil and rock saturated. On steep slopes gravity makes the saturated material move downhill.

Mudflows and landslides can also happen as a result of earthquakes and volcanic eruptions.

It's all one big cycle

The processes and changes which affect the landscape are connected. They are all part of a cycle.

▲ Landslides blocked the A85 near Stirling following heavy rain in August 2004. Rescue helicopters had to airlift 57 people to safety.

Rocks form.

Some of the weathered materials **erode** (wear away) land. Some are **deposited** (dropped). Eventually they might be turned into new rocks.

When rocks are exposed on the Earth's surface they start to **weather** and break up into smaller bits.

Weathered rock moves because of **mass movement**.

Weathered material might be **transported** by rivers and glaciers.

Did you know?
In 1966 heavy rain caused a coal tip to slide onto a school in Aberfan in Wales. 116 children and 28 adults died.

Did you know?
Climate change is likely to mean we'll get more frequent, intense rainfall. And that means more landslides.

In one end . . . out the other

In geography we say that landscapes are part of a **system.** This is a technical way of saying there are:

◆ **Inputs** – things that go into the system
◆ **Outputs** – things that come out of the system
◆ **Processes** – things that happen in the middle

This diagram might help to explain it a bit better.

Inputs
- Weather conditions – how hot, cold or wet it is.
- The action of a glacier, a river or the sea.
- Volcanic activity.
- Gravity.
These inputs can shape the rocks and soil, and so the landscape.

→

Processes
- Weather conditions cause the rocks to break up.
- Lava from volcanic eruptions, mudflows, etc. create new land.
- Gravity causes mass movement (it can be fast or very slow).
- Glaciers, rivers and the sea erode, transport and deposit material. These all affect the landscape.

→

Outputs
- A changed landscape.

More about rivers, glaciers, erosion, transport and deposition later!

Landscapes are changing all the time. These photos show how one bit of the coast at Happisburgh in Norfolk (pronounce it *Haisbro*) changed in just a short space of time, because of the process of erosion. And it is *still* changing.

▲ *Happisburgh in 1996.*

▲ *Happisburgh in 2004. Homes disappear into the sea at a rate of about one a year.*

Activities

1 Describe how soil creep, mudflows and landslides happen.
2 Choose two of the inputs in the diagram above. Explain how you think they could shape the landscape.
3 The photos of Happisburgh show a changing coastal landscape. Find out about another type of landscape which has changed and describe what has happened.

Water and drainage basins

This unit is about the water cycle and how water ends up in the sea.

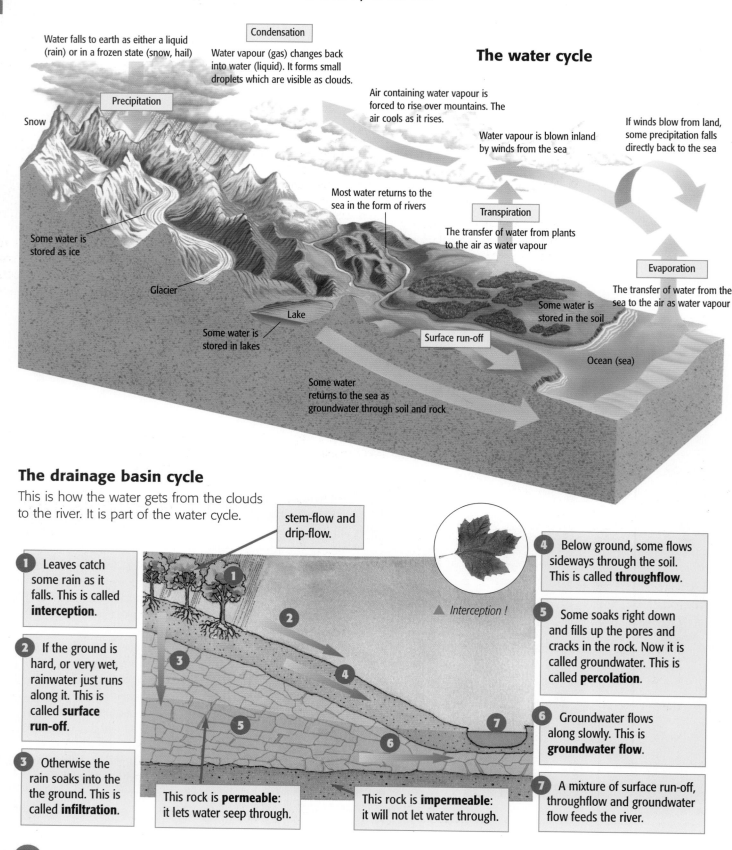

The water cycle

Water falls to earth as either a liquid (rain) or in a frozen state (snow, hail)

Condensation
Water vapour (gas) changes back into water (liquid). It forms small droplets which are visible as clouds.

Precipitation

Snow

Air containing water vapour is forced to rise over mountains. The air cools as it rises.

Water vapour is blown inland by winds from the sea

If winds blow from land, some precipitation falls directly back to the sea

Most water returns to the sea in the form of rivers

Transpiration
The transfer of water from plants to the air as water vapour

Some water is stored as ice

Glacier

Lake

Some water is stored in lakes

Surface run-off

Some water is stored in the soil

Evaporation
The transfer of water from the sea to the air as water vapour

Ocean (sea)

Some water returns to the sea as groundwater through soil and rock

The drainage basin cycle

This is how the water gets from the clouds to the river. It is part of the water cycle.

stem-flow and drip-flow.

1 Leaves catch some rain as it falls. This is called **interception**.

2 If the ground is hard, or very wet, rainwater just runs along it. This is called **surface run-off**.

3 Otherwise the rain soaks into the the ground. This is called **infiltration**.

▲ Interception !

This rock is **permeable**: it lets water seep through.

This rock is **impermeable**: it will not let water through.

4 Below ground, some flows sideways through the soil. This is called **throughflow**.

5 Some soaks right down and fills up the pores and cracks in the rock. Now it is called groundwater. This is called **percolation**.

6 Groundwater flows along slowly. This is **groundwater flow**.

7 A mixture of surface run-off, throughflow and groundwater flow feeds the river.

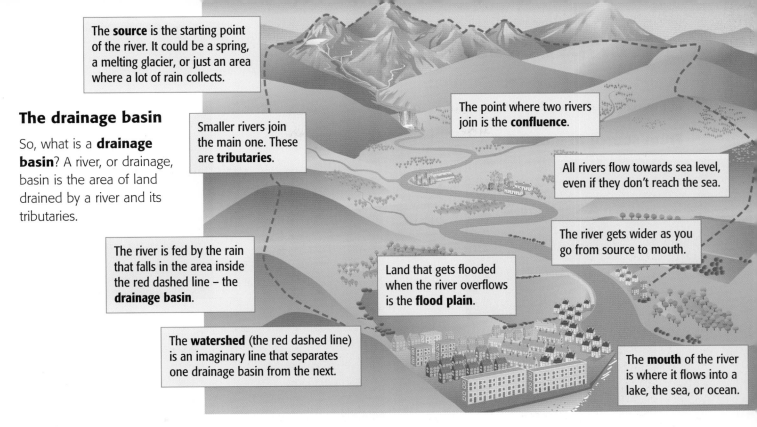

The **source** is the starting point of the river. It could be a spring, a melting glacier, or just an area where a lot of rain collects.

The point where two rivers join is the **confluence**.

Smaller rivers join the main one. These are **tributaries**.

All rivers flow towards sea level, even if they don't reach the sea.

The drainage basin

So, what is a **drainage basin**? A river, or drainage, basin is the area of land drained by a river and its tributaries.

The river is fed by the rain that falls in the area inside the red dashed line – the **drainage basin**.

The river gets wider as you go from source to mouth.

Land that gets flooded when the river overflows is the **flood plain**.

The **watershed** (the red dashed line) is an imaginary line that separates one drainage basin from the next.

The **mouth** of the river is where it flows into a lake, the sea, or ocean.

The river's long profile

This diagram shows a river's long profile – a slice along its length. The slope of the river gets flatter, and the bed gets smoother as you go downstream.

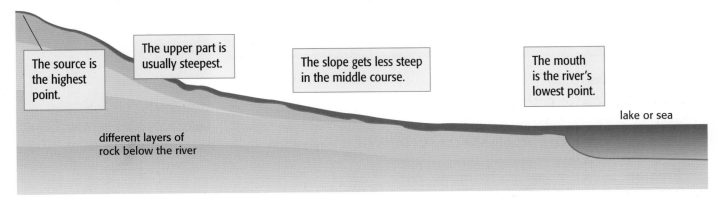

The source is the highest point.

The upper part is usually steepest.

The slope gets less steep in the middle course.

The mouth is the river's lowest point.

lake or sea

different layers of rock below the river

Activities

1 Copy the simplified diagram of the water cycle on the right and complete it using these labels.

| transpiration | precipitation | surface run-off |
| evaporation | groundwater | condensation |

2 Make and label your own simplified diagram of the drainage basin cycle.
3 What is the difference between:
   a source and mouth
   b watershed and drainage basin
   c tributary and confluence?

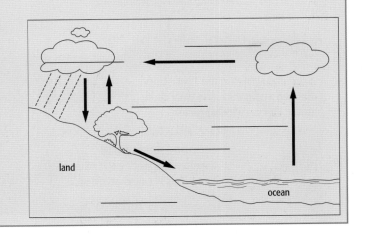

land

ocean

River processes

In this unit you'll learn the basics about rivers and what they do.

From source to mouth

The river near the source:
- narrow
- shallow
- slow-flowing (because of friction)
- has large bedload

The river in the middle:
- wider
- deeper
- faster flowing
- has smaller material in it

The river near the mouth:
- wide
- deep
- fast-flowing
- has mainly suspended load

North Pennines

River Tees

Hartlepool

Newton Aycliffe

Stockton

Redcar

Barnard Castle

Darlington

Middlesbrough

Yarm

Scotch Corner

N

What do rivers do?

Rivers have energy. That means they can do work. The work they do is **erosion** and **transportation**. When they run out of energy they have to stop doing work, so they drop what they're carrying. That's called **deposition**.

Erosion

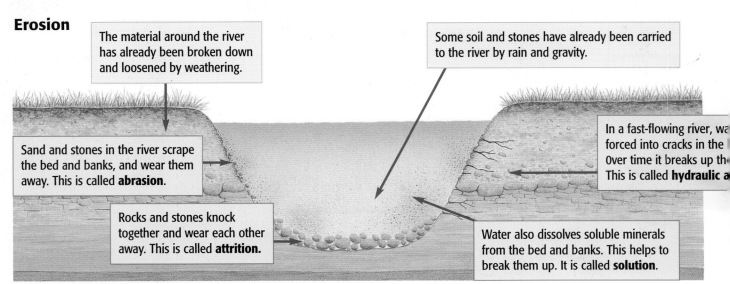

The material around the river has already been broken down and loosened by weathering.

Some soil and stones have already been carried to the river by rain and gravity.

Sand and stones in the river scrape the bed and banks, and wear them away. This is called **abrasion**.

In a fast-flowing river, wa... forced into cracks in the ... Over time it breaks up th... This is called **hydraulic a...**

Rocks and stones knock together and wear each other away. This is called **attrition**.

Water also dissolves soluble minerals from the bed and banks. This helps to break them up. It is called **solution**.

The more energy it has, the faster a river can erode.

Transportation

The material a river carries is called its **load**.

The more energy it has, the larger the load a river can carry.

Heavier material is carried along the bottom. It is called the **bedload**.

Sand grains and small stones just bounce along. This is called **saltation**.

Dissolved material is carried along as a solution. You cannot see it.

Larger stones and rocks get rolled along. This is called **traction**.

Small particles of rock and soil are carried along as a **suspension**. They make the water look cloudy or muddy.

Deposition

The deposited material is called **sediment**.

But dissolved material stays in the water and is carried out into the lake or sea.

As the river slows down, it deposits the largest stones and pebbles first, then smaller ones, and finally, the smallest particles.

The less energy it has, the more material a river deposits.

Activities

1 Make a larger copy of this table. Use the map and photo boxes to complete it.

part of the river	description	velocity	width	depth	particle size
upper					
middle					
lower					

2 Use this writing frame to write about the work that rivers do.

Rivers have energy so …
When a river has lots of energy it can erode. Ways it can do this are:
◆ hydraulic action: this means …
◆ …
Rivers can transport the material they have eroded as long as they have enough energy. Material can be carried by …
If a river doesn't have enough energy it drops (deposits) its load …

3 Copy this sentence, but only include the correct word from the brackets.

Rivers have high energy when they are flowing (fast / slowly), or when there is (a lot / a little) water in them.

4 a What is erosion?
   b How do rivers erode?

The river's upper course

In this unit you'll learn about the river near its source. Again we're using the River Tees as our case study.

Near the beginning . . .

Near its source the river is in a steep V-shaped valley. The OS map shows part of the upper course of the River Tees. Rivers in their upper course have some typical features you should look out for.

The river channel

Near its source the river flows quite slowly, because there's lots of friction with the **large bedload** it's carrying. The bedload is large because there hasn't been enough time for attrition to make the particles smaller. The channel cross-section (a slice through the river channel) looks like this.

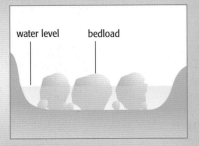

water level   bedload

V-shaped valley

Rivers near their source are a long way above sea level. This means they have a high gravitational potential energy. So they erode mainly downwards (vertically). That makes the steep valley sides. The slopes can't stay vertical because that's not stable, so the soil and rock on the slopes slide down – and that makes the V-shape.

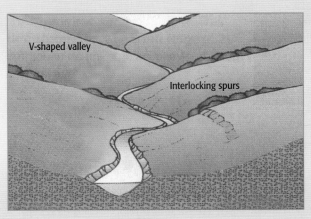

V-shaped valley

Interlocking spurs

Interlocking spurs

These are alternate hills that stick out like the teeth of a zip in the river's path. The river in the upper course doesn't have enough energy to erode the spurs, so it has to flow around them.

Waterfalls

Some rivers have waterfalls in the upper course. High Force on the River Tees (pictured on the right) is a famous one. At over 23 metres high, it's the highest waterfall in the UK!

How waterfalls are formed

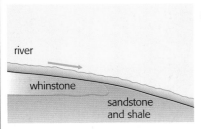

river

whinstone

sandstone and shale

1 Waterfalls happen when the river crosses a band of harder rock. In the Tees valley the hard rock is whinstone.

3 The erosion of the softer rock continues and undercuts the hard rock. The hollow at the bottom is called the plunge pool. It's full of bits of rock from above so there's lots of abrasion here. The force of the falling water means lots of hydraulic action too.

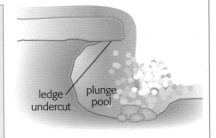

ledge undercut

plunge pool

whinstone

sandstone and shale

2 The softer rock gets eroded more quickly by abrasion and hydraulic action. This makes a ledge.

4 Eventually the ledge (overhang) collapses. The process keeps going and the waterfall moves backwards. In front of it, it leaves a steep-sided gorge.

Did you know?
The Angel Falls in Venezuela have a total drop of 979 metres – it's the highest waterfall in the world.

Did you know?
Niagara Falls attract about 14 million tourists every year – 50 000 of them honeymooners!

Did you know?
Khone Falls stretch 10.8 km (6.7 miles) across the Mekong River, between Laos and Cambodia – it's the world's widest waterfall.

Activities

1 Use the OS map to make a cross-section along AB of the Upper Tees valley. Add annotations (explaining labels) to explain about the V-shaped valley. This enlargement of part of the OS map will be clearer for making your cross-section.

2 What are interlocking spurs?

3 Make a flow diagram to explain how High Force developed. Remember to include diagrams of each stage too!

4 a Draw a sketch diagram of High Force from the photograph opposite. Label the plunge pool, gorge, and name the two rock types.

 b Choose the correct words from the box to complete this paragraph:

Waterfalls are formed where a river flows over a band of hard rock next to a softer rock. The softer rock is eroded by _____ and abrasion. The power of the water creates a deep _____ below the waterfall and undercuts the softer rock until the overhang eventually collapses. This causes the waterfall to _____ upstream, forming a gorge.

| plunge pool | advance | hydraulic action | retreat | traction | meander |

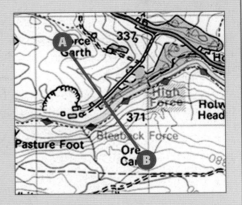

The river's middle course

In this unit you'll learn about the middle course of the river. Again we're using the River Tees as our case study.

What's happening here?

In the middle course, rivers aren't as high above sea level as they are in the upper course. So they erode sideways (laterally) as well as vertically. This means they are wider and deeper than upstream.

There's more water because tributaries have joined, and because more water has arrived from throughflow and surface run-off. The river **meanders** (twists) from side to side as it erodes laterally.

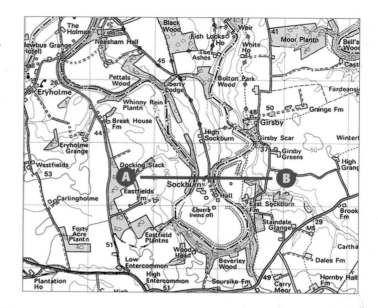

Meanders

It all starts when there is variation in the velocity across the river channel. This means more erosion on one side and more deposition on the other. This, in turn, means that the flow downstream is affected and the faster water (called the **thalweg**) swings to the other side.

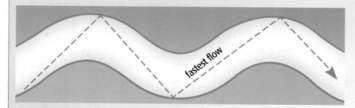

fastest flow

On the side where the fast water is, there is more erosion. This makes the river deeper and cuts into the bank, to make a **river cliff**. On the other side, where the slower water is, there is deposition. This makes a shallower area of sediment called a **point bar**. The gentle slope down to the point bar is called the **slip-off slope**.

The cross-section of the meander looks like this:

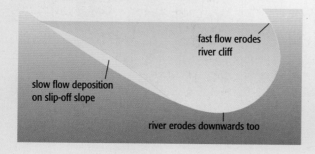

fast flow erodes river cliff

slow flow deposition on slip-off slope

river erodes downwards too

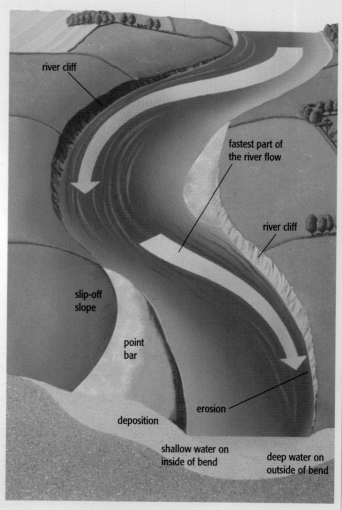

river cliff

fastest part of the river flow

river cliff

slip-off slope

point bar

deposition

erosion

shallow water on inside of bend

deep water on outside of bend

Oxbow lakes

This is how oxbow lakes form.

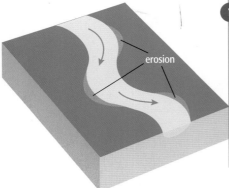

1 The faster water erodes the outside of the bends and there is deposition on the inside. This makes the meanders get more sinuous (wiggly!). This is called meander migration. Sometimes the scars of old meander bends can be seen next to the river.

2 The meander bend gets tighter. A really tight meander is called a **swan's neck meander**.

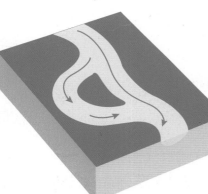

3 When there's a lot of discharge (in a flood or after a storm) the river has more energy, so it erodes a new channel straight across the neck of the meander. It erodes it by hydraulic action and abrasion.

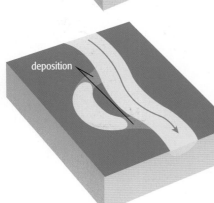

4 The river now uses the new channel because it's easier, even when the water level goes down. The old channel becomes an **oxbow lake** when deposition seals its two ends to separate it from the river. Eventually it gets filled in with debris and soil and might have trees in it.

oxbow lake

swan's neck meander

Activities

1 Use the OS map to make a cross-section along AB of the Middle Tees valley. Add annotations (explaining labels) to explain about the meander.

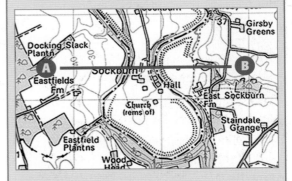

2 **a** Make a sketch map of the meander loop in the map extract.

   b Then make another for the future course of the river that you expect. Add annotations (explaining labels) to say why it will change.

3 **a** Draw a cross-section of the river channel at a meander. Label the river cliff, point bar and slip-off slope.

   b The river is eroding at the river cliff. Explain how.

The river's lower course

In this unit you'll learn about the lower course of the river. We're still using the River Tees.

Towards the end

The lower course of the river is the flattest part. Here the river flows in a deep, wide channel. It flows fast because there is much less friction. The load it carries is small, and it carries it by suspension and solution.

The sea comes up the river at the mouth. At low tide the edges are exposed. That leaves **mudflats** at the sides of the river.

The land here is mainly used for industry, like docks and factories that need to import or export heavy goods by sea.

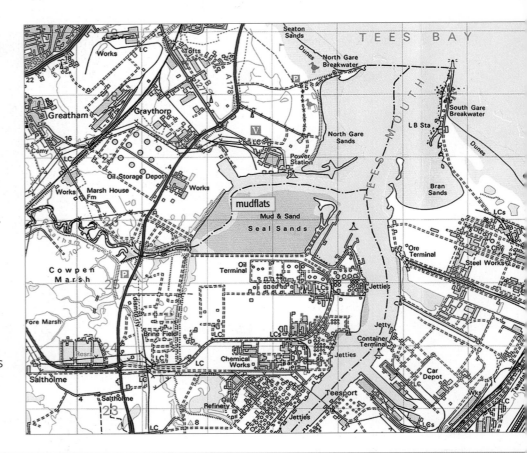

The floodplain

This is the land on either side of the river in the lower course. It is the land that gets flooded — so that's why it's called the floodplain! The floodplain is very fertile for crops because, when the river floods, it leaves behind fine silt called **alluvium**.

Many thousands of years ago, the sea level was higher. That meant rivers didn't have to cut down so far to reach the sea. Then the sea level dropped, and so the river had to cut down further to reach it. This has left **terraces** in the floodplain.

When the river floods, it deposits some of its load. The biggest stuff gets dropped first. It eventually builds up to leave mounds at the sides of the channel. They're called **levées**.

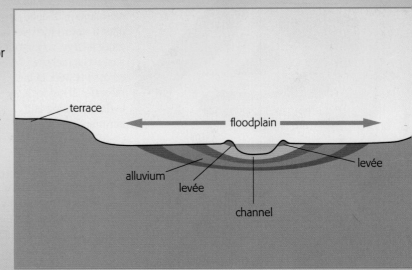

River mouths

Some rivers have estuaries, some rivers have deltas, and some rivers just have a narrow mouth. It all depends on the local rock type, the amount of load the river is carrying, and the strength of the sea.

Estuaries

The River Tees has an estuary. This is a wide, deep mouth. Estuaries are really useful for shipping, so they usually have ports and factories along them.

The Tees estuary. ▶

Deltas

A delta happens when the river has lots of load. When it reaches the sea the water flow slows down, so it drops its load. If the waves or currents aren't too strong and the land doesn't slope too steeply, the load builds up to make a delta. The sediment blocks the river so it has to divide up into lots of different channels called **distributaries**. Deltas can be different shapes, but the two main types are **bird's foot** deltas like the Mississippi delta and **arcuate** deltas like the Nile delta.

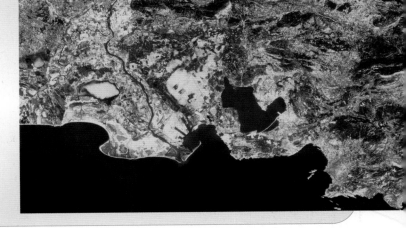

The Rhône delta from space. ▶

Activities

1 Use the words from the box to complete this paragraph. (Hint: use the map to help you.)

| mudflats | fast | small | flat |
| industry | marshland | deep | |

The lower course of the River Tees is _____. There is a lot of _____ along it. There is also _____ on the northern bank. Here the river flows in a _____, wide channel. It flows _____ because there is much less friction. The load it carries is _____, and it carries it by suspension and solution. The sea comes up the river at the mouth. At low tide the edges are exposed. That leaves _____ at the sides of the river.

2 a What is a floodplain?
  b What is alluvium? How does it get there? What is it useful for?
  c How are terraces formed?
  d What are leveés? How are they formed?
  e Now make a diagram of a floodplain and label the channel, alluvium, levées, and terrace.

3 a Make a sketch map of the Tees estuary, using the OS map or the photo.
  b Add a suitable title
  c Add labels to show the industry, the flat land, and the wide mouth.

4 Make a sketch map of the delta photo. Give it a title so you know which delta it is. Write annotations (explaining labels) to say what has happened to make the delta.

5 What do you think would happen to the delta if:
  a sea level went up? Why?
  b a dam was built further up the river? Why?

Glacial landscapes

The big picture

This chapter is about glaciers and the landscapes they create. These are the big ideas behind the chapter:

◆ Glaciers are like rivers, except they're made of ice and they flow very slowly.

◆ Glaciers erode, transport and deposit material.

◆ Glaciers create lots of different landforms by erosion and deposition.

◆ You can recognise glacial landforms on maps.

◆ There are many competing demands for the use of upland landscapes.

◆ Tourism can create problems which need to be managed.

Your goals for this chapter

By the end of this chapter you should be able to answer these questions:

◆ What is a glacier? Where do you find them? How do they change the landscape?

◆ How are these formed?
corries, arêtes, pyramidal peaks, glacial troughs, truncated spurs, hanging valleys, drumlins, eskers, kames

◆ Name four landforms created by glacial deposition.

◆ What do these terms mean?
melt-water, crevasse, plucking, abrasion, striation, moraine, freeze-thaw weathering, U-shaped valley, misfit stream, till

◆ Which glacial landforms can you recognise on an OS map?

◆ How is the landscape used in the Cairngorms?

◆ How important is tourism in the Cairngorms? Give some facts and figures.

◆ What conflicts does tourism cause?

◆ Give some examples of solutions to the problems that tourists cause. At least six, and nine if you can.

◆ Why was the Cairngorm Mountain Funicular Railway built? And why is it still causing conflict?

And then . . .

When you finish the chapter, come back here and see if you've met your goals!

Did you know?
◆ The last ice age ended about 10 000 years ago.
◆ Most of Britain was covered by ice, and much of our landscape is the result of ice erosion and deposition.

Did you know?
◆ Today, glacial ice covers about 10% of the Earth's land surface.
◆ During the last ice age, it probably covered about 30%.

Did you know?
◆ A glaciation or ice age is when massive amounts of ice spread over the Earth.
◆ We are currently in what's called an inter-glacial – a non-ice age.

Did you know?
The most severe ice age in the history of the Earth occurred 800 million years ago, when glaciers got close to the equator.

Your chapter starter
Look at the photo on page 22.
What is it? What's it made of?
Where could it be? Have you ever seen anything like this?
What could the person (or their dog) be thinking?
What's the link between glaciers and global warming?

That's a long way for his little legs.

Introducing glaciers

In this unit you'll learn what glaciers are, where they're found, and how they shape the landscape.

What is a glacier?

A glacier is like a river – only it's made of ice and it flows much, much more slowly. A glacier is made when lots of snow gets squashed into ice and then slides downhill. The ice goes down the easiest route, so it follows old river valleys down from the mountains.

Glaciers are really big so they make massive impacts on the landscape.

▲ The Russell glacier, Alaska.

Where are glaciers found?

Today we can find glaciers anywhere its cold enough. Most big mountain ranges have glaciers, like the Alps, the Rockies, the Andes, and the Himalayas. Places that get lots of snow have huge masses of ice that form an **ice sheet**, like Greenland, Iceland, and Antarctica. But in the past other places had glaciers too.

Where did they used to be?

There have been many **ice ages** since the formation of the Earth. In the last Ice Age, lots of the UK was covered by ice, and that means there were lots of glaciers!

The map shows where the ice was. The ice didn't melt until 10 000 years ago. We can still see the effects of this ice in the landscape of the UK.

How do they move?

Slowly. But with great power. Glaciers move between about 7 and 10 km a year. Much slower than a river, but wow do they make a difference to the landscape! There is usually some **melt-water** at the bottom and this helps them move. The middle moves faster than the edges, and sometimes the glacier hits an obstacle so it slows down. All this means the ice gets stretched and squashed, so it cracks. These cracks are called **crevasses**.

How do glaciers change the landscape?

Just like waves and rivers, glaciers have energy. That means they can do work. The work they do is eroding and transporting material.

Glaciers can erode rocks in two ways – by **plucking** and by **abrasion**. Plucking happens when the ice freezes on to a rock. Then when the ice moves again it pulls (plucks) the rock with it. This rock is then stuck underneath the glacier.

Did you know?
The world's longest and largest glacier is the Lambert Glacier in Antarctica – it's 400 km long and covers 1 million sq km.

Did you know?
About 75% of the world's freshwater is stored in glacier ice.

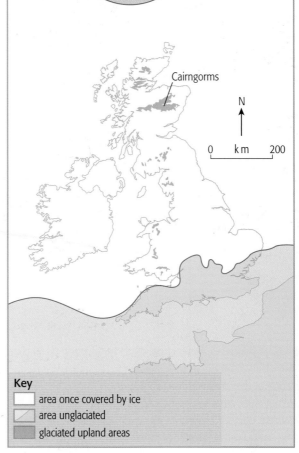

Cairngorms

N

0   km   200

Key
☐ area once covered by ice
▨ area unglaciated
▨ glaciated upland areas

▲ Mind the ice!

Abrasion is like the action of sandpaper. It takes place when rocks and pebbles stuck in the bottom of the ice grind over the bedrock. This can make scratches in the rock, called **striations**.

The glacier carries lots of material with it. This material is called **moraine**. Some moraine is under the ice (**ground moraine**). Moraine can also be inside the glacier if it has fallen into crevasses, or fallen from the surrounding mountains and then been covered by new snow. Moraine can also be on top of the glacier if it has fallen off the mountain slopes above the ice. It gathers at the side of the glacier to make **lateral moraines**. If two glaciers join up, one lateral moraine will get stuck in the middle. Then it's called a **medial moraine**. The drawing below and the photo on the left show moraines on a glacier.

There's lots of surface moraine because there's a weathering process going on. This is called **freeze-thaw weathering**. On the slopes above the ice, water gets into cracks in the rock. Then when the water freezes, it gets bigger. This forces the crack wider. Eventually the rock breaks off where the crack is.

Did you know?
The world's fastest-moving glacier is the Columbia Glacier in Alaska – it covers 35 metres per day.

Did you know?
Many of the world's glaciers are retreating – getting shorter and smaller – because of global warming.

▼ *A slice through the ice.*

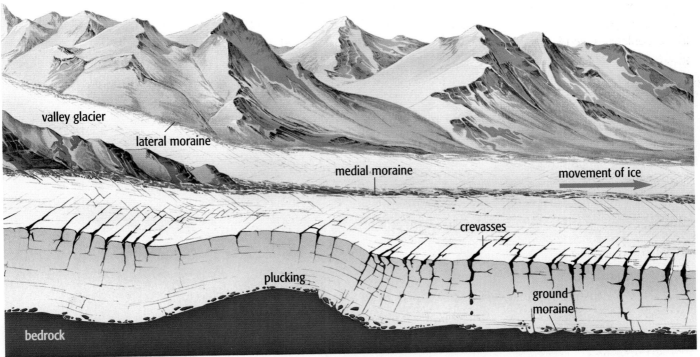

valley glacier
lateral moraine
medial moraine
movement of ice
crevasses
plucking
ground moraine
bedrock

Activities

1 a Make a large copy of this mind map. Use a whole page.
  b Add to it using the information on these pages. You may need to add more 'legs'.
  c Extra research from books or the Internet could make this more detailed. Think about examples, or facts and figures.
2 Answer in full sentences in your book:
  a What is freeze-thaw weathering?
  b How does it work?
  c What do you think the effects of this process might be on the landscape? Why?

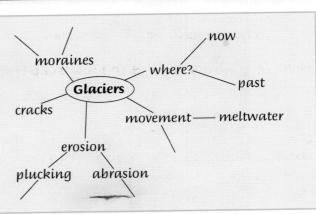

now
moraines
where?
past
Glaciers
cracks
movement —— meltwater
erosion
plucking abrasion

Glacial landforms – erosional features

In this unit we'll look at some glacial landforms and how they were made.

Lake District

What landforms do glaciers make?

Glaciers make lots of features, some of which have strange names! The ones we will be studying are corries, arêtes, pyramidal peaks, troughs, truncated spurs, hanging valleys, ribbon lakes, till, drumlins, eskers, and kames. Some are made by erosion and some by deposition.

The Lake District was covered by ice during the last Ice Age, so it has lots of examples of glacial features.

The first three erosional features are …

Corries

These can also be called **cirques** or a **cwms** – they're all names for the same thing, so don't get confused.

- Corries start as sheltered hollows near the top of a mountain.
- Snow collects there.
- The snow fills up the hollow and gets squashed to make ice.
- The ice moves downhill because it is pulled by gravity.
- But it doesn't move straight down. It moves in a rotational (curved) way.
- As it moves, it is plucking and abrading, so it makes a deep semi-circular hollow – this is the **corrie**.
- Plucking and freeze-thaw mean that the **back wall** of the corrie is very steep.
- The ice erodes less at the front edge, so a **lip** is left.
- When the ice melts, a small lake might be left behind the lip. This is called a **corrie-lake** or a **tarn**.

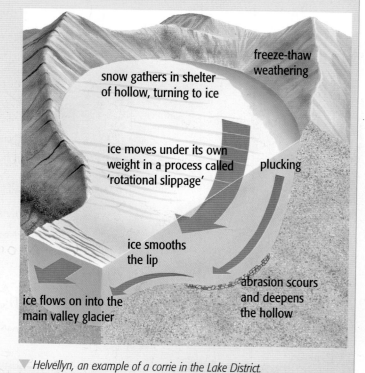

freeze-thaw weathering

snow gathers in shelter of hollow, turning to ice

ice moves under its own weight in a process called 'rotational slippage'

plucking

ice smooths the lip

ice flows on into the main valley glacier

abrasion scours and deepens the hollow

▼ Helvellyn, an example of a corrie in the Lake District.

steep back wall

corrie

tarn

lip

Arêtes

If two corries form next to each other they will leave a sharp ridge between them. This is called an **arête**. ('Arête' is French for stop!) This photo shows Striding Edge, a famous arête in the Lake District.

the arête

Pyramidal peaks

These are made when three or more corries form around a mountain. They cut backwards to leave a **'horn'** or **pyramidal peak** in the middle. There isn't a good example of a pyramidal peak in the Lake District, but there is in Wales – Mount Snowdon, shown in this photo.

the peak

Activities

1 Make a flow diagram to show how corries are made. Start like this … ➡

> Snow collects in a sheltered hollow at the top of a mountain …
> ⬇

2 Use these beginnings to makes notes on arêtes and pyramidal peaks:
   ◆ An arête looks like …
   ◆ An arête is formed when …
   ◆ An example of an arête is …
   ◆ A pyramidal peak is made when …
   ◆ An example is …
3 Draw a diagram of one of the photos on these pages. Add explaining labels (annotations) to explain how the feature was formed.

Erosional features continued

Now you'll learn about the other erosional features.

The final three erosional features are …

Glacial troughs, truncated spurs, and hanging valleys.

When a glacier moves downhill it usually takes the easiest way. That often means down an old river valley. See the interlocking spurs and the tributaries?

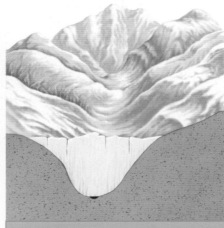

The glacier carves its way through the rock. It erodes a deeper and wider valley by **abrasion** and **plucking**.

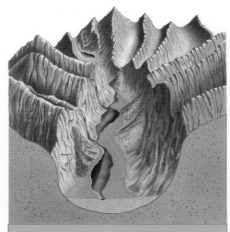

When the ice melts, a **glacial trough** is left behind. You can see that the old interlocking spurs have been cut-off to leave **truncated spurs**. The old tributaries are left hanging high up on the valley sides – so they're called **hanging valleys**.

Glacial trough

This is Martindale Valley in the Lake District.

Glacial troughs can also be called **U-shaped valleys** – because they're shaped like a U!

Steep valley sides. Some material has slumped down to make the sides a bit gentler over the years.

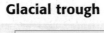

Misfit stream. This is a small stream in the bottom of a glacial trough – it looks too small to have made the valley.

Flat valley floor.

truncated spurs

Truncated spurs

When the glacier erodes the old river valley, it cuts off the **interlocking spurs**. This leaves **truncated spurs**. Truncated is really just another word for 'cut-off'. This photo shows Wast Water in the Lake District. You can see the ends of the spurs that have been truncated on the left-hand side of the photo.

Hanging valleys

This photo shows a hanging valley in Norway. You can clearly see the high-level tributary valley, from which there's a sharp fall to the level of the lower, main valley. The extra depth of the lower valley is due to more severe glaciation, because it contained more ice. To the left of the hanging valley is a truncated spur – so this photo's got it all!

hanging valley

Activities

1 **a** Draw a field sketch of the photo of the hanging valley.
   b Annotate it with explaining labels about the hanging valley, truncated spurs, and glacial trough.
2 Match up these beginnings and endings and write them out correctly.
   A glacial trough is . . .
      . . . the ends of interlocking spurs that have been cut off by the glacier.
   A hanging valley is . . .
      . . . a tributary valley that enters a main valley part way up the valley side.
   Truncated spurs are . . .
      . . . the eroded valley left by a glacier.
3 Write down this beginning: 'Misfit streams are . . .' and then finish off the sentence.
4 A thinking question! Why do you think there's a lake at the bottom of the valley of Wast Water? Make rough notes of your ideas.

Did you know?

The ice covering Antarctica is over 2.6 miles thick in some places!

Glacial landforms – depositional features

In this unit we'll look at some more glacial landforms and how they were made.

Depositional features

Deposition is when material is dropped by the glacier. This material is a lot of jumbled up bits of clay, sand, gravel, and boulders. It is called **till**.

Terminal moraine and ribbon lakes

As a glacier moves, it pushes material (**moraine** – a jumble of unsorted rocks, clays and sands) in front of it. When the ice melts this is deposited as **terminal moraine**. It shows the furthest point the glacier reached. If the glacier remained still for a long time, the terminal moraine could form a big ridge across the valley. Sometimes water gets trapped behind the terminal moraine, in the glacial trough (created by erosion). This makes a **ribbon lake**. This one is Derwent Water in the Lake District, with the town of Keswick next to the lake.

Drumlins

When a glacier is moving slowly, it doesn't have very much energy. This means it can't erode and transport material – it can only shape the clay underneath it. This makes smooth hills. Some people say they look like eggs – and a basket of eggs where there are lots together.

What happens when the ice melts?

The glacier drops its load! This makes lots of features.

Eskers and **kames** are quite small features, so they don't get given individual names.

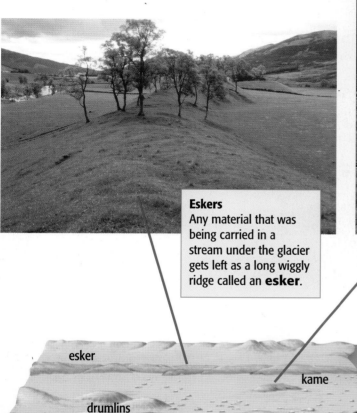

Eskers
Any material that was being carried in a stream under the glacier gets left as a long wiggly ridge called an **esker**.

Kames
Any debris that was in a crevasse gets dropped to the valley floor in a heap called a **kame**.

esker

kame

lake dammed by terminal moraine

terminal moraine (unsorted) deposits)

drumlins

till

Activities

1　**a**　What is a terminal moraine?
　　b　What is a ribbon lake?
　　c　How can a terminal moraine tell us about global warming?
2　Look at the photo of Derwent Water. Why do you think the settlement (Keswick) was built there? Try to come up with three reasons.
3　Write a series of true and false statements based on this chapter so far. Take turns with the rest of the class to read out your statements for the other students to decide if they are 'true' or 'false'.
4　Make revision cards of all the features you have learnt about in this chapter. For each card, write the feature on one side and on the other write:
　◆ a description of it
　◆ how it was formed
　◆ an example.

Glacial landforms on maps

In this unit you will see what glacial landforms look like on maps.

▼ *This map extract is from the Ordnance Survey Landranger series, Map 90, Penrith and Keswick. 1 : 50 000 scale (2 cm to 1 km, 1.25 inches to 1 mile).*

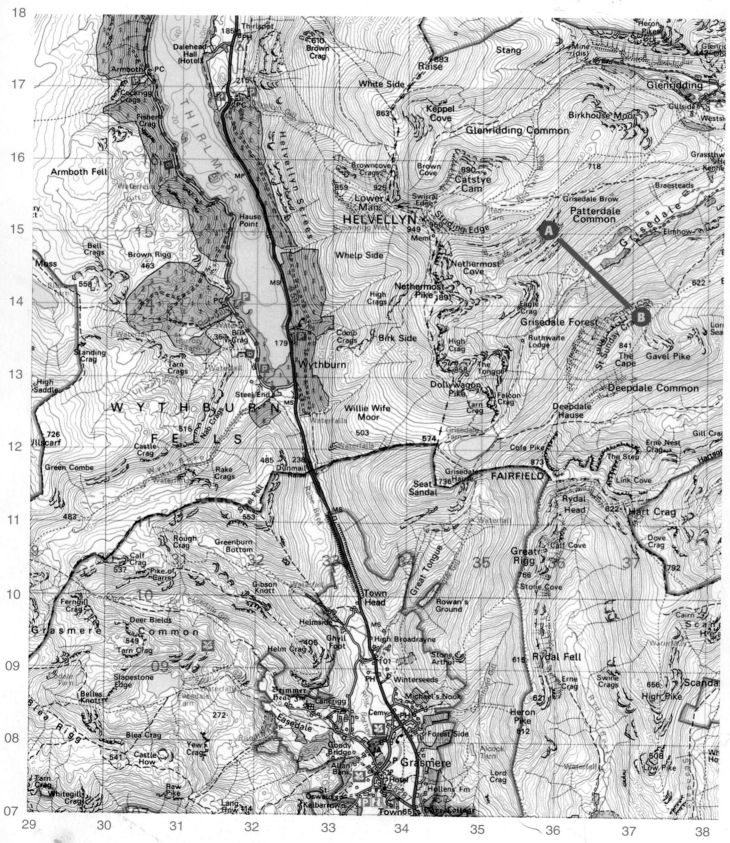

Activities

1 a How is height shown on an OS map?
  b How is steepness shown on an OS map?
  c Describe the overall **relief** of the area in the map.
2 Match up these grid references with the place names:

342151	Alcock Tarn
321131	car park
349079	spot height 949 on Helvellyn

3 Match up these places or locations with the correct landform type.

Brown Cove   ribbon lake   corrie lake   truncated spurs

glacial trough   hanging valleys   Thirlmere   Striding Edge

along the eastern edge of Thirlmere   Red Tarn   corrie   along the eastern edge of Thirlmere   Grisedale   arête

4 Draw a cross-section of the transect A-B marked on the map. (Hint: the bolder contour lines go up in 50-metre gaps.)
5 Why is Grasmere Village built in square 3307?
6 Why is the A591 built where it is?
7 What type of forestry has been planted on the shores of Thirlmere? Why do you think that is?
8 a Look at the photo below. What grid reference was the photographer standing at?
  b Which direction was the camera pointing in?
9 Make a large copy of the table below. Use the map and the previous pages to complete it.

feature	example	description	explanation of how it was formed
corrie			
tarn			
arête			
pyramidal peak	Snowdon		
glacial trough			
truncated spur			
hanging valley			
terminal moraine			
ribbon lake			
drumlins	------		
esker	------		
kame	------		

Thirlmere viewed from Helvellyn

Competing demands in the Cairngorms

In this unit you'll find out how people use the land in an area that was glaciated.

People have to make a living

The Cairngorms is an upland area in north-east Scotland. It became a National Park in 2003 and is the largest in the UK, covering 3800 km². The Cairngorms were glaciated during the last ice age.

There aren't just glacial landforms in the Cairngorms. There are people too! Over 16 000 of them. And they have to make a living. What do they do, and how do their jobs cause conflict in the countryside?

The Cairngorms National Park. ▶

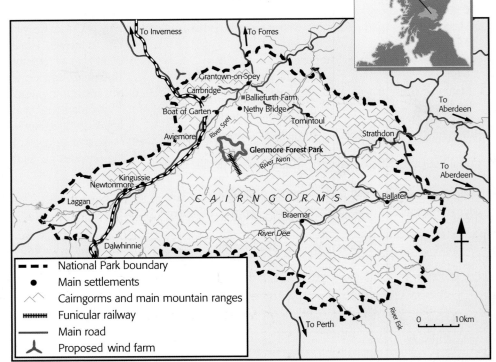

Cairngorms

- – – National Park boundary
- • Main settlements
- ⋀ Cairngorms and main mountain ranges
- ▥ Funicular railway
- — Main road
- 人 Proposed wind farm

Forestry

Nearly 12% of the Cairngorms are forested, usually with coniferous trees (normally pine trees). These grow quickly and are used for timber and paper-making. The steep slopes aren't very useful for arable farming (the soil is too poor), so forestry is an efficient use of the land.

Recently, there have been concerns about coniferous plantations. Native insects, birds and mammals can't cope with the pine trees, because there is less food and the leaf litter is acidic. The trees are planted in straight rows – this is unnatural and causes **visual pollution**, spoiling the view (see the photo). Foresters using heavy machinery like chainsaws and logging trucks also cause air and noise pollution.

So now some forestry plantations, such as the Glenmore Forest Park (in the Northern Cairngorms), are being planted to support native tree species, in particular the ancient Caledonian Pinewood. New trees are also planted more randomly.

Farming

Balliefurth Farm is a pastoral farm on the banks of the River Spey. It is a small-scale, low-intensity farm which has received a National Farmers Union Excellence Award for its good environmental practice. It has managed to increase biodiversity.

The farm has 170 hectares of land, with about 75 cows and 180 sheep. 37 hectares are woodland. The climate is too cold and the soil too thin for many arable crops to grow properly. 70 hectares of the farm are on the River Spey flood plain and are flooded about every three years.

Lambs only fetch about £25 each in the market now. This is because there's less demand for red meat generally in the UK, and because meat is imported more cheaply from other countries. Even wool doesn't make much – it costs the farmer more to shear the sheep than he makes selling the wool! If he doesn't shear the sheep they get infested with maggots.

Balliefurth Farm gets extra money from the EU's Common Agricultural Policy (see Unit 6.6). This provides 42% of the farm's income. Another 14% comes from tourism, including a successful bed and breakfast business and self-catering accommodation.

▲ *Alistair MacLennan – the farmer at Balliefurth Farm.*

Wind power

The Scottish Executive wants to produce 18% of Scotland's energy from renewable sources by 2010. And wind energy will help achieve this. The Cairngorms have some of the highest wind speeds in Britain – gusts over 100 mph occur several times a year.

Wind farms provide a clean form of renewable energy. But many people object to them, particularly in, or near, National Parks. They can cause visual pollution in a natural landscape.

The Cairngorm National Park Authority objected to plans to build a 34-turbine wind farm at Glenkirk, Tomatin. The closest turbine would have been 380 metres outside the park boundary, but the wind farm would have been visible from the park and could affect people's enjoyment of the area. It might also have affected protected species, such as golden eagles.

Did you know?

The weather station on the top of Cairngorm recorded the highest UK wind speed of 173 mph in March 1986.

▲ *Wind farms (like this one at Lammermuir) have a dramatic impact on the landscape.*

Activities

1 a Why aren't the Cairngorms suitable for arable farming (growing crops)?

b What does biodiversity mean?

2 Draw a mind map to show the different uses of the Cairngorms mentioned in this Unit. Add links between the uses to explain how they are connected. Add notes to your links to explain how the different uses might conflict.

Tourism in the Cairngorms

In this unit you'll find out about tourism in a glaciated area of the UK.

Thanks for visiting

Tourism in the Cairngorms is really important to the local, and the Scottish, economy. The Cairngorms is one of six areas in Scotland with the biggest potential for growth of the tourist industry.

The area gets over one million visitors a year from all over the world. Many stay overnight. This means jobs in hotels, B&Bs, cafes, restaurants, shops and in transport. And farmers and other local businesses can sell their produce either directly to the tourists, or to local shops.

At least 3000 people have jobs related to tourism in the Cairngorms. Tourism makes about £500 million a year for the Highlands of Scotland. Tourism and tourist-related businesses make up about 80% of the economy. The average length of visit is four days, the average group size is three people and average spend is £54 per person per day! – this shows how important tourism is.

What visitors do in the Cairngorms

- Walking
- Climbing
- Skiing
- School trips
- Mountain biking
- Canoeing/kayaking
- Historical attractions
- Wildlife spotting
- Deer stalking
- Fishing
- Sightseeing
- Photography

Welcome to the Cairngorms

The Cairngorms – a landscape of breathtaking beauty and fantastic scenery. Climb Ben Macdhui, the second highest mountain in the UK. Walk or mountain bike in one of the most beautiful parts of the country. Climb one of the winter snow-filled buttresses of the northern corries, or ski one of the many runs across three ski areas.

The Cairngorms is a land of contrasts with unique mountainous areas of moorland, forests, rivers, lochs and glens. Take a trip up the funicular railway and see the spectacular views from near the top of Cairngorm across Loch Morlich into the beautiful Strathspey valley.

Visit the picturesque surroundings of Kingussie, Newtonmore, Tomintoul and Grantown-on-Spey to find that ideal gift. Or relax in one of the locally run bars or restaurants whilst enjoying a quiet dram of Scotland's finest (whisky).

The Cairngorms is a land of wildlife, including 25% of Britain's threatened species. You can see golden eagles, osprey, capercaillie and, if you're lucky, the Scottish crossbill, the only bird unique to Britain.

So, tourism's good then?

Well not all good – it can cause conflicts …

- Skiing is one of the most controversial land uses in the Cairngorms. Chairlifts are unsightly. Skiing damages vegetation and compacts and erodes the soil, which can lead to flooding. Reseeding damaged areas alters the natural vegetation.
- Footpaths get eroded. Feet trample the soil and damage vegetation. When it rains the water runs off the slopes and takes soil with it. The paths get deeper and that causes even more run-off. They end up rocky and dangerous, and look ugly. The vegetation takes a long time to grow back as the climate is cool (and the ground is sometimes snow-covered). It costs about £100 per metre to mend a path.
- Salaries for workers in tourism are low. But the attractive location means that many tourists want to buy a holiday home which has driven house prices up, so local people can't afford them. It now looks like this problem is being tackled – as the newspaper article shows.
- Tourists come to the Cairngorms in the summer, and in the winter for skiing. But this leaves 'dead' times (September – December and April – June) when there is a shortage of jobs. Many people in the Cairngorms have seasonal jobs or are self-employed.
- Cars are a real problem in the Cairngorms National Park – nearly 90% of visitors come by car. Many of the roads are narrow, which can lead to traffic congestion, local people being unable to get around easily, and the risk of emergency vehicles not being able to get through. In winter roads can be icy – making driving dangerous.
- Litter is a big problem. It creates visual pollution and can be dangerous to wild animals and birds. It attracts crows and gulls, which disturb the natural bird life.
- Some towns and villages get swamped by visitors, making them too busy for local people. They are called 'honeypot' villages, with the tourists like bees around them! Examples are Aviemore and Braemar.
- Dogs owned by tourists often worry sheep (they chase them). In lambing season that could mean a ewe (a female sheep) miscarries. Uncontrolled dogs disturb wildlife.

Cairngorms set to change housing rules

There has been a problem in the National Park over the lack of affordable housing. The park authority is planning a new rule – if people want to buy a new house in the Park, they will have to have lived there for at least 3 years, or work there.

If people want to buy or use existing houses as holiday homes, they will have to get planning permission.

Did you know?

- 4 of Scotland's 5 highest mountains are within the Cairngorm National Park.
- The Cairngorm National Park is 40% larger than the Lake District National Park and twice the size of Loch Lomond and the Trossachs.

Activities

1 Draw a spider diagram to show the problems that tourism causes in the Cairngorms.
2 Make up a scene where there is conflict between tourists and locals. Include the reason for the conflict. Write it as a role play.

3 Find out these things about either Aviemore or Braemar:
- where it is
- why tourists go there
- a map to show where things are
- a bit about its history

Present your findings on one side of A4 only. Remember to put it all in your own words.

Managing tourists in the Cairngorms

In this unit you'll find out how some of the problems in the Cairngorms can be managed.

Looking for solutions

◆ Mending footpaths by planting new grass, or if the path is badly eroded, laying a new path of quarried stone, e.g. the path leading from the Corrie Cas Ski area into Coire An t-Sneachda.

◆ Placing bike hire centres across the park to reduce traffic congestion. The Forestry Enterprise is developing an extensive cycle network.

◆ Advertising public transport and displaying timetables in tourist information centres and local shop windows.

◆ Developing new routes and encouraging visitors to use existing public transport. Extending services to meet demand.

◆ Ensuring that more local people can buy their own homes (see Unit 2.7).

◆ Co-ordinating and extending car park charges that contribute to environmental conservation.

◆ Increasing the use of ranger services and upgrading ranger bases for information and education.

▲ *Walking a track specially bulldozed for tourists in the eastern Cairngorms.*

◆ Introducing a tourism signage system to protect more fragile parts of the National Park.

◆ Upgrading some path networks to make them wheelchair-safe and suitable for mobility scooters.

◆ Attracting more tourists at different times of the year and out-of-season by improving the seasonal spread of guided walks and the Park's events programme, e.g. the Aviemore Mountain Film Festival.

◆ Promoting local brands including crafts and produce (e.g. Balliefurth Farm beef and lamb – see Unit 2.6)

◆ Assessing and developing the potential for more opportunities for exploring the Park by foot, cycle, horse and canoe.

◆ Talking to coach operators. The National Park is considering producing a coach drivers' handbook.

Cairngorm National Park Authority

The National Park Authority has many jobs including carrying out research, giving grants and loans, providing information and educational services, and providing facilities to encourage people to visit for leisure purposes (including camp sites, accommodation, meals and refreshments).

The National Park's aims are as follows:
- To conserve and enhance the natural and cultural heritage of the area.
- To promote sustainable use of the natural resources of the area.
- To promote the public's understanding and enjoyment (including recreation) of the area's special qualities.
- To promote sustainable economic and social development of the area's communities.

Cairngorm Mountain Funicular Railway

People have been skiing in the Cairngorms for years! The original chairlift was built in 1961. By 1990, most of the original infrastructure was becoming difficult to maintain. The chairlifts and tows had to shut in high winds. The Cairngorm Chairlift Company wanted to replace some tows with a funicular railway (a train pulled by cables over a track). It caused a lot of conflict.

For the funicular

The boss of the Highlands and Islands Enterprise said 'This project is of national importance for Scotland's tourist industry. It is important for visitors and the environment.'

Against the funicular

Groups opposing the funicular included the WWF and RSPB. They said 'The railway will drastically increase the number of visitors to the area. What about the effect on the environment and wildlife?'

A compromise was reached and a 'closed system' of visitor management is now operated. In the winter only skiers can leave Ptarmigan Station (the top station). In summer no-one can leave Ptarmigan Station to walk on the Cairngorm plateau. This is to protect the fragile mountain environment. People can visit the restaurant, visitor centre and shops, but that's all.

Even though the Cairngorm Mountain Railway attracts about 162 000 non-skiing visitors and 80 000 skiing visitors each year, the funicular still has problems. Since it has been built, mild weather and poor winter snow conditions have meant fewer skiers, and it is increasingly dependent on other users. Groups are campaigning to allow walkers to leave at the top station.

Did you know?
The Cairngorm Mountain Railway is 2 km long and the highest railway in the UK. At the top is the UK's highest restaurant, highest retail outlet and highest underground station.

Activities

1 Draw a consequence map for the Cairngorms funicular railway. Start like this:

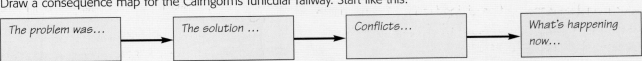

The problem was... → The solution ... → Conflicts... → What's happening now...

2 Is tourism in the Cairngorms sustainable? Think about the problems of tourism and some of the solutions.

The big picture

This chapter is about weather. These are the big ideas behind the chapter:

◆ Weather is the day-to-day state of the atmosphere, and can change very quickly.

◆ Weather consists of different elements, like precipitation, temperature etc. Each one is measured in a different way.

◆ Air moves around the world in huge blocks called air masses.

◆ Depressions and anticyclones control our weather in the UK.

◆ Synoptic charts and satellite images are used for weather forecasting.

◆ Weather and climate affects the things we do.

Your goals for this chapter

By the end of this chapter you should be able to answer these questions:

◆ What do these weather terms mean, and how are they measured?
precipitation, temperature, air pressure, humidity, wind direction, wind strength (speed), visibility, cloud type, cloud cover, sunshine

◆ Why can our weather change so quickly?

◆ Name at least three different air masses and say what kind of weather they bring to the UK.

◆ What type of weather do you get with:
a winter anticyclone? a summer anticyclone? a depression passing over?

◆ What do synoptic charts and satellite images show us, and how are they used?

◆ How do these types of rainfall form?
frontal, relief, convectional

◆ What type of climate do we have in the UK?

◆ How do our weather and climate affect what we do?

And then . . .

When you finish the chapter, come back here and see if you've met your goals!

Did you know?
The driest place in the world is the Atacama Desert in Chile. Parts of the desert haven't had a single drop of rain since records began.

Did you know?
The wettest place in the world is Mount Wai-'ale-'ale in Hawaii. It gets between 11 600-13 000 mm of rain a year. Several other places think they're the wettest too!

Did you know?
In 1970, 38 mm of rain fell on Guadeloupe in the Caribbean in just one minute – the most rain ever recorded over that period of time.

Did you know?
◆ The highest temperature ever recorded is 57.8 °C, in Libya, on 13 September 1922.
◆ The lowest is -89.2 °C, in Antarctica, on 21 July 1983.

Your chapter starter

Look at the photo on page 40.
What is it?
Where do you think it is?
What do you think might happen to the house?
Have you ever seen anything like it?

I see the Wizard of Oz is on again.

Measuring the weather

In this unit you'll find out about weather and how we measure it.

What is weather?

Weather is the day-to-day condition of the atmosphere.

Over the short-term, the atmosphere can change quickly. What's the weather like today? Warm or cool? Wet or dry? Cloudy or clear? Windy or calm?

The changes in the atmosphere can be measured. The results are used to produce quite reliable weather forecasts for a few days.

The elements of weather

Weather can be divided into a number of elements as the diagram shows. Each element is measured in a different way.

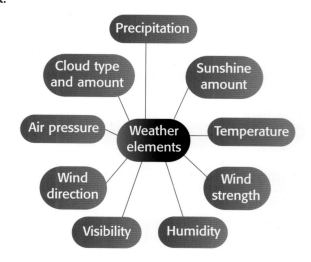

Measuring the weather

Precipitation is all forms of moisture from clouds — rain, hail, sleet and snow. It's measured in a **rain gauge**, in millimetres (mm). This should be located in an open space, away from buildings.

Temperature measures the heat in the air. Most geographers use a **maximum and minimum thermometer** to measure temperature in degrees Centigrade (°C). Maximum and minimum thermometers record the maximum and minimum temperature of the air. Thermometers should be kept inside a **Stevenson Screen**.

Air Pressure is the force the atmosphere exerts on the Earth's surface. It is also known as atmospheric pressure. It's measured by a barometer, in millibars (mb). Barometers are delicate pieces of equipment and should be stored carefully. Most geographers keep them inside a Stevenson Screen. Generally, air pressure is high if it's above 1000mb, low if it's below this figure. It's the single most important weather element, because it controls all the other elements mentioned here.

Cool air sinks. The pressure of the air on the ground increases. The air warms up as it reaches the ground, so no water vapour condenses and no clouds form. The skies stay clear and there's no rain.

high pressure

cool air sinking

Warm air rises. The pressure of the air on the ground decreases. The air cools as it rises, moisture condenses to form clouds, and rain follows.

warm air rising

low pressure

Wind direction is recorded by identifying the direction the wind is coming from using the eight points of a **compass rose** (eg N, NE, E, SE, etc). **Wind vanes** are used to record direction and should be located in open spaces or on top of tall buildings.

Wind strength (**speed**) is measured with an **anemometer**, in knots, kilometres or miles per hour. Anemometers should be located in open spaces or on top of tall buildings. A simple observation scale known as the Beaufort Scale can also be used. The scale goes from 0 to 12: 0 = calm (smoke rises vertically); 6 = strong breeze (difficult to use umbrellas); 12 = hurricane (great damage to property).

Visibility is how far we can see. It's measured by a visibility meter, in metres or kilometres.

A beam of light is sent out and a sensor measures how much arrives.

Humidity is the percentage of water vapour in the air. It's measured with a **hygrometer**. Hygrometers should be stored inside a Stevenson Screen.

Cloud type. There are five main types of cloud: stratus (layered), cumulus, nimbus (rain bearing), cumulonimbus, cirrus (ice).

Cloud cover is how much of the sky is covered by cloud. It's measured in eighths or oktas, just by looking. (See Unit 3.4.)

Sunshine is measured in hours using a **sunshine recorder** or **heliograph**. Although these are quite rare and expensive, some geographers still use them.

Weather stations

A weather station is a place where all of the weather instruments are placed together. This makes it easier to check them all in one go and record the daily weather.

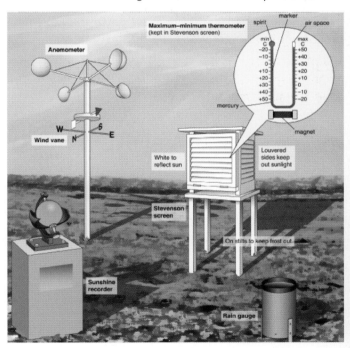

▲ A weather station.

Many people now use automatic weather stations like the one on the right linked to a computer to measure and record the weather. You might be lucky enough to have one at your school. Lots of automatic weather stations are now linked up to the Internet so it's easy to find out what the weather is like somewhere. You can also take visual observations by looking at web cams.

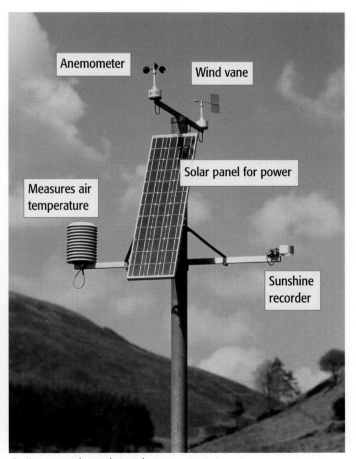

▲ An automatic weather station.

Activities

1 **a** What is atmospheric pressure?
   b Explain how it controls the weather elements.
2 Choose five weather elements. Describe what they are, and how they are recorded.

Air masses and anticyclones

In this unit you'll learn about the effects of air masses and anticyclones.

Air masses

You know that some parts of the world are really hot, and others are really cold. Because of this air moves around – just like the air does in a cold room when you turn on a heater.

Air moves around the world in huge blocks called **air masses**. An air mass can be thousands of kilometres across. It can be warm or cold depending on whether it originated in tropical or polar areas, and damp or dry depending on whether it originated over the sea, or land.

Many different air masses cross Britain. That's why our weather can change so quickly. But if an air mass moves very slowly, or doesn't move at all for a while, we can get the same weather for days.

Did you know?
The weather doesn't change much from day-to-day at the tropics (or the poles) because they have the same type of air mass all year.

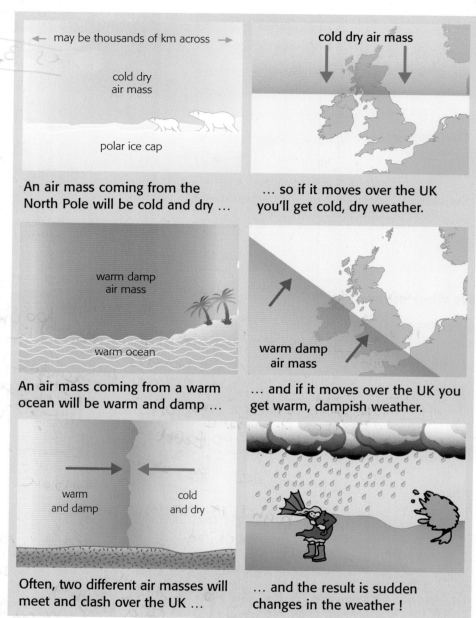

← may be thousands of km across →

cold dry air mass

polar ice cap

An air mass coming from the North Pole will be cold and dry …

cold dry air mass

… so if it moves over the UK you'll get cold, dry weather.

warm damp air mass

warm ocean

An air mass coming from a warm ocean will be warm and damp …

warm damp air mass

… and if it moves over the UK you get warm, dampish weather.

warm and damp   cold and dry

Often, two different air masses will meet and clash over the UK …

… and the result is sudden changes in the weather !

Greenland

Arctic Circle

Arctic Maritime brings cold, wet air from the Arctic Circle, creating very cold weather and bringing snow in the winter.

Polar Maritime brings wet, cold air from Greenland and the Arctic Ocean, creating cool, wet weather.

Tropical Maritime brings warm, moist air from the Mid-Atlantic Ocean, creating mild, cloudy and wet weather.

Polar Continental brings cold, dry air from Central Europe and Siberia during the winter.

Europe

Tropical Continental brings hot, dry air from North Africa, creating hot, dry weather during the summer.

Africa

N

Air masses, and the weather they bring. ▶

The anticyclone

Two large-scale weather systems control our weather in the British Isles:

1 The **anticyclone** – which is associated with high pressure and results in clear calm weather.

2 The **depression** – which is associated with low pressure and results in cloudy, wet, and windy weather (see Unit 3.3).

Air pressure is shown on maps by **isobars**. These are lines of equal pressure. In anticyclones, the isobars are far apart. This means the air pressure doesn't change much over a large distance, so winds are light. In depressions, the isobars are close together, indicating stronger winds.

Anticyclones have high air pressure, light winds, clear skies, and dry conditions. But there are differences between winter and summer.

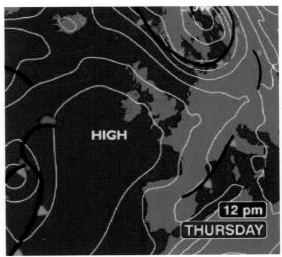

Winter anticyclones

In winter, the cloudless skies we often get with anticyclones allow heat to escape. The ground cools quickly at night, cooling the air above it – water vapour condenses and freezes on cold surfaces, giving **frost**. It also condenses on dust and other particles in the air, giving **fog**. This fog can linger into the day, until the heat of the sun evaporates it away. The days are often clear, cold, and bright. Water can freeze into **ice**.

Summer anticyclones

In summer, an anticyclone brings very different weather. The cloudless skies mean the sun is strong and the days are hot. But, because there's no cloud, evenings can be cool. The ground cools at night, so water vapour condenses to form **dew**. No cloud means no rain – which can lead to a **drought**. However, on very hot days, the hot air may rise quickly, cool, and form big black clouds leading to **thunderstorms**.

If a summer anticyclone stays over the British Isles for a few weeks, we talk about a **heat-wave**. There was a famous one in 1976; more recently, we had one in 2003.

Activities

1 a What is an air mass?
   b Why do some air masses bring warm weather, and others bring cold weather?

2 Suggest reasons for the weather associated with a summer anticyclone.

The depression

In this unit you'll learn about the formation of depressions, and how they affect our weather.

How a depression forms

Our weather is wet and windy. The weather system that gives us these conditions is called the **depression**. It's a low pressure weather system that moves across the country from west to east, from the Atlantic Ocean. It brings rain.

Depression systems form over the ocean at the boundary where warm light air from the tropics meets colder heavier air from the poles. The different air types don't mix, and the less dense warm air rises above the cold air to produce a **front**. Moisture condenses to form clouds and **frontal rainfall**.

Remember:
The warm front has warm air behind it.
The cold front has cold air behind it.

The development of a depression occurs in a number of distinct stages, with a lifecycle that usually lasts 5 or 6 days.

Stage 1: Birth
* Cold polar air meets warm tropical air along a polar front.
* The less dense warm air rises over the cold – this starts to lower the air pressure.

Stage 2: Maturity
* Warm air is drawn or 'sucked' into the low pressure centre and the colder air is sucked in behind it.
* The rotation of the Earth causes the system to spiral in an anti-clockwise direction.
* At the warm front, warm air rises over the cold air. Cooling and condensation occurs, resulting in clouds and precipitation along a frontal zone.
* At the cold front, heavy cold air sinks below or undercuts the warm air in the warm sector. Again the warm air is forced to rise resulting in a thick zone of cloud and heavy precipitation.

Stage 3: Old age and death
* The cold front travels faster than the warm front and eventually 'lifts' the warm air off the ground from the warm sector. This is called an occlusion.
* When cold air replaces the warm air the fronts disappear and the depression dies.

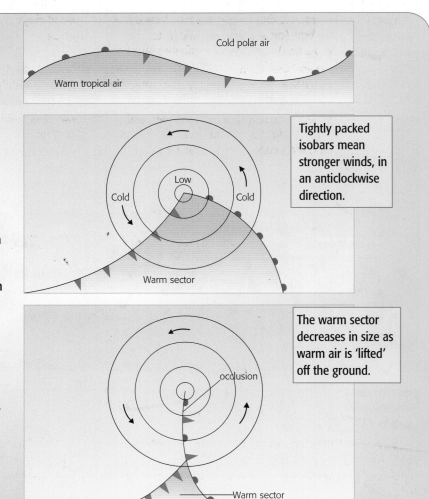

Cold polar air

Warm tropical air

Tightly packed isobars mean stronger winds, in an anticlockwise direction.

Low

Cold

Cold

Warm sector

The warm sector decreases in size as warm air is 'lifted' off the ground.

occlusion

Warm sector

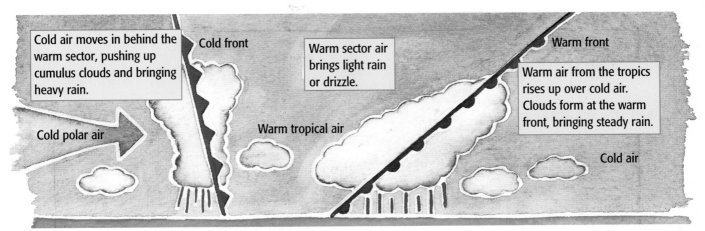

Cold air moves in behind the warm sector, pushing up cumulus clouds and bringing heavy rain.

Cold front

Warm sector air brings light rain or drizzle.

Warm front

Warm air from the tropics rises up over cold air. Clouds form at the warm front, bringing steady rain.

Cold polar air

Warm tropical air

Cold air

▲ *Frontal rainfall in a depression.*

As a depression system moves across the British Isles, there's a definite pattern to the weather. Meteorologists use this pattern to forecast the weather as accurately as possible, but the nature of the weather and its variability makes forecasting very difficult.

Weather associated with the passage of a depression

	Ahead of the warm front	Passage of the warm front	Warm sector	Passage of the cold front	Cold sector
Pressure	starts to fall steadily	continues to fall	steadies	starts to rise	continues to rise
Temperature	quite cold, starts to rise	continues to rise	quite mild	sudden drop	remains cold
Cloud cover	cloud base drops and thickens (cirrus and altostratus)	cloud base is low and thick (nimbostratus)	cloud may thin and break	clouds thicken (sometimes with large cumulonimbus)	clouds thin with some cumulus
Wind speed and direction	speeds increase and direction is SE	veers SW and becomes blustery with strong gusts	remains steady, westerly slightly	speeds increase, sometimes to gale force, sharp veer NW	winds are squally NW
Precipitation	none at first, rain closer to front, sometimes snow on leading edge	continues, and sometimes heavy rainfall	rain runs to drizzle or stops	heavy rain, sometimes with hail, thunder or sleet	showers

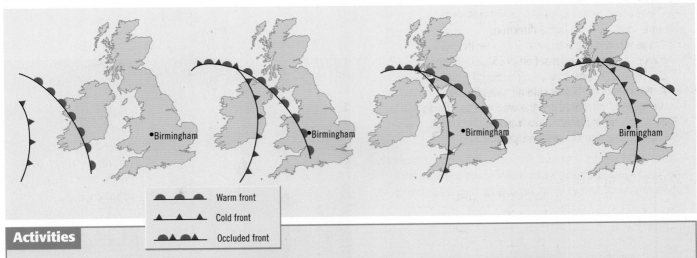

Warm front

Cold front

Occluded front

Activities

1 Using the diagram, produce a TV or radio weather forecast for Birmingham for the next 24 hours. Make reference to each part of the depression.

2 Describe and explain five differences between the weather associated with a depression and the weather associated with a summer anticyclone.

Synoptic charts and satellite images

In this unit you'll learn how to read synoptic charts and satellite images.

> Remember the precipitation process!
>
> **C**ooling ➡ **C**ondensation ➡ **C**loud formation ➡ **P**recipitation

What will the weather be like?

Most of our weather comes with the prevailing winds from the south-west, so we look mostly towards the Atlantic Ocean for clues about what will happen next.

Below is an Atlantic synoptic chart, or weather map. It's like many you see on TV. It clearly identifies the position of the weather systems looked at so far in this chapter:

- the anticyclone – a region of high atmospheric pressure
- the depression – a region of low atmospheric pressure.

The depression

This is a classic depression. It has a leading warm front, a warm sector, and a following cold front. The isobars are tightly packed, indicating strong winds.

It's likely this system will move across the British Isles in the next few days. The fronts will bring cloud and rain. The warm sector will bring slightly drier weather.

The anticyclone and high-pressure ridge

This large area of high pressure indicates an area where the air is sinking. As this air sinks towards the ground it will warm up and evaporate moisture. As few clouds can form, there will be clear skies. Over a cool sea there could be some fog. The isobars are much further apart than in the depression – this indicates calm winds.

In summer this system will provide warm temperatures, and maybe thunderstorms will develop. In winter it will provide cooler temperatures, with frost and fog.

Approaching the British Isles you can see a smaller ridge of high pressure – this should also bring settled weather. The winds blow in a clockwise direction.

An occlusion

The warm and cold fronts have merged here, lifting all the warm air off the ground.

Without a constant supply of warm air the storm will die out after a period of quite heavy rain. The occlusion marks the end of the depression system.

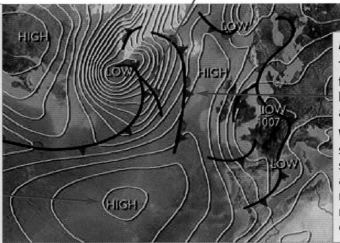

▲ *An Atlantic synoptic (pressure) chart.*

Precipitation

This chart shows how the cloud and rainfall pattern across the Atlantic matches up with the pressure systems. You should be able to match up the frontal bands of cloud and rain, and the clear conditions, with the synoptic chart.

All the rainfall shown is frontal. Notice how the isobars are close together, indicating stronger winds. With high pressure the isobars are much further apart, producing calmer conditions.

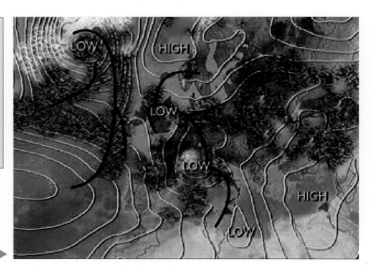

A pressure / precipitation chart. ▶

Satellite images

This is a visual image of the cloud cover associated with weather systems. Satellite images help weather forecasters to see what weather is heading our way. The skill lies in seeing how the atmospheric pressure is linked to the weather system and the amount of cloud and rain.

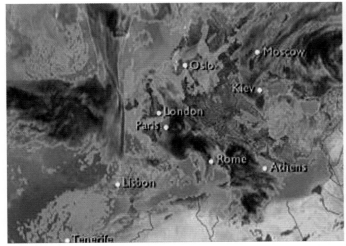

▲ A satellite image of cloud cover.

Weather symbols

If you know a bit about weather symbols, it's possible to interpret synoptic charts in more detail. The symbols describe the weather conditions at a place at a particular time, and can be used to anticipate how the weather conditions may change.

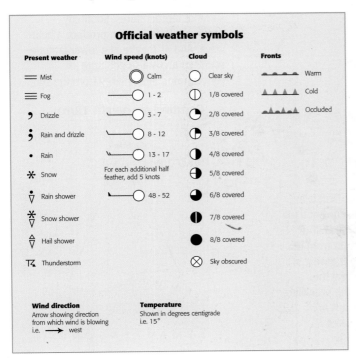

Official weather symbols

Present weather	Wind speed (knots)	Cloud	Fronts
Mist	Calm	Clear sky	Warm
Fog	1 - 2	1/8 covered	Cold
Drizzle	3 - 7	2/8 covered	Occluded
Rain and drizzle	8 - 12	3/8 covered	
Rain	13 - 17	4/8 covered	
Snow	For each additional half feather, add 5 knots	5/8 covered	
Rain shower	48 - 52	6/8 covered	
Snow shower		7/8 covered	
Hail shower		8/8 covered	
Thunderstorm		Sky obscured	

Wind direction
Arrow showing direction from which wind is blowing i.e. ➝ west

Temperature
Shown in degrees centigrade i.e. 15°

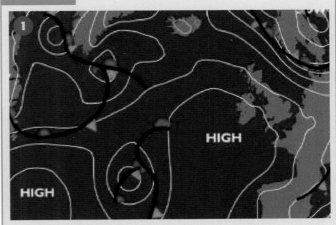

▲ A synoptic chart for 11 August.

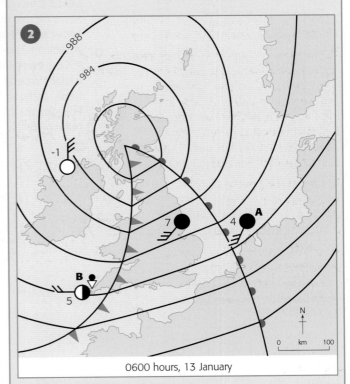

0600 hours, 13 January

▲ A synoptic chart of a depression system.

1 Study synoptic chart 1. Write a brief forecast about the general conditions expected for the British Isles on 11 August.
2 Study synoptic chart 2.
   a Describe the specific weather conditions at places A and B.
   b Suggest how and why the weather conditions for place A may change over the following 24 hours.

The climate of the British Isles

In this unit you'll learn about the climate of the British Isles – and three types of rainfall

Mild and wet

The British Isles has a **temperate**, **maritime climate** – our climate is generally mild and fairly wet because it's moderated by the sea. In the summer the sea cools the climate and in winter the sea insulates us, keeping us warmer than most other places at our latitude.

But the climate does vary across the British Isles. Look at the map and the four climate graphs.

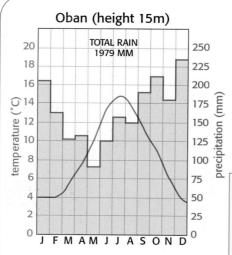

Oban (height 15m)
TOTAL RAIN 1979 MM

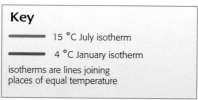

Key

15 °C July isotherm

4 °C January isotherm

isotherms are lines joining places of equal temperature

Why?
Colder temperatures in the north are due to both the higher latitude and the mountainous relief (air cools by 1°C for every 100 metres). So winter temperatures are quite harsh. Arctic air from the North Pole can also blast Scotland, reducing temperatures further.

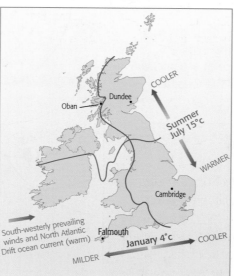

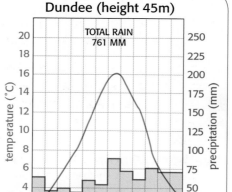

Dundee (height 45m)
TOTAL RAIN 761 MM

Why?
Warm air from Europe helps to lift summer temperatures. Southerly continental winds often produce a heat-wave. And as they're at a lower latitude, southern areas also get more concentrated heat energy from the sun.

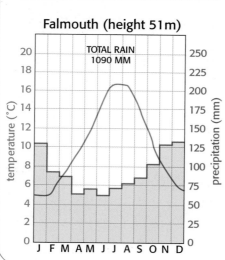

Falmouth (height 51m)
TOTAL RAIN 1090 MM

Why?
The North Atlantic Drift is a very warm ocean current that starts in the tropical Gulf of Mexico. The warmth from this water helps keep the west of Britain milder during the winter months – the prevailing south-westerly winds are warmed by this water.

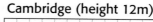

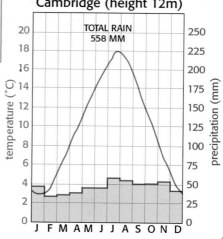

Cambridge (height 12m)
TOTAL RAIN 558 MM

West is wetter!

Three types of rainfall are responsible for all the precipitation received in the British Isles. These are:

1 relief rainfall (sometimes called orographic rainfall)
2 convectional rainfall
3 frontal rainfall (see Unit 3.3).

Remember the precipitation process!

Cooling ➡ **C**ondensation ➡ **C**loud formation ➡ **P**recipitation

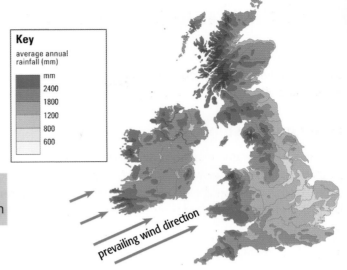

Key
average annual rainfall (mm)

mm
2400
1800
1200
800
600

prevailing wind direction

Relief rainfall

Warm moist air blows in, rises over hills or mountains, cools, condenses into clouds – and we get rain.

Warm moist air arrives from the Atlantic Ocean and rises over the mountains on the western side of Britain – the Cambrians, Pennines, and Grampians. The mountain peaks can receive quite high totals, up to 2000 mm annually. Once the air has passed over the mountains, it begins to descend and gradually warms as it reaches a lower altitude. This produces drier conditions and is known as the **rain shadow**. Our mountains tend to be wetter on the windward, western sides and drier on the leeward, eastern sides.

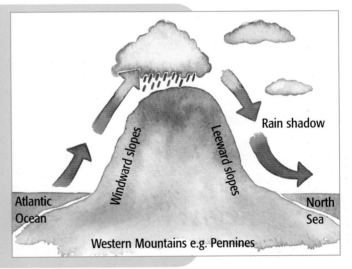

Convectional rainfall

During the summer, strong heating from the sun causes the ground to heat up rapidly. This can then set up rising pockets of warm air known as **convection currents**. The warm air rises rapidly to a high altitude where it cools and water vapour condenses to form clouds. With time, particularly by late afternoon, thick cumulonimbus clouds can form – and these can produce heavy rainfall, and sometimes thunderstorms. This process helps to explain why Cambridge often has its wettest month in July or August.

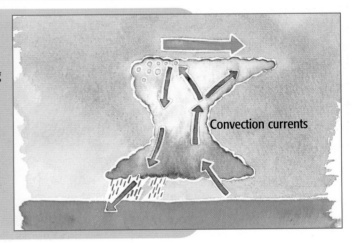

Convection currents

Activities

1 **a** Draw your own sketch map of the British Isles, and divide it into the four climate areas.
   b Using the climate graphs, annotate your map (add explaining labels) with key information about the climate. Remember to include data as part of your answer and remember to use the following terms: maximum temperature, minimum temperature, annual range, and total precipitation.

2 Compare two climate areas of the British Isles. Explain the differences in the climate patterns you identify using the information given.

3 Describe and suggest reasons for the distribution of rainfall across the British Isles (shown by the map above).

Climate and human activity in the UK

In this unit you'll learn how the weather and climate of the UK affects human activity.

Come rain or shine

The UK's weather changes from day to day. But the climate is more predictable. Most of our weather arrives from the Atlantic Ocean as depressions, which bring cloud, rain, and wind. The air is **temperate** (warm) and **maritime** (wet from the ocean), so our weather is mostly warm and wet.

In winter, northerly arctic blasts can cause sharp drops in temperature and can bring snow, especially in Scotland. In summer, heat-waves from North Africa and the Mediterranean can bring sweltering temperatures of around 25-30 °C. If prolonged, southern parts of the UK can experience drought.

The climate affects what we do – the crops we grow, the holidays we take, the sports we play.

Alternative sources of energy

Our wet and windy climate could provide us with alternative, renewable sources of energy. Fossil fuels (coal, oil, and gas) won't last forever, and carbon dioxide emissions from burning fossil fuels are contributing to global warming, so the government is looking for alternatives.

Hydro-electric power (hep) uses the power of running water to generate electricity. The western side of the UK is much wetter and more mountainous than the east. So this is where the hep stations are located. Most are in Scotland. The Dinorwig station in Wales is inside a huge mountain chamber. However, set up costs are high and finding the right location is difficult.

We're the windiest country in Europe – so there's plenty of potential for **wind power**. Most of our windfarms are on the western side of the country – because the high land is exposed to the prevailing wind. The first offshore windfarm – North Hoyle, off the coast of North Wales – started generating electricity in 2003. At least 30 more offshore windfarms are planned or being built already. Wind power is clean and non-polluting. But a thousand turbines will generate only 1% of our energy needs.

Remember:
- weather is the short-term state of the atmosphere – it can change from day to day
- climate is the average weather over a longer period of time.

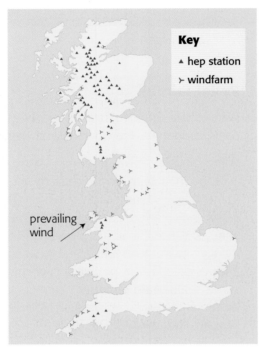

Key
- ▲ hep station
- ⊢ windfarm

prevailing wind

▲ A windfarm in Cumbria.

Farming

There's a direct link between type of agriculture and climate. Eastern England has a drier, warmer, sunnier climate, with an average of five or six hours of sunshine per day in the summer – so arable crops such as wheat and barley ripen well. The western side of the UK has a wetter climate – this produces good pasture for cattle, so pastoral farming dominates.

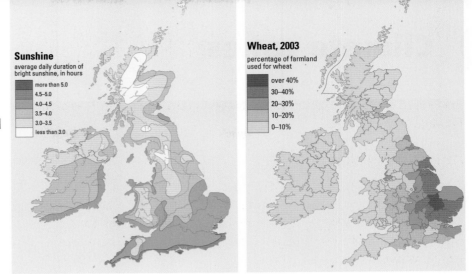

Flooding

Flooding can hit almost any part of the UK. But the western side of the UK often suffers more than other areas because it gets a lot of heavy rain, especially in the autumn and winter months. Carlisle in Cumbria was closed off by flood waters in the winter of 2004. A flash flood caused havoc in Boscastle in Devon in August 2004. The threat of flooding affects how we use land, for example where we build new homes and roads.

▲ Game off.

Tourism

The UK is the world's sixth most popular tourist destination, but many visitors enjoy our landscape and historical attractions whilst shouting 'shame about the weather!'. The tourist industry earns the country over £30 billion a year and provides many jobs in hotels, restaurants, souvenir shops, and attractions – although many of these jobs are for the summer only. There are many seaside resorts, especially along the warmer, sunnier south coast. The wetter parts of the country, such as the Lake District and Highlands of Scotland, rely on their stunning landscape to attract walkers, climbers, and mountain bikers.

▲ Summer work.

Sport and leisure

We play different sports at different times of the year. Traditionally it's been football in winter, cricket in summer. There are more outdoor events in the summer. We take most of our holidays in the summer, because that's when the weather's better.

Activities

1 Compare and explain the patterns shown by the two maps above.
2 Think of three further examples of how climate has a direct impact on human activity in the UK. Explain clearly the link between activity and climate.
3 Using the information on these pages and your own ideas, construct a mind map which illustrates the links you have thought of. You could even show how some activities are interrelated.

The big picture

This chapter is about climate. These are the big ideas behind the chapter:

◆ The world can be divided into climate zones – large areas with a similar climate.

◆ Climate depends on several factors – the effect of latitude is the main one.

◆ Different ecosystems are determined by climate.

◆ Climate affects people, but people have a major impact on the environment.

◆ Climate change will affect us all.

Your goals for this chapter

By the end of this chapter you should be able to answer these questions:

◆ How do these factors influence climate?
latitude, distance from the sea, prevailing wind, altitude, ocean currents

◆ How are ecosystems related to climate?

◆ Describe one of these climates:
hot desert, Mediterranean, tundra region climate, equatorial

◆ Where do you find the climate you described? And how does the climate affect people living there?

◆ What impact have people had in the climate zone you described?

◆ What examples can you give of sustainable management in the climate zone you described?

◆ What is climate change, and what's causing it?

◆ Give as many examples as you can of the possible effects of climate change.

◆ What can governments do about climate change? And what can *you* do?

And then . . .

When you finish the chapter, come back here and see if you've met your goals!

Did you know?
Global warming could cause:
◆ Arctic ice to melt and the extinction in the wild of animals like the polar bear
◆ the spread of malaria in Africa and North America.

Did you know?
Global warming could cause the warm North Atlantic Drift to be turned off – that would lead to a much colder Britain.

Did you know?
Scientists think it's unlikely that we can avoid dangerous climate change.

Did you know?
In Barrow, Alaska, average temperatures have increased 2.5–3 °C in the last 30 years.

Your chapter starter

Look at the photo on page 54.

What do you think the climate is like in this place?

Where do you think this is?

What's happening in this climate zone?

What do you know about polar bears?

How about seal tonight?

Global climate explained

In this unit you'll learn about the global distribution of climate – and the key factors behind this distribution.

Climate around the world

Climate is the *average* weather in a place. It's a summary of what the weather is usually like, based on measurements taken over a long time, usually 30 years.

Climate varies around the world. But we can divide the world into climate zones – large areas with a similar climate. Some are shown on this map, and by the climate graphs and statistics.

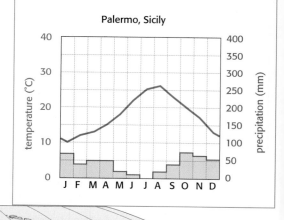

Palermo, Sicily

A Mediterranean climate has hot, dry summers and warm, wet winters. This climate is found on the west coast of continents roughly between latitudes 30° and 40°, and around the Mediterranean sea.

The desert climate is hot and dry throughout the year. Rain does fall – but not very often. Hot deserts are found around the Tropics of Cancer and Capricorn.

Barrow

Tropic of Cancer

Palermo

Khartoum

Arctic tundra regions are found in the Northern Hemisphere in areas with a polar climate. It's cold all year with a small amount of precipitation every month.

Manaus

Equator

Tropic of Capricorn

An equatorial climate is hot, wet, and humid all year round. There are no seasons. Equatorial areas lie in a band around the equator.

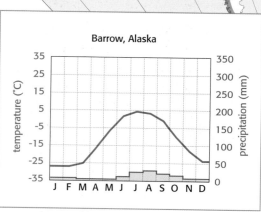

Barrow, Alaska

Key

Polar	Temperate
Desert	Mediterranean
Savanna	Equatorial
	Other climates

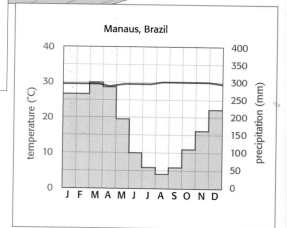

Manaus, Brazil

Desert	**J**	**F**	**M**	**A**	**M**	**J**	**J**	**A**	**S**	**O**	**N**	**D**
Khartoum, Sudan												
Temperature (°C)	23	25	29	32	35	34	32	32	32	32	28	25
Rainfall (mm)	0	0	0	1	4	5	46	75	25	5	1	0

Explaining global climate

The effect of latitude

Latitude is the main factor in global climate. The further you go from the equator, the cooler it gets.

This is because the Earth's surface is curved – which means the sun's energy isn't distributed evenly. The diagram shows how the energy received at the equator is much more direct and concentrated. This, and the thinner atmosphere, means the Earth gets hottest here.

The poles are colder. Here the greater curvature of the Earth means the sun's energy is spread over a larger area. This, and a thicker atmosphere, means colder temperatures. Ice forms and reflects heat back into space, making conditions even colder.

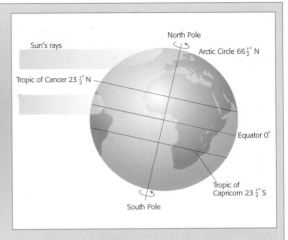

The effect of distance from the sea

The sea is cooler than the land in summer, but warmer in winter. This is because it takes longer to heat up, but is slower to cool down.

Because we're surrounded by sea, the climate of the British Isles is called a **maritime climate**. The sea moderates our climate, making temperatures more even throughout the year. So, our climate isn't as hot in summer or as cold in winter as it could be. Without the seas around us, winter temperatures could fall to -20 °C.

A long way from the sea, the interiors of the large land masses have a **continental climate**, with cold snowy winters and hot dry summers. Siberia and central areas of the USA have this type of climate.

The effect of altitude

Temperatures decrease by 1°C for every 100 metres in altitude (height above sea level). Therefore, mountainous areas are always cooler. Relief rainfall (Unit 3.5) also makes for a wetter environment.

The effect of the prevailing wind

The prevailing wind is the direction the wind blows from most often.

For the British Isles, the prevailing wind is from the south-west. It blows over a warm ocean, so the British Isles is warmer in winter than it could be, given our northerly latitude. And because it blows over the ocean, it also brings moisture – and that means rain.

Our climate would be much colder if the prevailing wind came from the north, from the Arctic (think how we get our coldest weather in winter when the north wind blows).

The effect of ocean currents

Ocean currents are warm or cold, and these affect the climate of coastal areas. For example a warm current called the North Atlantic Drift helps warm the British Isles in winter, by warming the prevailing wind.

Activities

1 Describe the global distribution of these climate zones:
   a equatorial   c desert
   b Mediterranean   d polar

2 a Use the climate data opposite to draw a climate graph for Khartoum.

b Compare two of the climate zones with the information shown for the temperate climate (in Unit 3.5). Use statistical data from the graphs as part of your comparison.

3 Suggest reasons for the differences you have described in question **2**.

Climate and ecosystems

In this unit you'll find out what an ecosystem is, and how ecosystems are related to climate.

What is an ecosystem?

An ecosystem is a unit made up of two parts:

◆ living things (plants, animals, bacteria)

◆ and their non-living surroundings or **environment** – air, water, soil and the climate.

In any ecosystem, the living things interact with the environment and each other. For example, caterpillars in a wood breathe the air, feed on leaves, and get eaten by birds. If it gets too cold, they die.

How big is an ecosystem?

An ecosystem is any size that you choose to study. It could be a pond, a field, a wood, a tropical rainforest or even the whole Earth.

How are ecosystems related to climate?

The world can be divided up into eight big ecosystems, or **biomes**. Each one has its own type of vegetation. Individual biomes are mainly determined by climate. This is because climate affects the growth conditions for vegetation. It does this in a number of ways:

◆ precipitation – particularly the total amount and how it's distributed through the year

◆ temperature – especially the seasonal pattern and the length of the growing season

◆ the number of sunshine hours – which determines the amount of light for photosynthesis

◆ rates of evaporation, transpiration and humidity.

Other factors such as geology (rock type), soils, relief and the drainage of water are also important.

The map on the right shows the distribution of the world's main biomes.

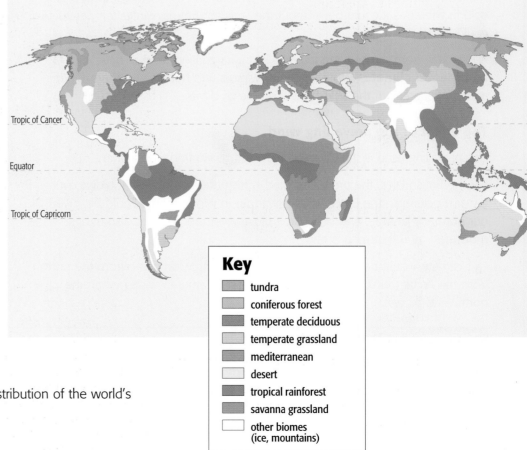

Tropic of Cancer

Equator

Tropic of Capricorn

Key

- tundra
- coniferous forest
- temperate deciduous
- temperate grassland
- mediterranean
- desert
- tropical rainforest
- savanna grassland
- other biomes (ice, mountains)

How we humans fit in

Unlike most animals, we've spread all over the world.

◆ We've moved into every ecosystem (although some climates don't suit us too well).

◆ Our numbers have grown quickly. Now there are over 6.5 billion of us.

◆ We consume a lot. Over 40% of the plants now growing on the Earth will be consumed by us and our livestock (our cows, sheep …).

◆ We use a lot of land. Not just to live on, but to grow food, and provide water and fuels, and dump waste, and so on. Experts say we each 'use' 2 hectares of land (about 1.5 football pitches) in our lifetime. This is called our **ecological footprint**.

There are problems with this

◆ The more land we use up, the less there is for the Earth's other 6 million species.

◆ As we've spread through ecosystems, we've tended to take them over – and drive many other species to extinction.

◆ In places, we've treated the soil so badly that we've ruined it.

◆ We burn a lot of fossil fuels, and now we think this is causing global warming. That will affect every ecosystem on Earth.

We can change

We need food, fuel, water and shelter.

But we are learning that we must get them in a **sustainable** way. This means in a way that doesn't harm us, or other species, and isn't wasteful.

In other units in this chapter you'll look at four parts of the world in detail:

◆ deserts in a hot desert climate region

◆ Mediterranean regions

◆ tundra in a polar climate region

◆ tropical rainforests in an equatorial climate region.

You will learn what the climate is like and how humans have used, damaged and are starting to repair damaged areas.

Did you know?

Rhinos are killed for their horns. The horn fetches high prices as a traditional medicine in the Far East.

Did you know?

On average, 130 species of plants and animals become extinct each day.

▲ *The endangered black rhinoceros.*

Activities

1 Write your own definition for these terms:
   a ecosystem
   b ecological footprint.

2 Look at the map showing the distribution of the world's main biomes. Choose one of the following and describe its distribution: deserts, Mediterranean, tundra or tropical rainforests.

3 Think about the information in this unit. Will it affect how you think about the world around you? Explain your answer.

4 'The greatest pest ever known.' Is this a fair description of us humans? Justify your answer.

Hot desert climate

In this unit you'll learn about hot deserts and how the climate affects the people living there.

Dunes, camels and cacti

Hot desert climates (sometimes called tropical deserts) are found around the tropics of Cancer (23.5° N) and Capricorn (23.5° S), and on the western side of continents. About 20% of the Earth's land surface is desert, and deserts are some of the driest places on Earth. There are lots of different types of desert, including the ones shown here.

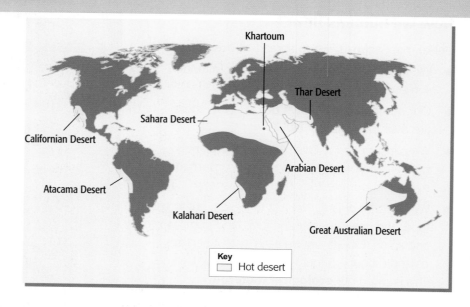

Khartoum

Thar Desert

Sahara Desert

Californian Desert

Arabian Desert

Atacama Desert

Kalahari Desert

Great Australian Desert

Key
☐ Hot desert

▲ Hammada (rock desert), Algeria.

▲ Reg (stone desert), Israel.

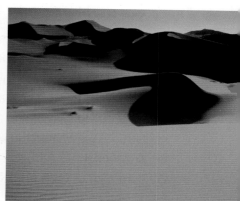

▲ Erg (sand desert), Namibia.

Climate control

Temperature

Hot! Hot! Hot! Daytime temperatures can rise to over 40 °C during the summer. But, hot deserts can get very cold at night as there is no cloud cover to keep the heat in. So, hot deserts can have a high temperature range.

Precipitation

Dry! Less than 250 mm of rain a year. It may not rain in a hot desert for many months (even years). When it does rain it is often a torrential downpour. A heavy desert storm can bring up to 1 mm of rainfall per minute. Normally dry stream channels, called **wadis**, fill up quickly after heavy rains causing dangerous flash floods.

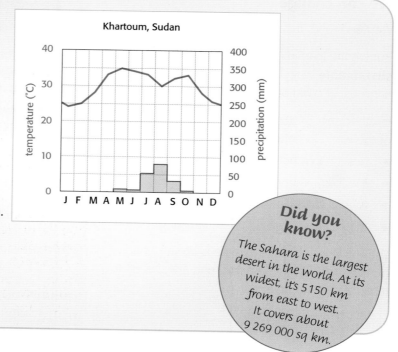

Khartoum, Sudan

temperature (°C)

precipitation (mm)

J F M A M J J A S O N D

Did you know?

The Sahara is the largest desert in the world. At its widest, it's 5150 km from east to west. It covers about 9 269 000 sq km.

Coping with the climate

◆ Traditionally, in order to survive in a desert, most inhabitants were **nomadic** (e.g. the Bedouin, see photo). They travelled from place to place in search of food and water for themselves and their animals – sheep, goats and camels. In the 1950s and 60s many Bedouin started leaving their traditional nomadic life to live and work in the cities of the Middle East as their grazing areas shrank and population increased.

◆ Water is very limited. Wells, **oases**, rivers and streams often run dry. When it does rain the water quickly disappears into the ground. Some countries (e.g. Niger) have built large dams across rivers to provide drinking and **irrigation** water for people.

◆ Other countries (e.g. Dubai) have started to get their water from the sea using the process of **desalination** (removing the salt). But this is very expensive and would be impossible for countries without a coastline.

◆ Where irrigation water is available, a variety of crops can be grown, including cash crops.

Desert tourism

Deserts have become popular tourist destinations recently. The desert landscape can be spectacular, with strange rock formations that have been weathered and eroded by the wind.

New types of adventure sport are becoming popular in hot deserts, e.g. sandboarding (like snow and skate boarding) and dune bashing (racing dune buggies).

Vegetation

Vegetation has adapted to survive in the harsh climate.

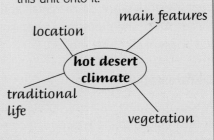
Did you know?
Between 1964 and 2001, the average annual rainfall at Quillagua, in the Atacama Desert, Chile, was just 0.5 mm.

▲ Sandboarding in Peru.

- Some plants have long (7–10 m) taproots that tap into groundwater sources.
- Other plants have horizontal root systems that lie just below the surface.
- Some plants store water in their roots, stems, leaves or fruit (these are called **succulents**).
- Small leaves or spines, glossy and waxy leaves all reduce water loss.
- Seeds can stay dormant for years, but can germinate quickly when it rains.

Activities

1 Make a larger copy of the mind map in your book. Add extra legs to put all the information from this unit onto it.

main features

location

hot desert climate

traditional life

vegetation

2 Describe a hot desert climate.

Human impact in hot deserts

In this unit you'll learn about the spreading of deserts, how people have helped to cause this problem and how we might be able to stop the process.

The Sahel

The Sahel is a strip of land south of the Sahara Desert that runs right across Africa. It's about 500 km wide. The Sahel is under intense pressure from human activity and in some places the quality of the land has declined so much that it's turned into desert. This process of land degradation is called **desertification**. To make matters worse, the countries that make up the Sahel are all LEDCs with rapidly growing populations.

Desertification

Desertification happens when human and climatic processes combine so that the land can't support vegetation.

Land that was once fertile enough for farming starts to suffer soil erosion and eventually turns to desert. In the Sahel, prolonged drought and human activity have resulted in millions of hectares of land being lost to the desert each year. This can contribute to major human disasters, such as the 2005 famine in Niger. The rains failed, so crops didn't grow. Nearly 4 million people were affected by starvation. A massive international aid effort sent emergency food supplies to the country.

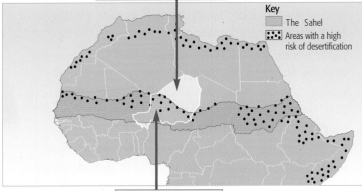

Northern Niger is in the Sahara Desert. This area is virtually rainless.

Key
- The Sahel
- Areas with a high risk of desertification

Southern Niger is in the Sahel. This area has moderate but unreliable rainfall.

Did you know?

The word 'Sahel' literally means 'shore of the sea of sand'.

The causes of desertification

Overcultivation

Population growth has put pressure on the farmland to produce more and more food. This intensive use of the land exhausts it of nutrients – so crops no longer grow and soil is lost through wind and water erosion.

Overgrazing

Permanent and nomadic pastoral farmers have to let their livestock graze on marginal land closer to the desert. Once the protective vegetation cover is eaten, the soil is likely to be eroded.

Deforestation

Across the Sahel, 80% of domestic energy comes from burning firewood. Increased population means increased demand for wood, and so the land is cleared of trees. Again, the soil becomes vulnerable to erosion.

▲ *The advancing desert.*

Climate change

The climate of the Sahel has become much drier over the last forty years. The graph shows that twenty two out of the last thirty years have been drier than average. Less rainfall means poorer grazing and lower crop production. Underground water reserves have been used up. Population pressure makes the problem worse.

These causes combine to create a 'spiral into desertification' (see below right).

Sustainable land management

There are a number of land management practices that if used well can stop, and even reverse, the process of desertification. These include:

◆ Tethering cattle and goats to limit the area they can graze. This has the added advantage of creating manure in one place that can then be spread as a fertiliser. Fodder (animal food) is taken to the animals.

◆ Farmers diversifying into a more varied range of crops and trees. This helps bind the soil together and prevents erosion. And the vegetation puts a continual supply of nutrients back into the soil.

◆ Harvesting fuelwood from branches – rather than taking the whole tree – prevents deforestation.

◆ Building stone lines to trap soil and water when the rains arrive. This prevents erosion and can help increase crop production (see Unit 10.8).

◆ Controlled burning of grasses to prevent the spread of devastating wildfires.

◆ Planting more trees to help bind the soil together and stop it getting washed away by rain, and blown away by the wind. Trees like the Kad Tree are popular because it is drought resistant and its leaves provide food for cattle.

◆ The development of fuel-efficient stoves like the **Jiko**. These are very cheap and use about half the amount of wood an open fire does. So, not as many trees are cut down.

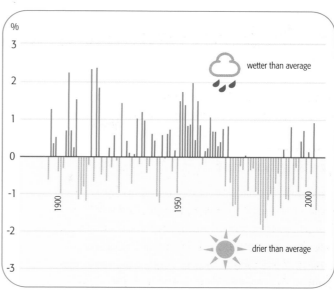

▲ The Sahel has mostly been drier than average since 1970.

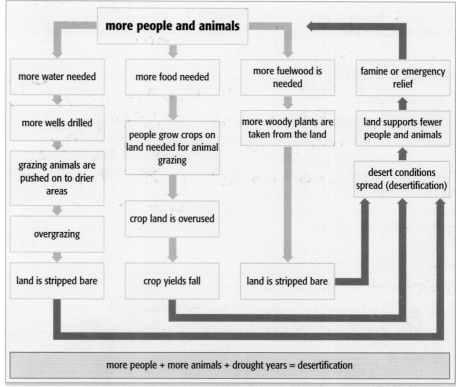

more people + more animals + drought years = desertification

▲ Jiko stoves are becoming common in East African homes

Activities

1 Write a definition of 'desertification'.
2 How far has desertification been caused by people? Justify your answer.
3 What does the 'spiral of desertification' mean? Explain it in your own words.

Mediterranean climate

In this unit you'll learn about areas with a Mediterranean climate and how the climate affects people living there.

Feeling hot, hot, hot …

You'll find Mediterranean climates on the west coasts of continents, roughly between latitudes 30° and 40° north and south of the equator, and around the Mediterranean Sea. Regions with a Mediterranean climate include much of California, the Western Cape in South Africa, central Chile and the coastal areas of South West Australia. Places with a Mediterranean climate are really pleasant places to live in, and are popular with tourists.

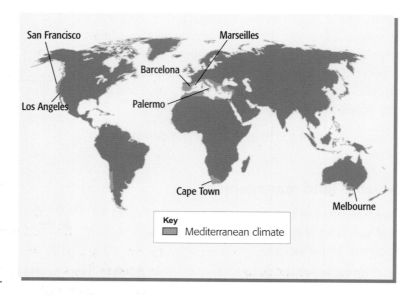

San Francisco
Marseilles
Barcelona
Los Angeles
Palermo
Cape Town
Melbourne

Key
Mediterranean climate

Climate control

Temperature

Temperatures in the summer can be high – up to nearly 30 °C. But even in the warmest places with a Mediterranean-type climate, temperatures don't get as high as in a hot desert region. Winters are mild and temperatures rarely reach freezing (except in areas with a high altitude). The average winter temperature is 10 °C.

Precipitation

On average, the annual precipitation is less than 1000 mm per year. Summer months can be very dry with little or no rain (though if it does rain it comes in short, heavy thunderstorms), and places with a Mediterranean climate can experience drought conditions. Winters, though, can be very wet.

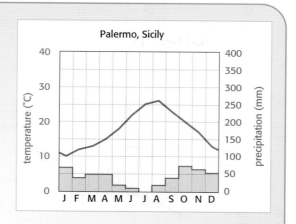

Palermo, Sicily

Seasons

The Mediterranean climate has two definite seasons:
- hot, dry summers
- warm, wet winters.

Wind

Winds can be strong in Mediterranean climate regions, particularly in areas right next to the coast.

Coping with the climate

- Winters are mild and wet enough to grow crops in some areas. In the summer, farmers need to **irrigate** their fields, a very expensive process.

- Cash crops such as citrus fruits can be grown. The crops are protected from the strong winds by **shelter belts**. These are rows of trees planted to shield valuable crops.
- Large reservoirs are built to provide water during the summer drought.
- In summer, vegetation is so dry that fires can break out and spread very quickly. Fields are often laid with fire breaks and fire crews are always on standby at times of risk. In August 2006, several thousand tourists and local people fled from a forest fire in northern Greece. The fire happened at the hottest time of year (the temperature that day was 42 °C) and during a very long dry spell. The flames were fanned by a seasonal northern wind called the **Meltemi**.
- The long hot summers attract tourists. The tourist industry provides important jobs for local people. Some hotels use solar power as a renewable source of energy.
- Traditionally, people in hot countries like Portugal and Greece take a **siesta** (short nap) in the early afternoon – the hottest time of the day.

▲ The blaze spread rapidly across the Halkidiki peninsula in northern Greece.

Vegetation and land use

▼ Cross-section through a Mediterranean landscape.

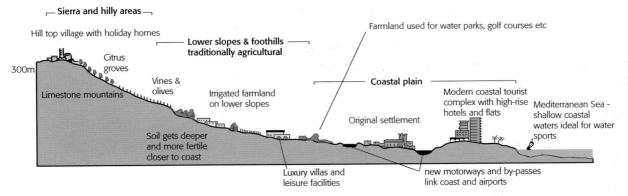

— Sierra and hilly areas —

Hill top village with holiday homes

Farmland used for water parks, golf courses etc

— Lower slopes & foothills —
traditionally agricultural

Citrus groves

300m

Vines & olives

Limestone mountains

Irrigated farmland on lower slopes

— Coastal plain —

Modern coastal tourist complex with high-rise hotels and flats

Mediterranean Sea - shallow coastal waters ideal for water sports

Original settlement

Soil gets deeper and more fertile closer to coast

Luxury villas and leisure facilities

new motorways and by-passes link coast and airports

Mediterranean regions have two natural types of vegetation – woodland and scrub. In Europe there are two types of scrub:

- **maquis** – a dense mass of shrubs found on granite and other impermeable rocks
- **garigue** – sparser low-lying scrub with plants like lavender and rosemary, found on limestone and other permeable rocks.

All the vegetation has to adapt to the summer drought.

- Leaves are small, waxy or glossy, or plants have thorns, to reduce water loss.
- Thick bark protects against heat and water loss.
- Long tap roots reach groundwater supplies.
- Life cycles avoid the summer – plants germinate in the winter rain, flower in the spring and are dormant in the summer.

Activities

1 Make a larger copy of the mind map in your book. Add extra legs to put all the information from this unit onto it.

location main features

Mediterranean climate

land use vegetation

2 a Describe a Mediterranean climate.
  b Give four main differences between the climate graph for Palermo and the climate graph for one of the other climates you have studied.

Human impact in the Mediterranean

In this unit you'll find out how tourism has affected a Mediterranean landscape, and how the Mediterranean Sea is being misused.

How Benidorm was transformed

SPAIN
Benidorm

▲ Benidorm in Spain, in 1960. A fishing town with 6200 residents, two great beaches and just a few hotels.

▲ Benidorm by 1995. 55 000 residents and 350 000 tourists at its busiest time. (Most of them British!)

In 1957 the first **package tour**, from the UK, arrived in Benidorm. Tourists loved the sunshine, peace and quiet. News spread fast and with grants from the Spanish government lots of new hotels were built. There was very little planning control and new buildings were often poor quality. They caused **visual pollution** and scarred the beautiful landscape. New bars, clubs and restaurants spoilt the peace and quiet, contributing to **noise pollution**. By the end of the 1980s Benidorm was really starting to go downhill.

Did you know?

On average a tourist in Benidorm uses 880 litres of water a day ... a local person uses 250.

Benidorm today - doing better

In the 1990s the Spanish government took more control of development. Bad hotels were improved and modern hotels were built. A theme park was built to attract tourists all year. Today Benidorm gets around 4 million visitors a year and the area generates 1% of Spain's **GDP**.

Coastline under pressure

Tourists generate high levels of waste, and in many cases sewage systems can't cope, so raw sewage is washed into the sea. Every year hundreds of tons of sand are lost from the Costa Blanca (in shoes, clothing and sandwiches)! Over-use of Benidorm's beaches has led to erosion and damage.

Water shortage

Benidorm uses huge amounts of water for swimming pools (30 000 of them!), showers and golf courses. The level of water in aquifers has fallen, so farmland is drying out. Sea water is seeping into the aquifers so Benidorm has to pipe water from the River Tajo, 480 km away.

Sustainable management

The Spanish and local governments have been tackling the problems:

◆ Providing grants to support clean-up operations.

◆ Developing sustainable tourism policies to ensure that the local area isn't harmed and can be enjoyed by future generations.

◆ The government is keen to introduce a sound-limit in nightclubs and limit the number of people who are allowed in.

◆ The EU awards 'blue flags' to beaches which meet high standards of beach cleanliness and water quality.

The Mediterranean – use and abuse

The UN's Environment Programme estimated that every year:
- 650 million tons of sewage
- 129 000 tons of mineral oil
- 60 000 tons of mercury
- 3800 tons of lead
- 36 000 tons of phosphates
are dumped into the Mediterranean.

The sea is a major transport route. About 100 000 tons of crude oil are discharged every year from accidental spills and illegal tank cleaning.

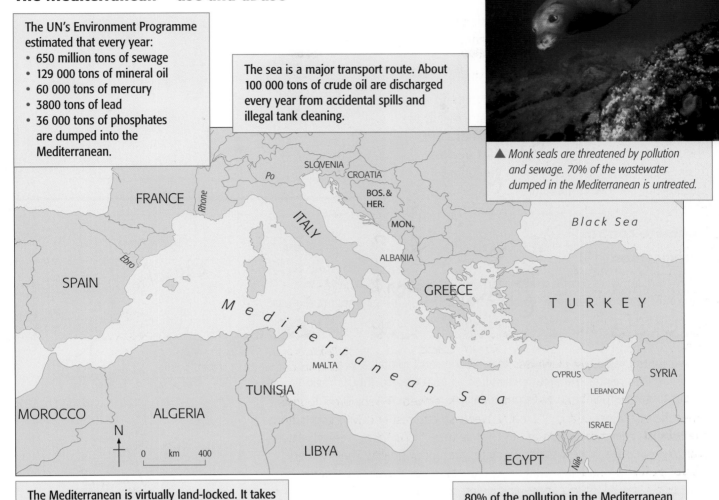

▲ Monk seals are threatened by pollution and sewage. 70% of the wastewater dumped in the Mediterranean is untreated.

The Mediterranean is virtually land-locked. It takes almost 100 years to renew the water.

80% of the pollution in the Mediterranean comes from the land.

Sustainable management

The Mediterranean Action Plan (MAP) was adopted by Mediterranean countries and the EU in 1975. It aims to:

◆ protect the environment

◆ deal with coastal zone management, assessing and controlling pollution, protecting ecosystems and preserving biodiversity.

The Barcelona Convention is the legal part of the MAP. It has reached agreements on:

◆ eliminating land-based pollution

◆ action plans

◆ using clean technologies

◆ taking measures to reduce the risk of pollution from accidents.
Not all the Mediterranean countries have signed the agreements – so the sea is still at risk from pollution.

Pollution reaches the Mediterranean via rivers. The Po, Ebro, Nile and Rhône carry large amounts of agricultural and industrial waste.

Activities

1 a Draw a spider diagram to show the problems tourism has caused in, and around, Benidorm.
  b Draw another spider diagram to show how Benidorm's problems are being tackled.
2 What problems is pollution likely to cause in the Mediterranean?
3 The Mediterranean region is likely to see a big rise in tourism in the next 15 years. How can the landscape and the sea be protected?

Tundra regions

In this unit you'll learn about the Arctic tundra and how the climate affects people living there.

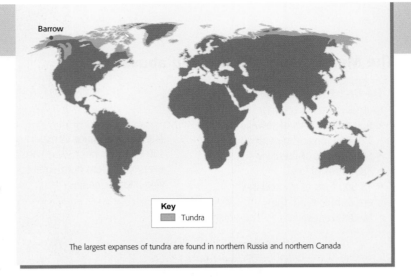

Key
◻ Tundra

The largest expanses of tundra are found in northern Russia and northern Canada

Land of the midnight sun

Arctic tundra regions are found in the Northern Hemisphere in areas with a polar climate, mostly to the north of the Arctic Circle. Tundra comes from the Finnish word *tunturia*, which means treeless plain. Trees don't grow very well in the tundra because of the low temperatures.

Climate control

Temperature

Very cold. In winter temperatures often drop to at least −25 °C and in summer temperatures rarely go above 10 °C. There's a big temperature range.

Precipitation

Low. Tundra regions receive less than 250 mm of rainfall a year. With so little rainfall the area is classified as cold desert. Tundra regions tend to get a small amount of precipitation every month.

Daylight

Anywhere north of the Arctic Circle experiences at least one day a year when the sun doesn't set, and one day when the sun doesn't rise. The further north you go the more daylight you get in summer, and the more darkness in winter. Prudhoe Bay (northern Alaska) has two months of the year when the sun doesn't set, and two months when it doesn't rise.

Wind

Very windy, with winds blowing over 48–97 km/h. The winds are very cold when they blow off the Arctic ice cap.

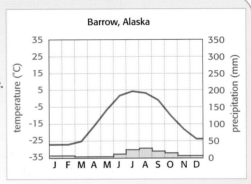

▼ *Houses built on stilts in Chukotka, Siberia, Russia.*

Did you know?

The greatest temperature range recorded is around the Siberian 'cold pole', in eastern Russia. Temperatures in Verkhoyansk have spanned 105 °C, from −68 °C to 37 °C.

Coping with the climate

◆ Low temperatures mean the ground is permanently frozen (permafrost) for most of the year. This makes building difficult. When the ice on the surface melts, the water can't drain away because of the permafrost below. In summer the ground becomes marshy.

◆ Houses are built on wooden or concrete stilts, so that heat from the buildings doesn't thaw the permafrost and make the building subside.

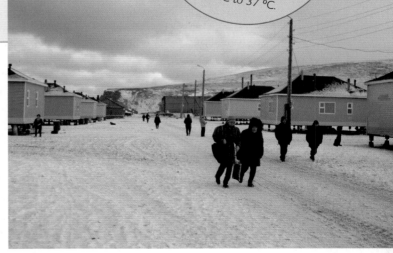

- Water and sewage pipes are enclosed in a *Utilidor* which is heated by steam to stop it freezing.
- Oil pipelines are built above ground level and insulated. Oil storage tanks are heated to stop them from freezing.
- Cars have to be plugged into an electricity supply all night (it can be night for 24 hours!) to stop the engine freezing (see photo).
- The Inuit (**indigenous** people living in Arctic coastal areas) traditionally relied on fish, sea mammals, and land animals for food, heat, light, clothing, tools, and shelter. In winter some Inuit chose to live in igloos, while others used snow to insulate their houses made from whalebone and caribou hides. Traditionally Inuit are **nomadic**.
- Other indigenous tribes live inland, e.g. the Athapaskan Indians of northern Alaska. One group of Athapaskans, the Gwich'in Indians, supplement their diet by hunting caribou. Each year around 180 000 caribou pass their village as they migrate.
- Now igloos and skin tents have been replaced with a more modern lifestyle and permanent housing. But the Inuit and the Athapaskan Indians still have strong traditions and values.

Vegetation

There are about 1700 kinds of plants in the arctic and sub-arctic, and vegetation has adapted to survive in the harsh climate.

▲ Yellow electric cables hang down in a car park in Alaska to power car heaters in the winter, to stop the engines freezing.

▲ Alaskan caribou migrate north to spend the summer on the coastal plain of the Arctic Ocean.

- Plants have short roots as the ground is often frozen.
- Plants are low-growing to avoid the strong, cold winds.
- Plants have a short life-cycle adapted to the short growing season.
- On south-facing sheltered, drier slopes brightly coloured flowers grow.
- In poorly drained areas mosses grow and rocks are covered in lichen.
- Small stunted shrubs might grow near rivers or streams.

Activities

1 Make a larger copy of the mind map in your book. Add extra legs to put all the information from this unit onto it.

location   main features
Tundra
traditional life   vegetation

2 a Describe the climate at Barrow.
  b Give four main differences between the climate graph for Barrow and the climate graph for one of the other climates you have studied.

Human impact in the tundra

In this unit you'll find out about the effects of resource exploitation in the tundra.

Oil – black gold

Prudhoe Bay is located on the northern coast of Alaska. Oil was discovered there in 1968 but production didn't begin until 1977. Production peaked in 1988 at about 2 million barrels a day, but fell to below 1 million a day in 2005. It is estimated that all the oil will be extracted by 2015.

Oil from Prudhoe Bay is transported by pipeline to the closest ice-free port, Valdez, 800 miles away. Building the pipeline presented special challenges:

◆ The climate makes working conditions very difficult (especially in winter).

◆ The pipeline had to cross three mountain ranges and lots of rivers and streams.

◆ Almost half the pipeline had to be built on stilts to avoid melting the permafrost.

◆ In places it had to be 6 metres high to allow caribou to migrate.

◆ Pumping stations were installed so that oil could be shut off if there was a leak.

Globally there's a shortage of oil, and the US government is keen to exploit other oil reserves in the Arctic. There are significant reserves in the Arctic National Wildlife Refuge (ANWR) east of Prudhoe Bay and there have been many heated debates about whether the oil should be extracted. Look at the next page for some of the arguments.

Activities

1 Should drilling for oil be allowed in the ANWR? Justify your answer.

2 What are the likely impacts of drilling for oil? Think about the effects on people and the environment.

3 How could the development of the oil reserves be managed sustainably?

Oil spill devastates Alaska ... again

Fifteen years after the *Exxon Valdez* devastated the Alaskan coast there's another oil spill.

A freighter ran aground on one of the Aleutian Islands. The ship was carrying 1.8 million litres of heavy oil and 21 000 litres of diesel.

The spilled oil threatens a wildlife refuge – home to sea otters (pictured), seals, halibut and crabs. The oil spill is small compared to the *Exxon Valdez* spill, but the oil is difficult to break up and will be dangerous for the wildlife in the refuge.

For

The Inupiat Eskimos have lived in the Arctic for thousands of years. 'We live as our elders taught us, and rely on the land and resources for our physical, cultural and economic well-being. The oil industry around Prudhoe Bay has brought us benefits, including jobs. We have seen how development can exist alongside our natural resources and way of life. We believe we can only afford to keep most of our land as wilderness if we can develop a smaller area such as the Coastal Plain of the ANWR for oil.'

For

The ANWR consists of 19 million acres. The US government wants to use just 2000 acres to ensure the nation's energy supply. Drilling in the ANWR could produce 16 billion barrels of oil – equivalent to 30 years of oil imports from Saudi Arabia. Since drilling began in Prudhoe Bay over 20 years ago, the Arctic caribou herd has grown from 3000 to 27 500. No polar bears have been killed or injured as a result of extracting oil.

Did you know?

The Gwich'in Indians call the coastal plain of the ANWR The sacred place where life begins'.

Against

The Gwich'in Indians believe the Coastal Plain of the ANWR should be protected from oil and gas development. The elders called the village chiefs to hold a traditional gathering about the threat to the caribou birthing and nursing grounds. The Gwich'in believe that drilling would violate the human rights of their people because of the impacts it would have on their culture and way of life.

Against

The Natural Resources Defense Council says that 55% of Americans oppose drilling in the ANWR. They say drilling has nothing to do with energy independence, but is all about oil company profits. Drilling would be a disaster for the environment – look at Prudhoe Bay – there are mountains of sewage sludge, scrap metal, rubbish and over 60 waste sites that leak acids, pesticides, solvents and diesel.

Equatorial climate

In this unit you'll learn about equatorial climate regions and how the climate affects people living there.

Tree frogs and pythons and …

Places with an equatorial climate are found in the tropics (5° either side of the equator). And this is where you get tropical rainforests – where it's hot and wet all year. They are our most ecologically bio-diverse ecosystem.

◆ They are home to 50% of all life-forms on the planet.

◆ They produce 40% of the world's oxygen.

◆ The vegetation is luxurious and dense, and trees can grow to over 50 metres in height.

◆ They have been nicknamed the 'Worlds Largest Pharmacy' because of all the medical drugs which are found there.

The tropical rainforests now cover less than 6% of the Earth's surface. 200 years ago they covered twice as much.

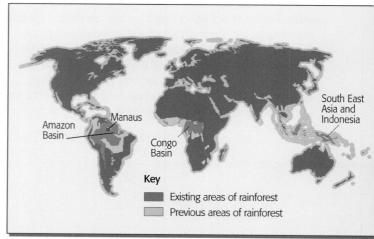

Key

- ■ Existing areas of rainforest
- □ Previous areas of rainforest

Climate control

Daily rhythm

There are no real seasons in the rainforest. Each day is similar to the next. But there is a daily pattern to the weather:

◆ 8.00 a.m. – dry with intense heat from the sun.

◆ 12.00 noon – high temperatures, up to 33 °C, and the formation of cumulus clouds.

◆ 6.00 p.m. – thick cumulonimbus clouds, thunderstorms, and torrential downpours of rain.

Temperature

The average daily temperature is usually about 28 °C. Only occasionally does it go above 35 °C. It never goes below 20 °C. The temperature range may be as little as 2 °C.

Precipitation

Typically, 2000 mm of rain falls per year – but it can be more. The atmosphere is sticky – it's hot and humid.

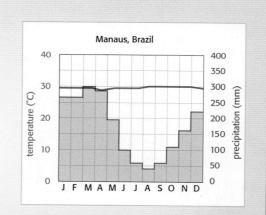

Coping with the climate

Very few people live in regions with an equatorial climate. They have a low population density. The dense tropical rainforest makes building roads and railways very difficult, so these areas remain isolated.

People who live in tropical rainforests, like the Amerindians in the Amazon Basin, farm traditionally using shifting cultivation.

- A small area of rainforest is cleared using low technology (e.g. stone axes and other hand tools).

- After the fallen trees have been allowed to dry, the area is burnt (see photo). This removes weeds and roots, and the ash provides a natural fertiliser. This type of shifting cultivation is called '**slash and burn**'.

- The area is planted mainly with manioc, but also rice, yams, cassava and pumpkins. Tobacco might be grown and sold as a cash crop. The forest provides other food including monkeys, fish and fruit.

- As soon as the trees have been cleared, the nutrient cycle is broken and the soil quickly loses its fertility. Heavy afternoon rain washes (leaches) nutrients out of the soil and contributes to soil erosion.

- After about 4–5 years the nutrients in the ground have become so poor that crops don't grow properly and tribes move to a new area of rainforest and start all over again.

- Because only a small area of rainforest is cleared, it can regenerate itself within 20–25 years.

Vegetation

- Trees are branchless and trunks are tall and thin – this helps them to reach the sunlight more easily.
- Trees have an evergreen appearance due to the continuous growing season. They shed their leaves at any time.
- Leaves often have **drip tips** to help shed heavy rain.
- Leaves can be waxy – to help shed rain and protect them from hungry insects.
- Some trees have large **buttress roots** to support them in shallow soil. Others spread their roots over the surface to capture as many nutrients as possible.
- **Lianas** are woody climbing vines which climb high into the canopy to reach the sunlight.
- **Epiphytes** are plants that grow in the branches of the trees.

Activities

1 Make a larger copy of the mind map in your book. Add extra legs to put all the information from this unit onto it.

location   main features

equatorial climate

traditional farming   vegetation

2 Describe the equatorial climate. Use the climate graph and climate control text to help.

Human impact in the tropical rainforest

In this unit you'll learn how people are clearing the Amazon rainforest – and how they're trying to preserve it.

Chainsaws and fires

For millions of years the rainforests were undisturbed. Small tribes of people lived there, but they were too few in number to alter the ecosystem.

But **deforestation** – the felling of trees – is now taking place very quickly. The world's rainforests may be all gone by 2030. It's claimed that in the Amazon one hectare of forest is cleared every second. That's the equivalent of two football pitches. Let's look at the reasons for this intense human activity.

Did you know?
- Quinine, a drug to help malaria sufferers, was developed from rainforest plants.
- Scientists think useful new drugs could be developed from other rainforest plants.

Economic exploitation

Mining
The Amazon rainforest has developed above a rich base of mineral resources. The most abundant of these is iron ore (haematite). It's exported to countries for steel making. Other metal ores include gold, platinum, copper, lead, and bauxite for aluminium. Vast areas have been cleared to gain access to these reserves. The Carajas Project near to Manaus (see the photo) is the largest open-cast mine of its type.

Logging
There's great demand for tropical hardwoods such as mahogany and rosewood. Consumers in MEDCs find these deep red woods attractive, and pay high prices for furniture and interior fittings made from them. But random logging means that for every tree cut down, at least 30 more may be destroyed in the process. Five million hectares of forest are lost in the Amazon each year as a result.

Cattle ranching
Large areas have been cleared for cattle. Since 1950, two-thirds of the Amazon's lowland forest has been turned into pasture for grazing and the production of beef. Zeebu cattle are reared, as they are best adapted to the humid conditions. But the quality of the grass soon declines as the nutrients are lost from the soil. Many ranches have simply increased in size because of this.

Peasant farming
Since the 1970s, the Brazilian government, concerned about overcrowded cities in the south of the country, has encouraged landless citizens to move to the rainforest, giving them land to clear for subsistence farming. This hasn't been very successful due to the infertile soils – without the forest canopy, there's nothing to replenish the soil with nutrients.

Do rainforests naturally regenerate?

They will, if only small areas are cleared and then left alone. But large-scale deforestation breaks the natural nutrient cycle. As the land is cleared, the soil becomes vulnerable to erosion and the nutrients get washed away by the rains. New tree shoots are unable to establish themselves and the landscape becomes barren. The ecosystem dies (see the photo on the right). Tribal communities lose their way of life. And the global oxygen and carbon dioxide balance changes, contributing to global warming.

Sustainable management

The exploitation of the Amazon's natural resources can help Brazil boost its GDP and improve the quality of life of its population. Activities like logging and mining need to continue. But if they happen in an uncontrolled way, irreversible damage could be done to the rainforest. So, sustainable forest management is required. This means meeting the needs of the present without harming the environment, and so allowing future generations the opportunity to meet their needs.

The state of Acre on the western tip of the rainforest is one area where sustainable approaches are proving successful. These long-term policies are underpinned by three aims:

◆ to protect the forest canopy and bio-diversity, preventing soil erosion

◆ to maintain the operation of the nutrient cycle

◆ to ensure the natural regeneration of the forest.

Activities

1 Describe, and add to, the range of human activities responsible for the rapid deforestation of the Amazon rainforest.

2 Which three sustainable management strategies shown in the spider diagram do you think are the most important? why?

3 Is 'slash and burn' farming sustainable (see Unit 4.9)?

4 What problems might sustainable management strategies cause? What would you advise the Brazilian government to do about these problems?

Agro-forestry
This is the practice of growing trees in combination with agricultural crops. This means farmers can take advantage of the protective canopy and the supply of nutrients from decomposing plant matter.

Forest Reserves
These are areas of forest that are completely protected from all activities, in a similar way to National Parks. They are often close to areas known as extractive reserves, which are dedicated to sustainable products, such as plants for medicines and latex from rubber tapping.

Tree measuring
The felling of a tree should only occur once it has reached a specific height. This ensures that younger trees have a chance of survival.

Sustainable management strategies

Afforestation
This is the planting of new trees once mature trees have been felled. This ensures the canopy is maintained.

Selective logging
Individual trees are felled only when they have matured. This helps preserve the existing canopy, and helps the slower growing hardwoods such as mahogany.

Education
A key component of any successful forest management strategy is to enable those who use the forest to become the stewards of the forest, protecting its future.

Climate change

In this unit you'll learn about the issue of climate change and the possible effects of global warming.

The big issue

Is global climate changing? If so, how quickly? What effects will it have?

A small rise in global temperature of just a degree or two could have a big impact. Already the Arctic ice seems to be melting. People and animals living there are already being affected. Some scientists predict more droughts, more floods, and more extreme weather events such as hurricanes.

What is climate change?

Over very long periods of time the Earth's climate has naturally changed. But now scientists think the natural cycles of change have been overtaken by rapid global warming. **Global warming** is the rise in temperature of the Earth's atmosphere.

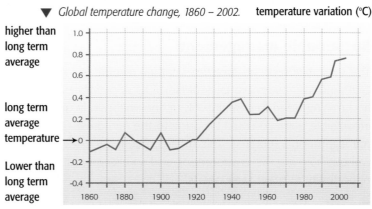

▼ *Global temperature change, 1860 – 2002.* temperature variation (°C)

What's causing it?

The scientific principle behind global warming is the **greenhouse effect**. This is an essential process – without it the Earth would be too cold for life.

But human activity is putting more of the greenhouse gases such as carbon dioxide (CO_2) and methane into the atmosphere. These activities include:

◆ burning coal and petrol (fossil fuels) for industry and transport – particularly car and air transport
◆ cutting down of rainforests and other forests
◆ farming – animal waste produces methane.

Although a few researchers disagree, most scientists predict that global temperatures will rise between 2.5 °C and 10.5 °C over the next 100 years. It's difficult to assess exactly how quickly this will happen, and what impact it will have on the planet.

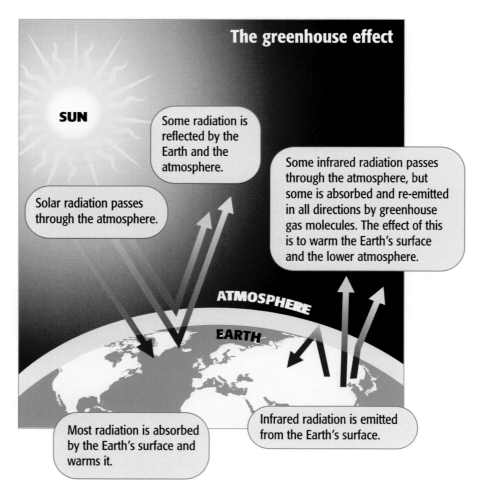

The greenhouse effect

SUN

Some radiation is reflected by the Earth and the atmosphere.

Solar radiation passes through the atmosphere.

Some infrared radiation passes through the atmosphere, but some is absorbed and re-emitted in all directions by greenhouse gas molecules. The effect of this is to warm the Earth's surface and the lower atmosphere.

ATMOSPHERE

EARTH

Most radiation is absorbed by the Earth's surface and warms it.

Infrared radiation is emitted from the Earth's surface.

What might happen?

Nobody knows for sure – but here are some predictions about what *might* happen:

◆ Sea levels could rise between 9 and 88 cm. This would mean: more coastal erosion; more coastal flooding; the loss of vital fertile land in low-lying areas like Bangladesh or the Mississippi delta.

◆ In many parts of the world, warmer weather would mean a longer growing season.

◆ More carbon dioxide (CO_2) in the atmosphere should make plants grow more energetically. Experts reckon the extra CO_2 would improve food output by 17%.

◆ People like warm climates; heating bills are lower and clothing costs are reduced.

◆ Many natural ecosystems could be lost – perhaps forever.

◆ There could be greater threats to human health as mosquitoes and other disease-carrying insects spread infection over wider areas.

So, not all the possible consequences of global warming are negative – some can even be benefits.

Did you know?
The concentration of CO_2 in the atmosphere has increased by more than 30% since 1800.

Did you know?
Computer models predict that if nothing is done the world will be warmer by 1.4-5.8 °C by 2100.

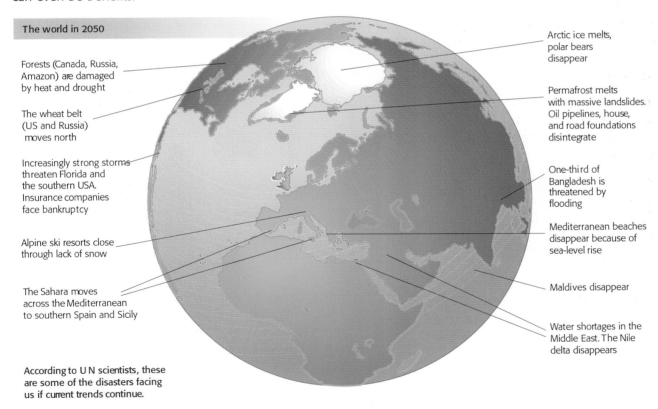

The world in 2050

Forests (Canada, Russia, Amazon) are damaged by heat and drought

The wheat belt (US and Russia) moves north

Increasingly strong storms threaten Florida and the southern USA. Insurance companies face bankruptcy

Alpine ski resorts close through lack of snow

The Sahara moves across the Mediterranean to southern Spain and Sicily

Arctic ice melts, polar bears disappear

Permafrost melts with massive landslides. Oil pipelines, house, and road foundations disintegrate

One-third of Bangladesh is threatened by flooding

Mediterranean beaches disappear because of sea-level rise

Maldives disappear

Water shortages in the Middle East. The Nile delta disappears

According to U N scientists, these are some of the disasters facing us if current trends continue.

Activities

1 Look at the graph of global temperatures. How much has the average temperature risen since 1861?

2 Explain the process of global warming.

3 Is there sufficient evidence to state that climate is changing?

4 Produce a diagram or table to show the impact of global warming on both MEDCs and LEDCs.

What can we do about global warming?

In this unit you will find out how we can tackle global warming.

What can governments do?

A lot of governments have been working really hard to cut down emissions of greenhouse gases. In December 1997, more than 160 nations signed an agreement called the **Kyoto Protocol**.

The Kyoto Protocol is an international agreement on climate change. It comits MEDCs to reduce greenhouse gas emissions to 5% below 1990 levels.

The aim is to keep greenhouse gases in the atmosphere at a level that would prevent dangerous changes in the climate.

For and against Kyoto

Not all countries were happy about the Kyoto Protocol. Some were for it, others objected.

EU – responsible for 24% of CO_2 emissions, agreed to the Kyoto Protocol.

Russia – responsible for 17% of CO_2 emissions – finally agreed to the Kyoto Protocol in 2004.

USA – responsible for 36% of CO_2 emissions – says the Protocol doesn't take into account emissions from developing countries, which it thinks will soon be emitting as much as it does. They pulled out of Kyoto in 2001. But, within the USA some cities, states and companies are acting to reduce emissions.

Japan – responsible for 9% of CO_2 emissions – wants all countries to agree to the Protocol.

Australia – responsible for 2% of CO_2 emissions – says they won't agree to the Kyoto Protocol until the USA does, and that it would mean a loss of jobs and would damage industry.

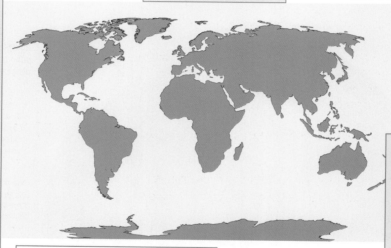

Emissions details are 1990 figures

Other organisations, e.g. the EU, agree that substances released into the atmosphere by human activities lead to other environmental problems, e.g.:

◆ acid rain
◆ poor air quality
◆ damage to, and dirtying of, buildings
◆ holes in the ozone layer
◆ poisoning ecosystems
◆ exposure to hazardous substances.

The UK has signed the Kyoto Protocol. On the right is a speech by a government minister, explaining the plans for cutting the release of greenhouse gases in the UK.

'In the UK, our first goal is to obtain 10% of our electricity from renewable sources by 2010, with the hope of doubling this by 2020 ... Wind energy will play a very big part ... both onshore and offshore wind generators. Wind generation projects currently amount to more than 2000 MW ... total UK windfarm capacity is currently around 650 MW. We estimate that nearly 500 MW of capacity will be built this year, or about four times as much as last year ... We are also encouraging the development of other forms of renewable energy, such as biomass, solar cells, and wave and tidal energy ... to create a much more varied renewable energy sector.'

Because we get so much rain and wind in Scotland some Scottish Ministers believe that Scotland could become self-sufficient in energy production by just using the renewable sources we have available.

Countries are also investing in technology that will help us use less fuel – by developing more efficient car engines, heating systems and so on. In Scotland we are trying to encourage more people to use public transport (see Unit 5.8)

What can I do?

Just look at a typical day …

Jed's Day

07.28: (as late as possible) Alarm rings on mobile. Switch on radio. Batteries dead. Chuck old batteries.
07.30: Stumble out of bed, go to loo – long flush. Pressure shower.
07.40: Get dressed, go downstairs.
07.45: Fill kettle. Boil kettle. Make cup of tea. Breakfast.
07.55: Run tap. Clean teeth. Turn off tap.
08.00: Get lift to school.
08.45 - 15.30: School – lessons, send texts, school dinner, fizzy drink from vending machine, chuck can in bin, listen to some MP3 tracks. Brain on screensaver.
15.45: Bus home. Buy drink in plastic recyclable bottle. Chuck bottle in bin. Download a ring tone; some more MP3 tracks.
16.15: Switch on computer to start homework. Actually use Playstation/TV.
18.00: Leave TV on standby, computer on screensaver. Have tea.

No, not **this** sort of car-sharing!

So what can you and I do to slow down the emission of greenhouse gases? Basically, use less energy based on fossil fuels.

This spider diagram shows some of the ways to use energy more wisely. Which ones do you do now, and which ones could you do if you wanted?

Low-energy light bulbs cost around £3 each. They can save £10 on electricity per year. A bulb used for 4 hours a day will last 10 years.

The average UK family spends £574 on central heating each year. Lowering the thermostat on the central heating by 2°C can save 15% or more on your heating bill.

USING ENERGY WISELY

If your TV is on standby 18 hours a day, and electricity costs 5 pence per kWh, you'll save £3.29 per year on your electricity bill just by switching the TV off!

Full loft insulation covering an area of up to 51 square metres costs about £220 and saves £92 in heating costs each year.

The average UK family uses 380 kWh of electricity each year on lighting, at 5 pence per kWh. Turning out a light that would otherwise have been left on can cut the lighting bill by 31%.

Activities

1 a Why do countries need to cooperate to reduce greenhouse gas emissions?
 b Why is it difficult to get everyone to agree?
2 What can Scotland do to reduce its production of greenhouse gases?

3 a List every resource you used today, from when you got up untill this lesson. Make a two-column table showing your activity and the resource used.
 b How could you use energy more carefully?

The big picture

This chapter is about settlements – the places where people live. These are the big ideas behind the chapter:

◆ All settlements, however big or small, have a site and at least one function.

◆ Settlements are ranked in order of size and importance (the biggest and most important at the top).

◆ More and more people are living in towns and cities.

◆ Land use changes across cities. The Burgess model shows land use in MEDC cities.

◆ Cities have problems of deprivation – but these problems can be tackled.

◆ Other problems include traffic (everywhere seems to have this problem!) and urban sprawl.

Your goals for this chapter

By the end of this chapter you should be able to answer these questions:

◆ What factors were important for the original sites of settlements? How many can you name?

◆ What is a settlement function?

◆ What is a settlement hierarchy, and what does a diagram of it look like?

◆ What is urbanisation? And what's the connection between industry and urbanisation?

◆ How does land use change across an MEDC city? Draw the Burgess urban model.

◆ Why do urban zones develop?

◆ Give examples of problems in MEDC cities. Then give some examples of how these problems can be tackled.

◆ Why is traffic such a big problem in Edinburgh? What is being done about it?

◆ Urban sprawl – what's causing it, and what are the problems? Can we stop it?

◆ Give examples of the developments on Edinburgh's greenbelt.

◆ What do these terms mean?
sphere of influence, CBD, urban model, urban zones, redevelopment, renewal, rural-urban fringe, counter-urbanisation, green belt

And then . . .

When you finish the chapter, come back here and see if you've met your goals!

Did you know?
Footprints found in the Mexican city of Puebla have been dated at over 40 000 years old.

Did you know?
The city of Bravos in Romania is becoming increasingly popular with the local bear population. They can be seen on the outskirts of the city at night looking for dinner in dustbins.

Did you know?
Urban areas generally have fewer married people, and lower birth rates, than rural areas.

Did you know?
In Edinburgh 43% of households have at least one car or van (some have more). The figure for Glasgow is 34%.

Your chapter starter

Out moose!

Look at the photo on page 80.
Where do you think this is? Why?
Why has this place been built here?
Is this place likely to have any problems? What might they be?

5.1 Site

In this unit you'll find out about the things people looked for when choosing a place to settle.

What is 'site'?

A settlement's **site** is the land it is built on: a hill or a plain, bog or dry land, or a location that has **resources**. A settlement's **situation** is its location in relation to its surroundings.

A

Drained marshland

B

C

D

E

F

Looking for a place to stay

The photographs opposite show locations that people have found useful.

◆ Water is always needed. So a site with a good water supply is a **wet point**.

◆ If a region is wet and low-lying, a slightly higher location is a **dry point**.

◆ If you live in lawless times, you'll be looking for a site that's easy to **defend** – perhaps on the top of a hill, or within a river meander.

◆ You might want **shelter** from the burning sun in hot areas like the Sahel.

◆ Or you might locate on the sunny side (or **aspect**) of a deep valley.

◆ Some settlements are located near passes (or **gaps**) through hills.

◆ Settlements often locate near river crossings, or where main transport routes such as rivers and roads meet, so they can **trade**.

◆ Many settlements are sited close to **resources** such as good farmland.

As times changed, the sites people preferred to settle on changed.

If the site is a really good one, the settlement will grow and adapt.

You can see from the second map here that London was a **route centre** by Tudor times. There's a bit of chicken-and-egg here – did London become important because it was a route centre, or did routes radiate to and from London because London was important?

Good sites were more important in the past, but are less so now. This is because we now have better technology. A settlement will grow almost anywhere, if there's a strong enough **economic** reason (if there's money in it!).

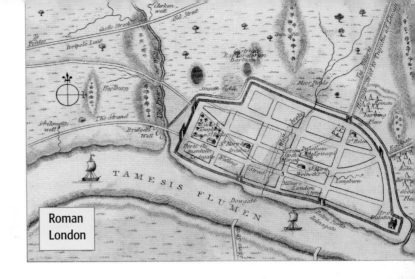

Roman London

Tudor London

Victorian London

Activities

1 Describe the site of your school.

2 For each of the sites listed A to F opposite, decide which of the site factors above apply, e.g. shelter, defence, etc. Some may have one, two, or more site advantages.

3 a Why do you think London's site was first chosen?

 b How do you think London changed and adapted to become a site with many advantages?

Settlement functions

In this unit you'll learn about the things that happen in settlements, and the role settlements play in our lives.

What is a 'function'?

A **function** is a job or process. An **urban function** is an operation that happens in a town or city. It could:

- sell expensive or rare goods, or services
- provide jobs – in industry or in services
- administer the area surrounding it
- have great museums and galleries
- be home to a football club
- have lots to do – movies to watch, places to eat
- have many schools and one – or more – universities
- be defensive – to protect itself and the surrounding area
- be a place of pilgrimage for one or more religions
- have specialist hospitals
- be a transport hub (**route centre**)
- be a port
- and have housing areas for all the workers.

All settlements perform one or more useful functions that give a good reason for their survival. Most settlements have several functions:

- A **hamlet** is a little group with only houses.
- A **village** has houses, and at least one other function – maybe a church, a village hall, a pub, and possibly a shop. It may be a meeting place for people and the goods and services they need, and not be very different from a thousand other villages. Some villages and towns have specialised functions. For example, the Welsh village of Hay-on-Wye has 39 bookshops, but a population of only 1450. Once a year it has a festival (pictured on the right), which draws around 8000 people.
- Lots of towns are **market towns**. Their markets may have been running for hundreds of years, and now they may have lots of supermarkets – but the open-air market still runs once a week.

Functions can change over time – e.g. a place may no longer have a defensive function.

Land use in urban areas (that's towns and cities) is mostly the result of the **primary functions** of the town or city – residential, industrial, retail, administrative, commercial and recreational.

Jerusalem is a holy place for me.

... and me!

... and me!

Glastonbury it ain't!

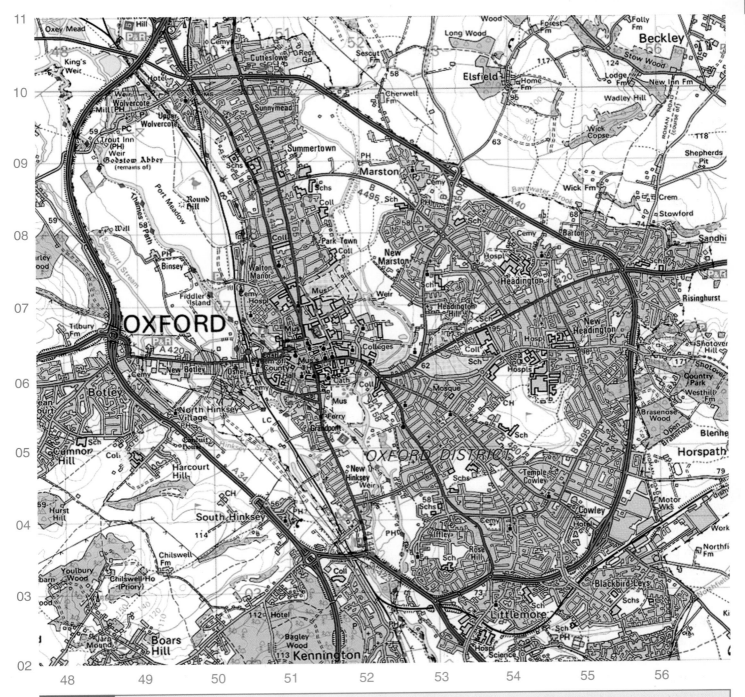

Activities

1 a What is an urban function?

b What do you think is the main function of Oxford? (Look at the OS map above.)

c What is the main function of the place where you live?

d Is there a market town near you? A route centre? An industrial town? A tourist centre? Give named examples.

2 When a settlement becomes a town or city, it has many functions, not just one. Using the OS map above, what is the evidence that Oxford is a university town? Give grid references in your answer.

3 Look for evidence for other functions of Oxford:
- a cultural centre
- a county town
- an industrial centre
- a historic town
- a recreational centre
- a route centre
- a tourist town
- a residential settlement

Provide a grid reference every time.

Settlement hierarchies

In this unit you will learn how settlements are ranked in order of size and importance.

How the hierarchy works

For this unit, you need to know the word **hierarchy** – a simpler word is **ranking**. On the right is a diagram of a **settlement hierarchy** – a ranking of settlements, with the biggest settlement at the top. Settlements at the top not only have larger populations, they also have more – and more varied – functions, and a bigger **sphere of influence** than settlements lower down the hierarchy.

There are two questions arising from this diagram:
- What are the definitions of each of these settlement types?
- Why is the settlement hierarchy shaped like a pyramid?

primate city (usually the capital)

conurbation
city

city

large town

small town

village

hamlet

isolated buildings/farmsteads

Definitions of settlement types

An **isolated building** (or isolated dwelling) is just a building on its own. There are definitions of hamlet and village in Unit 5.2. However, the real problems come in working out the difference between a **village** and **town**, and town and **city**.

Different countries have different ideas about this. The table on the right shows six examples of how big a settlement has to be in those particular countries in order to be called a town. And the size difference between **towns** and **cities** is just as variable, depending on the country you're in.

country	minimum population size to be a town	urban population as a % of country's total population
Sweden	200	83%
South Africa	400	57%
Israel	2000	90%
Belgium	5000	97%
UK	10 000	90%
Japan	30 000	78%

Why is the hierarchy shaped like a pyramid?

The width of each level of the pyramid is a rough indication of the number of settlements in each class. In the UK, London is the primate city. Then there are seven conurbations, fourteen large cities and seventeen small cities. (And 1.7 million postcodes!)

Even if there are difficulties over population sizes, it's still possible to rank settlements. There are four measurements:
- population size
- number and variety of functions
- the distance between a settlement and the nearest settlement of similar size
- the size of the **sphere of influence**.

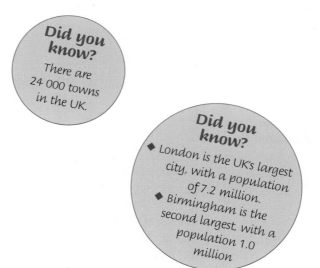

Did you know?
There are 24 000 towns in the UK.

Did you know?
- London is the UK's largest city, with a population of 7.2 million.
- Birmingham is the second largest, with a population 1.0 million

What's a sphere of influence?

The sphere of influence is the area surrounding a settlement that is affected by that settlement – it's the distance people will travel to use a shop or service. People who live within the sphere of influence depend on the settlement for services such as education, employment, retailing etc. The settlement is, in turn, 'served' by the labour supply from the sphere of influence.

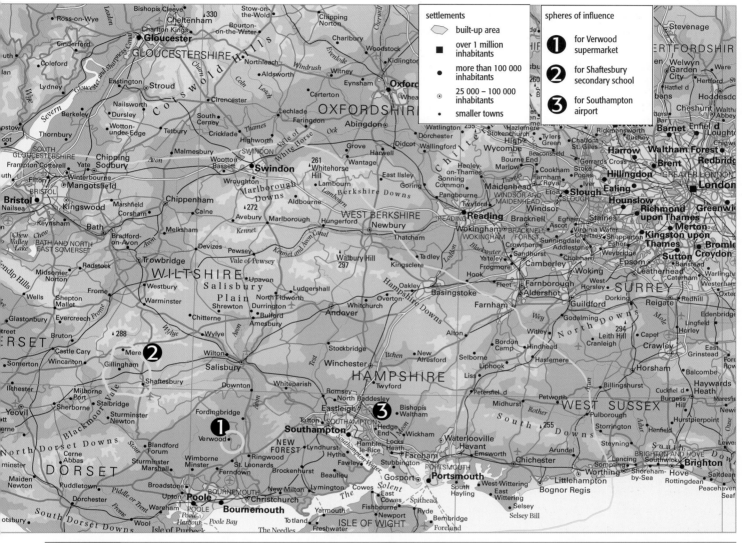

Activities

1 What is a hierarchy?
2 Give two reasons why a pyramid shape is a good symbol to show the idea of a settlement hierarchy.
3 London is the primate city in the UK. Name a UK conurbation, city, town, village, and hamlet.
4 What connection would you expect there to be between the minimum population size to be a town and the urban population as a percentage of a country's total population? Now look at the table opposite. Does this show the connection you expected? Explain why/why not.
5 What is a sphere of influence?

6 Using the map and key above, arrange these places between Bristol and London into a hierarchy with 5 levels: Bristol, Marshfield, Chippenham, Calne, Avebury, Swindon, Marlborough, Hungerford, Newbury, Thatcham, Reading, London.
7 Which settlement shown on the map above do you think has the largest sphere of influence?
8 Look at these pairs of settlements on the map. For each, say which you think has the largest sphere of influence:
 a Bristol, Chippenham,   b Oxford, Abingdon
 c Swindon, Reading,   d Salisbury, Abingdon

Urbanisation

In this unit you will learn how more and more people are living in urban areas.

What is urbanisation?

Urbanisation means a rise in the percentage of people living in urban areas (towns and cities), in comparison with rural areas.

	urban population as a % of total population				
	1950	1975	1990	2000	2030
World	38	38	43	47	60
MEDCs	55	70	73	76	84
LEDCs	18	27	33	40	56

Urbanisation in MEDCs

European and North American MEDCs, like the UK, urbanised during the late 18th and the 19th centuries.

As a country industrialises, the number of people living in urban areas tends to increase. Industrialisation in the 19th century attracted millions of workers to the new factories and the houses built by the factory owners. Today, 90% of the UK population lives in towns or cities.

A recipe for urbanising a 19th-century MEDC

You will need:
- ✔ efficient farming
- ✔ better industrial machinery
- ✔ lots of coal
- ✔ state-of-the-art transport.

Time needed:
About 25 years.

Directions:
1. Combine agricultural machinery with crop rotation and/or fertilisers. You should then have more than enough food for everybody, and you will free up a labour supply.
2. Using new steam-engine technology, coal and industrial machinery, build factories.
3. Build small back-to-back houses for workers.
4. Advertise for large numbers of workers (from step 1). You can then employ them and their children.
5. Use high-tech transport (firstly canals, then railways), to bring raw materials to factories, and to send finished goods to shops nationwide and empire-wide.

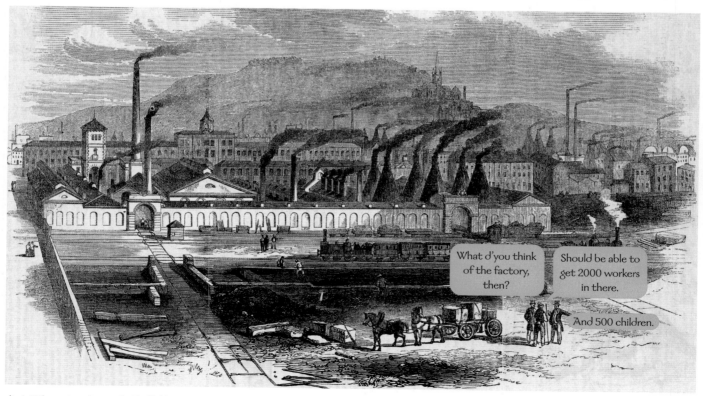

▲ *A 19th–century factory in Sheffield.*

Urbanisation in LEDCs

Is urbanisation in LEDCs following the same pattern as in MEDCs? Yes and no.

Yes

◆ In both MEDCs and LEDCs, people have been pushed from rural areas through the use of machinery.

◆ And, just as in MEDCs, people in LEDCs are pulled towards cities, for jobs.

No

◆ The other pushes from rural to urban areas in LEDCs are different. They include landlessness, drought, famine and civil war.

◆ There are different pulls, too – the chance of an education, of piped water, electricity, and much more entertainment.

◆ The settlement hierarchy is usually different in LEDCs. There's often one very big city, up to ten times bigger than the second city.

◆ Urbanisation is happening a lot later in LEDCs – only since the 1950s. And it's happening a lot faster than it did in MEDCs. You can see the evidence of this if you look at the location of the world's mega-cities – cities with over 10 million inhabitants (see the table on the right).

While LEDC cities continue to grow, many MEDC cities are losing population (more about this in Unit 5.9).

◀ *Mumbai, India: a mega-city.*

The world's mega-cities (population in millions in brackets)

1975	2000	2015 (projected)
Tokyo (19.8)	Tokyo (26.4)	Tokyo (26.4)
New York (15.9)	Mexico City (18.1)	Mumbai (26.1)
Shanghai (11.4)	Mumbai (18.1)	Lagos (23.2)
Mexico City (11.2)	São Paulo (17.8)	Dhaka (21.1)
São Paulo (10)	Shanghai (17)	São Paulo (20.4)
	New York (16.6)	Karachi (19.2)
	Lagos (13.4)	Mexico City (19.2)
	Los Angeles (13.1)	New York (17.4)
	Kolkata (12.9)	Jakarta (17.3)
	Buenos Aires (12.6)	Kolkata (17.3)
	Dhaka (12.3)	Delhi (16.8)
	Karachi (11.8)	Metro Manila (14.8)
	Delhi (11.7)	Shanghai (14.6)
	Jakarta (11)	Los Angeles (14.1)
	Osaka (11)	Buenos Aires (14.1)
	Metro Manila (10.9)	Cairo (13.8)
	Beijing (10.8)	Istanbul (12.5)
	Rio de Janeiro (10.6)	Beijing (12.3)
	Cairo (10.6)	Rio de Janeiro (11.9)
		Osaka (11.0)
		Tianjin (10.7)
		Hyderabad (10.5)
		Bangkok (10.1)

Activities

1 What is urbanisation?

2 Draw a graph of the data shown in the table 'urban population as a % of total population'. Make it a cumulative line graph (your teacher will show you how).

3 Which type of countries urbanised first – MEDCs or LEDCs? Why do you think this was?

4 What is the connection between industry and urbanisation?

5 Why is it that agricultural change and industrialisation are often referred to as a 'chicken and egg' cause of urbanisation? Explain your answer.

6 a On a world map, mark the location of all the mega-cities in 1975 from the table.

   b Now, using a different colour, mark on all the mega-cities in 2000.

   c Describe the changes shown on your map, in terms of number and location.

   d Is the trend you identified in answer c likely to continue until 2015? Explain your reasoning.

You are entering the twilight zone

In this unit you will learn how land use changes across a city – and how to recognise the different land use zones.

Inside the city

Travel through a typical MEDC city and you'll see how the **land use** changes.

What's land use, then?

It's what they use the land for. Buildings don't just spring up anywhere. Have you noticed that many cities seem to follow the same pattern of land use? Big shops seem to cluster in the middle, houses mostly get bigger and smarter as you move away from the centre, and garden centres and supermarkets are located at the edge. Let's go through the city, from the centre to the edge, and you'll see for yourself.

1 The Central Business District (CBD)

Here's the CBD. Lots to see and do: shops, cinema, clubs, bars, banks and offices.

Yeah, and to cram it all in, they have to build upwards.

The roads, canals, and railway lines all meet at the CBD.

2 The inner city – aka the twilight zone

But some people are doing up the old housing because it's near the city centre.

Look how fast it's changed! Old housing, corner shops. Lots of the factories have closed.

The streets make a grid pattern. Tenements or terraced houses were built for factory workers. Little or no green space.

3 The inner suburbs

The pavements are wider.

And the houses are bigger. There are parks.

The streets are curvier, and there's more open space – but the houses are still quite close together.

4 The outer suburbs

Trees, big houses, but a long way to work.

I wouldn't mind in that car.

Houses often in small groups. Parks, maybe woods, perhaps a golf course.

5 The rural-urban fringe

Great view here! They're building new houses and a shopping centre, though.

Can we take the bus back?

Almost in the countryside, but only 40 minutes by train from the city centre.

A man called Ed Burgess noticed this pattern in Chicago, and drew an **urban model** of it. This model is shown on the right.

An urban model is a simplified diagram of the way land is used in a city. Of course, real cities are much more complicated, but models help you to understand what's going on, why things are where they are, and where things might change.

The kind of journey shown on the opposite page is called a **transect**. Looking at transects helps geographers to understand how and why a city changes from the centre to the edge.

Burgess urban model

Key

1. Cen tra l Business Dis tric t (C BD)
2. inn er cit y
3. inn er sub urb s
4. outer s ubur bs
5. rur al- urb an frin ge

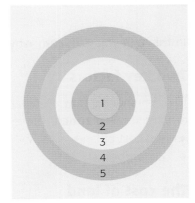

CBD

Activities

1. Draw a sketch of the photo above of Cardiff. Label the land use zones. (The CBD is labelled to help you.)

2. **a** Read the five sentences below. Which sentence matches which land use zone? Explain your answers.

   A Mrs Ponsonby can't decide which of her four bathrooms to use.

   B Izzy and her friends are off to town for a shopping spree.

   C They're knocking down the old houses and building posh flats.

   D Mr Brown is parking his car in his new garage. It only just fits.

   E Protesters are sitting in trees to stop the bulldozers clearing the site for a new football stadium.

   b Now try to write five sentences of your own to match with each zone.

3. For a town or city that you know, write an account of your journey from the town or city centre to the rural-urban fringe.

4. The words 'twilight zone' usually describe an inner city area as it begins to change from being an industrial zone. How could people 'brighten up', or improve, the twilight zone?

Urban zoning: why does it happen?

In this unit you will learn why urban zones develop.

Two key factors

Unit 5.5 showed how an urban area is made up of different districts – called **zones**. There are two basic causes:
- ◆ the cost of land
- ◆ accessibility.

The cost of land

The graph shows how much rent is paid, per square metre per year, at different distances from the centre of the CBD.

Think of getting the best land as a 'sale'. Different 'bidders' at the sale know where the locations they're interested in are to be found – and they know how much they can pay:

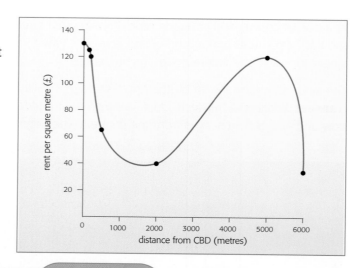

Everybody wants to locate at the heart of the city – but not everybody can afford it. We at Megacoffee can.

Rookems Solicitors want to be as central as possible, but we can't pay the huge rents that other businesses pay.

Obviously, we want to be close to the banks and our customers, but the only land that Loorolls Manufacturing can afford is 500 metres from the centre.

Yes, the house is big but the land is a third of the cost of city centre land – and it's only ten minutes by bus!

The zones develop as a settlement grows. Look at this map of the growth of Bedford.

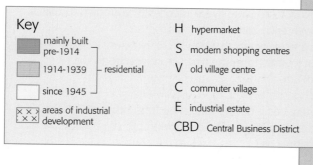

Key

▓ mainly built pre-1914	⎤
▒ 1914-1939	⎬ residential
☐ since 1945	⎦
⤫⤫⤫ areas of industrial development	

H   hypermarket
S   modern shopping centres
V   old village centre
C   commuter village
E   industrial estate
CBD   Central Business District

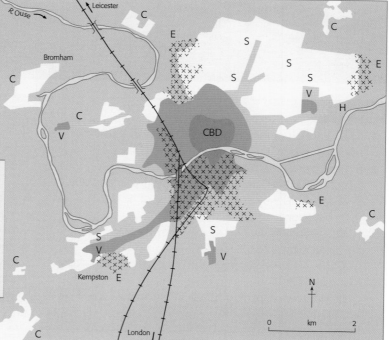

Is the CBD losing its charms?

The coffee shop, the solicitors and the factory owner in the cartoons opposite all wanted **good access** to the city centre, because that's where their customers were. But this has changed in the last 25 years or so.

In a way, the city centre has become too successful. People want to get there by car, and the older, narrower streets at the centre can't take the traffic. Street after street has been pedestrianised, car parks are now dotted around the CBD, and there are park-and-rides around the edge of the city, but for many shoppers getting into the city centre is too much of a hassle.

This is especially the case when out-of-town locations have vast superstores with free parking. Look again at the rents shown in the graph, and you can see that an out-of-town retailer will pay almost as much rent as companies in the city centre – but the store will be easily accessible (usually on a ring road) and will offer free parking. Now the buzzword is **accessibility**, especially by car.

Activities

1 **a** What is an urban zone?
   b What does accessibility mean?
2 Look at the graph of rents.
   a What happens to the cost of land as you move away from the city centre?
   b What influence does accessibility have on the cost of land?
   c Why would HMV be prepared to pay for a city centre location?
3 **a** Using the cartoons opposite, explain why different 'bidders' will pay different amounts of money for locations within the city.
   b Why is Burgess' land use pattern:
      commercial ➤ industrial ➤ residential
      often found as you leave the city centre in an MEDC? (Hint: It's all about your answers to questions **2** and **3a**.)
4 **a** What is the anomaly (doesn't fit the pattern) in land prices in the graph?
   b Why do you think this is?
   c Explain the negative side of the CBD.
5 Draw and label a land use sketch of the photo above. You should be able to include four land use zones: CBD, industrial, residential, recreational.

Urban problems in MEDCs

In this unit you will find out about deprivation in cities.

Richer zones, poorer zones

Geographers are interested in the location of rich and poor people at several different levels:

◆ globally (where the MEDCs and LEDCs are)
◆ nationally (within a country)
◆ locally (for example within a city).

The **inner city** (look at Unit 5.5 to check its location) has high levels of **deprivation**. It is the poorest zone of most MEDC cities.

Deprivation in the inner city

Factories developed in the 19th century, and factory owners and developers built houses for the factory workers. These were tenements or terraced houses. They were built to cram in as many people as possible.

In the second half of the 20th century, many of these factories closed because:

◆ other countries could make the same goods cheaper
◆ the local resources the factories needed ran out
◆ the machines and buildings were just too old.

Unemployment rose, and investors chose to put their money into more prosperous areas. This unemployment, together with cramped, ageing houses and schools, plus congestion as people tried to find parking spaces in the narrow streets, caused the better off people to move out to the suburbs.

Inner cities now have a higher-than-usual proportion of people who are:

◆ unemployed
◆ low-skilled and low-paid
◆ elderly
◆ single parents
◆ students
◆ ethnic minorities.

The rioting in Birmingham in 2005 highlighted some of the problems of the UK's inner cities. There can be tensions within the community. The unemployment, poverty, and lack of opportunities often result in high crime rates. Gangs develop to provide a sense of belonging, and as something to do. Adele's story highlights other difficulties.

My name is Adele.
Me and my mum live in a shared house. Our bit is not too bad, but some of the people who live here are scary. Sometimes there's used needles on the street. There's nowhere for young kids to play, and now the council want to close the primary school – they say it costs too much. And the council have agreed to build a new supermarket on our park. They say this will bring more jobs. My mum says these jobs will be low paid, low-skilled and mostly part-time.

Birmingham riots

A man was killed in clashes in the Lozells area of Birmingham last night. The riot, between Asian and black youths, broke out after a public meeting was held about an alleged sex attack on a teenage girl.

A group of more than 100 youths ran through the streets, attacking cars and motorists. Several cars were overturned and at least one was set alight. The mob was chased by police carrying riot shields.

The area has a strong African-Caribbean presence. Asian gangs have also sprung up in the area. There has been simmering tension between the two groups.

Adapted from newspaper reports, Sunday 23 October 2005.

Improving the inner cities

There has been a lot of **redevelopment** in the UK's inner cities.

Brindley Place in Birmingham is redevelopment on a grand scale:

◆ This part of Birmingham has a network of canals, which have been cleaned and smartened up.
◆ The accommodation runs from **social housing** to luxury flats. The buildings are roomy and modern.
◆ There are stylish bars and restaurants.
◆ There's the National Indoor Arena and the Sea Life Centre.

Brindley Place was started in 1994 and work is now complete. Brindley Place and the surrounding canal apartments cost about £400 million.

Developments like this provide many jobs. They try to mix the housing types, and provide lots to do in a safe, well-lit environment. This is one way to bring a higher quality of life back to our inner-city areas.

Before and after redevelopment at Brindley Place ▶

Activities

1 In theory, which zone of the city (see Unit 5.5) is most likely to be the most deprived? Why?
2 a Give three reasons why this zone in MEDC cities declined rapidly in the second half of the 20th century.
  b Why do you think industry left its location in the inner city?
  c Give three problems which would deter new industry from locating in the inner city.
  d Whereabouts in the city do you think industry has moved to?
3 Read Adele's story opposite. List five inner-city problems she mentions.
4 You are going to redevelop an inner-city area of your own. Make a large copy of the plan of an inner-city area on the right, but only copy the major roads, railway, and the canal. These things have to remain; everything else you can either knock down (**redevelop**) or keep but improve (**renewal**). Add labels to your map to show the changes you would make, explaining each one. Use the Brindley Place example to give yourself some ideas.

Key
- 19th century terraced housing
- 20th century housing
- industry
- ▌▌ derelict
- — major roads
- ── railway
- — canal

5 Now prepare a presentation (perhaps a PowerPoint presentation) saying how your plan helps:
  ◆ the local residents
  ◆ the environment
  ◆ the local heritage
  ◆ the city as a whole.

Traffic – everybody's problem

In this unit you will learn how one city is trying to solve its traffic congestion problems.

Edinburgh's transport problems

- Edinburgh has a population of 450 000 and a rapidly growing economy.
- It's estimated there will be a 14% rise in commuters between 1991 and 2015.
- Over 40 000 commuters enter the city every day.
- They come from expanding towns and villages in West Lothian and across the Forth in Fife.
- Over the past 20 years, growth in car ownership and car use has caused traffic levels on some city roads to increase by up to 60%.
- Over the past 10 years, car ownership in Edinburgh and surrounding areas has risen by 57%, compared to the UK average of 29%.
- Roads converge on the city centre.
- An outer by-pass circles the eastern, southern, and western boundaries of the city, but there is neither a northern by-pass nor a recognised inner ring road.
- The central area is under pressure from cars, lorries, and buses – many of which are entering the central area unnecessarily during through journeys.

▲ The joys of the open road.

What are they doing about it?

Edinburgh City Council is trying to solve these problems by:

- getting more people to use public transport by improving travel times and improving the options available
- reducing the number of cars carrying just the driver
- reducing traffic movement in the city centre
- working with neighbouring local authorities and rail networks to improve rail links for commuters.

▼ Edinburgh's transport network.

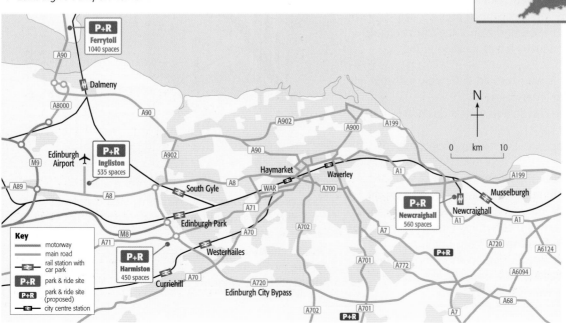

Public transport

Buses

To encourage commuters and shoppers to leave their cars behind, three large park and ride areas have been created. There's free parking, and frequent buses into the city centre.

Many travellers had complained that bus journeys were too slow. So the council has created green bus lanes for peak periods, to allow buses to move more quickly. Traffic light sequences at certain junctions can be changed in favour of buses. There are plans to have real-time bus information systems at bus stops. Two more large park and rides are being built to the south-east of the city.

Trams

To try to reduce the number of cars on the roads, the City Council planned a road-charging scheme. Car owners would have paid a toll on entering the city. The money raised was going to be ploughed back into the public transport system, especially the introduction of two new tram lines linking the north and south of the city. After four years of planning and consultation, a public referendum rejected the congestion-charging scheme. A reduced tram system is still being proposed, with the new system coming into operation by 2010.

▲ *Trams like this? An artist's impression of what one of the new Edinburgh trams might look like arriving at Edinburgh Park, Edinburgh's business park.*

Trains

Many of the existing train routes were operating at full capacity and not all areas were served by the trains. Working together, the City Council and the rail company opened two new stations, built longer platforms at others, and built larger park and ride areas to make the stations more accessible.

Edinburgh's newest rail station, Edinburgh Park, is served by a cross-city bus service and free shuttle buses for the nearby business park. The increase in rail commuters from West Lothian and Musselburgh to the east has been helped by the re-opening of the old Bathgate rail link and the creation of another five stations.

Further expansion is planned, with longer platforms to increase train size from two to six carriages, doubling the tracks, and creating even more parking spaces. Plans to re-open the Bathgate to Airdrie line and the Waverley Borders line, allowing even more commuters to get into Edinburgh, have been agreed by the Scottish Executive. Work on Waverley Station to allow more through-routes and to increase the number of trains per hour from 24 to 28 will boost the handling capacity of Edinburgh's main station.

Activities

1 Why does Edinburgh have traffic congestion problems?
2 Describe what the city council has done to try to get more people to use public transport.
3 Why do you think some people feel the tram system will not be completed?
4 Describe some of the improvements on the local railway network.

Urban sprawl

In this unit you will learn how our towns and cities are growing, and about some of the problems this is causing.

Spreading out

New growth is happening at the edges of towns and cities. This area, where the town or city meets the countryside, is called the **rural-urban fringe**. Urban growth in this area is often called urban sprawl. The word 'sprawl' tells us this growth isn't seen as a good thing.

However, most MEDC cities are losing population – people are moving out to smaller towns and villages nearby. This is called **counter-urbanisation**.

Why are people moving out of cities?

Reasons for counter-urbanisation include:
- Inner-city problems, like pollution, traffic and crime.
- Businesses moving to office parks and science parks. (They're not real parks, just groups of offices and researchers located on out-of-town sites.)
- Better transport and more car ownership.
- The peace and quiet of the countryside.

The same pattern – moving from the city to beyond the city limit – is happening all over the UK. On top of this, most cities have out-of-town developments: garden centres, golf courses, country parks, superstores, and science and office parks.

The elderly lady on the right clearly hates the changes to her town. But other people want new developments in the urban fringe:

My town's under attack …
It's being destroyed. There's not much parking, and it's expensive. Queues stretch back along all the main roads at rush-hour and on Saturdays. All the traditional shops have gone: butchers, fishmongers, grocers, furniture shops – because the rents keep going up and parking is free at out-of-town shopping centres. Whole streets are full of bars and cafes. Young people everywhere; no oldies like me. I'm too scared to be in the town centre after 10 p.m.

We need free parking, and so do our customers.

Multiplex cinema owner

With a bigger stadium, we could get bigger crowds and increase our income.

Football club owner

Yes, the superstore is doing OK – but we need to develop megastores.

Supermarket boss

The government wants us farmers to develop new ways of earning money. What about a golf course?

Farmer

The split-up wasn't too bad, but now I have to find a new house.

Divorcee

We need a bigger house!

Parents of triplets

Problems and issues

You can see from the cartoons opposite that there are good reasons for building in the urban fringe. But there are a lot of people who want to ban any further building there:

◆ environmentalists – they worry about damage to wildlife
◆ walkers and naturalists – they have access to less and less open space
◆ people already living in villages at the urban fringe – demand for houses has gone up so prices have risen, meaning locals can't afford to buy houses in their own village
◆ 'greens' – an increase in commuting leads to increased greenhouse gas emissions, and air and noise pollution.

Green belts

The government has been trying to preserve the countryside. One plan was to create **green belts**. A green belt is a zone around an urban area. New building is not totally banned, but it's hard to get planning permission for any new development. In 2005, Brighton and Hove Albion Football Club got permission to build a new stadium on a site inside an Area of Outstanding Natural Beauty. Much of the M25 cuts through London's green belt.

One of the main problems of the green belts is that they have led to people commuting further into work.

An alternative is to redevelop brownfield sites – abandoned sites within existing towns and cities, such as Lewes in Sussex (below).

East Linton is about 25 miles east of Edinburgh in East Lothian. Lots of people have moved to the village looking for a better quality of life. Many are commuters working in Haddington, or Edinburgh. They often shop or bank in the place they commute to.

Before 2004, East Linton lay just off the A1 which links London and Edinburgh. In 2004 East Linton was bypassed when a section of the A1 was up-graded to dual carriageway. The effect on the village was disastrous, as it had relied on passing trade to support its local economy. The high number of commuters living in the town, and the effect of the bypass, resulted in a number of local shops, the garage and the petrol station closing.

The villagers in East Linton formed an action group which resulted in East Lothian Council improving road signage to help direct traffic off the bypass to visit the town.

▼ *From this …*

▼ *… to this?*

Activities

1 Define:
   a counter-urbanisation   **b** rural-urban fringe
2 Give three reasons why people are leaving cities.
3 Give four attractions of the rural-urban fringe lifestyle.

4 Name four land uses (other than housing) that develop on the rural-urban fringe.
5 Choose two of these uses, and explain fully why the rural-urban fringe is attractive to them.

Edinburgh – green belt developments

In this unit you will learn about the pressures on Edinburgh's green belt.

Edinburgh's green belt

When the city bypass was built, it was decided to allow development in areas of green belt inside the new road. This was balanced by adding new areas of green belt to its outer fringes.

One of the biggest areas taken out of the green belt was the area around the Gyle. In the 1990s a huge shopping complex and a business park called Edinburgh Park were planned for this new development land.

Edinburgh's green belt. ▶

A green belt is a buffer zone around a large urban area where development is limited to protect the environment and stop urban sprawl.

It also helps to focus development on brownfield sites inside the city boundary.

Edinburgh Park

Edinburgh Park is Scotland's premier business park:
- ◆ It has attracted top-quality occupiers.
- ◆ The office blocks are high quality and many have won architectural awards.
- ◆ The planners created a high-quality work environment, with tree-lined boulevards and water features.
- ◆ It covers 58 hectares.
- ◆ It has over 100 000 square metres of office space.
- ◆ It was established in 1992.

Edinburgh City Council was pleased to support the development, because it reduced the amount of road traffic heading into the city centre. New transport links have been made and the new Edinburgh Park railway station, with a free shuttle bus service, helps workers to travel out from the city and in from the towns of West Lothian. Its closeness to the motorway network and Edinburgh Airport has also helped its growth.

The green belt has recently been altered again through the Edinburgh and Lothians Structure Plan 2015. The current economic boom in the Lothians region has greatly increased demand for green belt land – for transport, industry, and housing. In the western part of the green belt, several new developments have taken place or are planned.

Did you know?
Edinburgh's green belt covers 17 000 hectares.

Where will we build next?

Royal Bank of Scotland Global HQ, Gogar

The land was previously the site of a large mental hospital. Even though it was in the green belt, because it was already developed, the planners couldn't stop its re-development. The land was bought by the Royal Bank of Scotland (RBS) to be the site of its new £350-million global headquarters. It meant RBS could get its offices from across Edinburgh on to one site. There's more than 1 million square metres of office space. Facilities for the 3250 workers include a supermarket, chemist, florist, and a 480-seat terrace restaurant. To encourage workers to keep fit, there are cycling and running tracks, and a leisure centre and aerobics studio.

A new road junction and a bridge had to be built. City planners are hoping the site will link up with the new tram system which is being planned to run past it on its way to the airport.

To comply with council directives, RBS has produced a travel plan. It includes a private bus service linking all the key public transport points in Edinburgh, subsidies for staff using public transport, provision for cyclists, and a car-sharing initiative.

Developments at the airport

Edinburgh Airport is in the green belt. In the last 10 years, with the opening up of transatlantic routes and the growth of cheap airlines, there has been a huge increase in the number of passengers using the airport. Edinburgh City Council has realised the economic benefits of allowing the airport to expand, even though it's in the middle of the green belt. British Airports Authority, the owners of the airport, have expanded the terminal buildings and built large new multi-storey car parks. The bus companies, working with the City Council, have created a huge park and ride area with bus links to the city centre. Further developments are planned, including the extension of one of the tram lines out to the airport to create a faster route into the city.

Activities

1 The green belt is a dynamic area. Explain what this means.
2 What are the main functions of the green belt?
3 Why has Edinburgh City Council been forced to allow development in the green belt?
4 What sorts of things make the RBS Global HQ different from other office developments?
5 Why are conservationists not too happy about the developments at Edinburgh Airport?

The big picture

This chapter is about farming in the UK. These are the big ideas behind the chapter:

◆ All types of farming work as a system, with inputs, processes and outputs.

◆ Physical and human factors affect what type of farming happens where. And for most types of farming climate is the most important physical factor.

◆ Farmers, wherever they are, face problems and challenges.

◆ Farming needs to be made more sustainable.

Your goals for this chapter

By the end of this chapter you should be able to answer these questions:

◆ What do these terms mean?

system, inputs, processes, outputs, factors, intensive, extensive, commercial, subsistence

◆ How are farms classified?

◆ What type of farming happens where in the UK, and why?

◆ Give an example of an arable, pastoral and mixed farm in the UK. Where are your farms? What are the inputs, processes and outputs of the farms?

◆ Draw a systems diagram for one of your named farms

◆ What problems and changes do the UK's farmers face? And how have some real farms changed?

◆ What do these terms mean?
CAP, SPS, quota, set-aside, agribusiness, sustainable, agri-environment scheme

◆ List some of the ways that farming in the UK can become more sustainable, and give some examples.

And then . . .

When you finish the chapter, come back here and see if you've met your goals!

Did you know?
There are about 25 million sheep in the UK. That's nearly half a sheep for everyone!

Did you know?
2% of the UK's workers are employed in farming.

Did you know?
Farms are measured in hectares. A hectare is about the size of a football pitch.

Did you know?
◆ In Scotland 5% of the rural workforce work in farming.
◆ Between 1982 and 2005 the number of full-time workers in Scottish farming fell from 44 000 to 26 000.

Your chapter starter

Look at the photo on page 102.

What is this animal? What does it give us?

What type of farming is this?

What else do you know about farming?

Does farming have anything to do with you?

Stop looking at me like that.

Farming – what's it all about?

In this unit you'll start to think about farming,
and find out about farming systems.

Celebrity chef Rick Stein criticised what he called 'cruel' British battery farming methods.

British battery hen farmers say their methods aren't cruel.

Farming – or **agriculture** – it doesn't really matter what we call it. But what's it all about? What do farmers do? And how do they do it?

The answers are lots of different things, in different ways, in different parts of the world, as you'll see by the time you get to the end of this chapter.

Farmers produce the food we eat – from the beef that goes in our burgers, to the rice we have with our curry. Farming also includes things like flowers, fruit and fish. But farmers also look after the countryside.

Did you know?
Britain is the largest producer of chicken in Europe.

Did you know?
In 2004, 68 000 people were employed full-time in farming in the UK.

Think about these

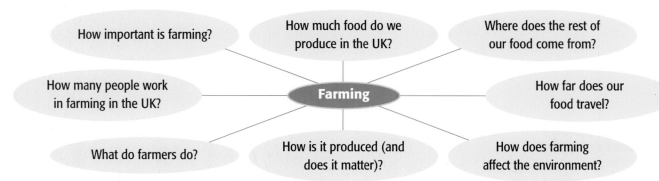

How important is farming?

How much food do we produce in the UK?

Where does the rest of our food come from?

How many people work in farming in the UK?

Farming

How far does our food travel?

What do farmers do?

How is it produced (and does it matter)?

How does farming affect the environment?

Some of these questions will be answered in this chapter, or even on these two pages. You might need to do some finding out of your own to answer the others.

What goes in must come out

In geography we say that farming is a **system**. This is just a way of saying there are:

- ◆ **Inputs** – things that go into the system
- ◆ **Outputs** – things that come out of the system
- ◆ **Processes** – things that happen in the middle

There might be some **feedback**, e.g. where some of the profits (if there are any) are put back into the system. The farming system diagram below shows how inputs, processes and outputs fit together.

Inputs can also be called **factors**. These are the things which affect farming, and a farmer's choice of what to produce.

Systems can be applied to any farm anywhere in the world.

Physical inputs
Climate
Temperature
Length of growing season
Rainfall

Relief
High or low
Steep or flat

Soils
Deep or thin
Rich or poor

Human and economic inputs
Labour (workers)
Machinery
Buildings
Markets and transport
Capital (money)
Seeds, animals
Animal feed
Fertiliser, pesticides, etc.
Government/EU policies, subsidies, loans

Processes
Rearing animals
Grazing/feeding
Lambing/calving
Shearing/milking

Growing crops
Ploughing
Planting
Spraying
Harvesting

Outputs
Animals and animal products
Milk, wool, eggs
Lamb, beef, pork, chicken
Lambs, calves, piglets, chicks

Crops
Wheat, oats, barley, etc.
Vegetables, fruit, flowers

In LEDCs farming may be subsistence (see Unit 6.2 for what this means), where there's no profit because the produce isn't sold – it's eaten by the farmer's family.

Feedback
In MEDCs there may be a profit which is reinvested.

Did you know?
British farmers look after more than 70% of the total land area of the UK.

Did you know?
British farmers produce nearly 65% of the food we eat in the UK.

Did you know?
There are over 2 million dairy cows in Britain. They produce 14 billion litres of milk every year.

Did you know?
Dairy cows are kept indoors in the winter and they eat silage (pickled grass) and cow cake (dried cereal). Tasty.

Activities

1 Why do you think 'battery farming' (for example of hens in cages) has become an important method of farming in the UK?

2 Do you think Rick Stein's opinion on battery farming will influence either farmers or the people who buy the eggs?

3 Do you think 'farmers produce the food we eat' is an accurate description of farming in the UK?

4 Choose two of the physical inputs in the systems diagram. Explain why they are important in farming.

Farming – what happens where?

In this unit you'll learn how farms are sorted, and why farming varies around the UK.

Classifying farms

Geographers find it helpful to sort things into different groups. The technical word for sorting is 'classifying'. Farms can be classified in three ways.

1   By what is grown or produced (**processes**):
    ◆   **Arable** farms grow crops.
    ◆   **Pastoral** farms rear animals.
    ◆   **Mixed** farms grow crops *and* rear animals. Some of the crops are used to feed the animals.
    ◆   **Market gardening**. These are small farms growing fruit and vegetables.

2   By how much **input** there is:
    ◆   **Intensive** farms have large inputs of labour, money or technology. They are usually quite small. Market gardening is intensive.
    ◆   **Extensive** farms have smaller inputs and are usually larger. Hill sheep farms are extensive.

3   By **output**:
    ◆   **Commercial** farms. The outputs are sold to make a profit, e.g. arable farms in East Anglia.
    ◆   **Subsistence** farms. Farmers produce food for themselves and their family. There is nothing left to sell, e.g. rice growing in the Philippines.

Farming types in the UK

So, what type of farming happens where? It's not haphazard – there's a **pattern** to it all, as the map opposite shows. If you try to grow wheat in the Lake District, it won't grow very well – and there are good reasons for that. Different **factors** are at work. A farmer's choice about what type of farming to do depends on physical and human factors. For most types of farming, physical factors are more important than human ones – and **climate** is the *most* important.

Remember – the map is very generalised *and* it doesn't show any towns or cities.

The north and west

◆   Cool summers, mild winters (but cold on mountains).
◆   Lots of rain, snow in winter, strong winds.
◆   Lots of high land and steep slopes. Poor, thin soils.
◆   Small fields, sheep graze on moorland.
◆   Not a lot of machinery.
◆   Not a lot of money.
◆   Poor transport links.
◆   Markets not close by.

Hill sheep farms are found in parts of Wales, northern England and Scotland in areas with these physical and human factors. Land here isn't suitable for other types of farming.

Dairy farming

Dairy farms keep cows for milk. They are found where:
◆   there is a warm, moist (not *too* wet) climate
◆   land is not *too* steep
◆   transport is good (to get milk to the market quickly)
◆   markets are close.

Farming types in the UK

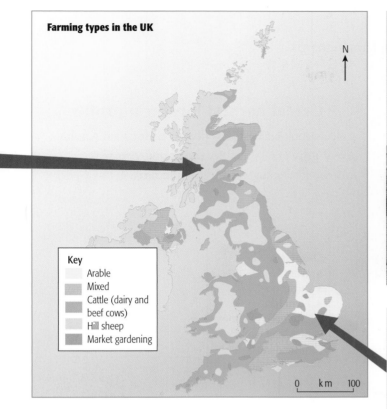

Key
- Arable
- Mixed
- Cattle (dairy and beef cows)
- Hill sheep
- Market gardening

0   k m   100

Mixed farms

These are found:

- between the crop-growing areas in the east, and animal-rearing areas in the west
- where the climate is just right – not *too* wet and not *too* dry, and where soils are good.

The south and east

- Warm sunny summers, cold winters.
- Less rainfall (falls when crops are growing).
- Lots of low flat land.
- Fertile, deep soils.
- Large farms, with large fields.
- More machinery.
- More money.
- Good transport links.
- Markets closer.

Arable farms are found mainly in eastern England in areas with these physical and human factors.

Market gardening

This is found:

- where transport links are good
- close to markets.

Lots of money is spent on labour, seeds, fertiliser, sprays, heating and lighting (for greenhouses).

This photo shows strawberries being grown.

Activities

1 Farming in the UK is usually classified as commercial. Why?
2 Wheat is an arable crop.
   a What physical and human factors do you need to grow wheat?
   b Why can't you grow wheat in the Lake District?

3 Why do you think climate is often the most important physical factor influencing farming?
4 'Farmers in the UK decide what to grow and where to grow it – technology is more important than climate to the modern farmer.' How far do you agree with this statement?

Farming – on the flat ... and on the edge

In this unit you'll find out about an arable farm and a hill farm in the UK.

Arable farming – Lynford House Farm

Lynford House Farm as a system

Remember we said in Unit 6.1 that farming is a system? Every farm can be described like this. Lynford House Farm is an arable farm in East Anglia run by Robert and Charles Sears. The diagram below shows the inputs, processes and outputs of the farm.

Cereal harvest hits farm profits

A disastrous harvest was predicted for East Anglia's cereal growers. A healthy profit one year was followed by a staggering loss the next.

Inputs
- 570 hectares of flat fen land
- Farm is just above sea level
- Warm, sunny summers – 17 °C in July
- 560 mm rainfall a year
- Fertile soil
- Fertiliser and pesticide
- Fuel for tractors, etc.
- 4 full-time workers plus contractors
- Machinery – lots! Includes combine harvester, tractors, sugar beet harvester, mower.
- Subsidy paid on the amount of land farmed (a subsidy is money from the government or EU).

Processes
- Ploughing
- Sowing
- Applying fertiliser and pesticides
- Watering
- Weeding
- Harvesting
- Maintenance – machinery, hedges, ditches, etc.

Outputs
- Wheat
- Sugar beet
- Farm has produced potatoes, peas and winter linseed in the past

Feedback
Profit is reinvested in the farm

Lynford House Farm

What's changing?

With farm incomes down, and no crystal ball to predict the future, Robert and Charles have been simplifying things. They have:

- increased technology (they use computers for crop-recording, accounts, wages and banking)
- not replaced recently retired workers
- rented out fields to other farmers for growing potatoes, lettuces and onions
- sold 8 bungalows on the farm to pay off loans
- considered building wind turbines (they decided not to as too many people were against it).

Farm buildings

▲ Lynford House Farm in the Cambridgeshire Fens, East Anglia.

Hill farming – Herdship Farm

Hill farmers win wildlife honours

Maurice and Kath Toward from Herdship Farm in Teesdale, have been presented with a Hill Farming Award. Their farm is a haven for birds like black grouse, lapwing, yellow wagtail, snipe and golden plover.

Herdship Farm

Kath Toward was originally a city girl from Liverpool. Her business brain and Maurice's love of his land mean they have survived in difficult times. This is what Kath said about the farm:

'It's about 229 hectares. The land goes from 450–600 metres above sea level. Our local weather expert says we have about 580 mm of rain a year. We've got about 22 hectares of flowering hay meadow. The rest is *very* rough pasture. And we use moorland.

Animals – we keep 12 cows. We've been paid to change these to a traditional British breed. And we have *loads* of sheep. 268 Swaledales and 180 North Country Cheviots. We produce our own silage for the cows, and hay for the sheep. The sheep need dipping and shearing, and we're very busy when they're lambing! Lambs are sold for meat, or they replace older ewes.'

▲ *Herdship Farm in Teesdale*

What's changing?

The National Trust thinks the incomes of some hill farmers will halve by 2010. This is because of a change in subsidies. Farmers will be paid according to how much land they farm rather than the number of animals they keep. So, some farmers will be worse off.

At Herdship Farm, Maurice and Kath have seen lots of changes. They are paid by the Environmental Stewardship Scheme to:
◆ create breeding bird habitats
◆ look after wildflower sites
◆ maintain historic sites, e.g. old lead workings, on their farm
◆ organise farm tours and walks for the public.

Kath says 'We now call ourselves land managers, not just farmers.'

My days here could be numbered – people reckon hill farming is close to collapse.

Activities

1 What is a subsidy?
2 Why do you think farmers are paid subsidies?
3 What other ways can you think of for Lynford House Farm to make money?

4 Draw a systems diagram for Herdship Farm. Describe and explain the main differences between this and the Lynford House systems diagram.

Mixed farming

In this unit you'll find out about two different examples of mixed farming.

Penllan Farm, Hereford

Penllan Farm is close to the English-Welsh border. It's a mixed farm run by David and Helen Morgan with lots of animals – 2300 sheep and 400 cows! It covers over 400 hectares. The farm is at a height of 60–250 metres above sea level, and rainfall varies from 600–1000 mm a year, depending on where you are on the farm. The soil is a silty loam.

Over the last ten years the Morgans have been worried about their falling income. About 25% of their income now comes from subsidies and grants.

Penllan Farm–facts and figures

Land use	
Arable land	139 hectares
Grassland	249 hectares
Woodland	10 hectares
Set-aside	12 hectares

Inputs	Outputs
Fertiliser (including chicken manure, farmyard manure and sludge from the water authority)	Wheat, barley, oats (some exported)
Pesticide	Potatoes (sold to supermarkets)
Feed for animals (some produced by the farm, some is bought in)	Turnips, straw and hay (grown for the animals)
Diesel for machinery	Cattle, lambs and ewes (sold to supermarkets, butcher and through livestock markets)
Stockman, tractor driver, part-time lady shepherd, 1 full-time and 1 part-time family member, plus contractors for jobs like hedge cutting, sheep shearing and muck spreading	Wool (fleeces)
Machinery includes tractor, combine harvester and baler	
Farm buildings are used for storing animal feed, corn, and housing animals	

Penllan Farm

▼ *The farming year begins in April.*

April	Calving, lambing, sow oil seed rape, spray cereals
May	Lambing, spray cereals, clear manure from sheds
June	Sheep work – shearing, drenching for worms, footbathing, spraying, have holiday!
July	Sheep work – drenching, footbathing, begin harvest
August	Harvesting (cereals, straw, etc.)
September	Harvesting, ploughing, begin planting
October	Put cows in sheds, finish planting
November	Put cows in sheds, feed cows and sheep, send corn to buyer
December	Feed cows and sheep
January	Feed cows and sheep, put sheep in sheds, shear sheep
February	Feed cows and sheep, calving
March	Feed cows and sheep, calving

Organic farming in the Highlands, Scotland

Organic farms don't use artificial fertiliser, herbicide or pesticides – so they're great for the environment, animals and people. They're also good news as far as jobs go. In Scotland organic farms provide 64% more new jobs than non-organic farms (the figure for England is 21%).

Ardalanish Organic Farm is a mixed farm on the Isle of Mull in the Inner Hebrides.

> **Did you know?**
> Organic farming will help to regenerate farming as an employer and boost rural economies.

Ardalanish Organic Farm

Aeneas and Minty MacKay keep native Kyloe cattle and Hebridean sheep at Ardalanish Farm. The cattle are a native breed – they're small, hardy and black. The way the animals graze helps to conserve the natural environment and improves habitats for wildlife.

Crops are grown on small fields on the 'inbye' land (low-lying land near the farmhouse). The MacKays grow oats, hay and turnips to feed the animals in the winter. They also grow tatties, carrots and winter veg to sell locally.

The farm has got its own weaving loom, and the MacKays use wool from their own sheep to make jumpers, scarves and tweed. They want to buy fleece from other farmers as a way of encouraging people to keep native breeds, and to farm organically.

You can visit the farm to meet the cattle and sheep, and walk the farm trail.

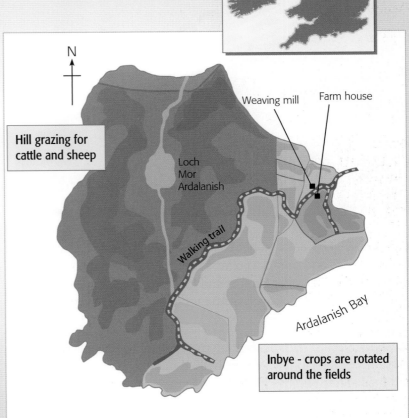

> **Did you know?**
> Most organic farms are mixed farms.

Activities

1 Draw a systems diagram for each of the two farms in this Unit. How are they similar? How are they different?
2 Why do organic farms provide more jobs than non-organic farms?
3 Why do you think most organic farms are mixed farms?

Is farming in crisis?

In this unit you'll learn about some of the problems facing the UK's farmers.

Food in the shops

In early September, fruit and veg grown in the UK, like apples, carrots and green beans are in season. But in the supermarket we see apples from the USA, carrots from South Africa and beans from Kenya.

What's going on?

The food we eat has changed. We want different types of food to those that people ate 50 or so years ago. And, we want them cheaper.

◀ What's this...

... got to do with this? ▼

Most people shop at the supermarket. Everything's in one place, it's open for hours and seems to offer us bargains. Supermarkets are very powerful. They offer farmers and food producers the chance to sell to huge numbers of people. And for some farmers that's where it can all go horribly wrong.

The supermarkets' size means they can choose their suppliers and decide how much to pay farmers both at home and abroad. The food market has become **global**, and farmers in the UK compete with those abroad. A UK pig farmer spent lots of money to make his farm meet the needs of the RSPCA's Freedom Food Scheme. The supermarket he supplied with meat then bought cheaper Danish bacon instead, produced with lower welfare standards, so the supermarket could offer shoppers a better deal.

Farmers have other problems, such as money (income). Robin Spence is a dairy and livestock farmer in Dumfries, Scotland. Farmers there feel lucky if they make £12 000 a year – and they work every single day. Robin gets just over 18p a litre for his milk. Compare that with the price in the supermarket!

More problems

Increased demand for more, and cheaper, food has led to other problems.

Soil erosion

Repeated ploughing, especially in autumn and winter, means the soil is exposed at the wettest, windiest time of year. The Fens in East Anglia (where Lynford House Farm is) are flat, with little to slow down gales. So, the soil is eroded.

Removal of hedgerows in the past didn't help. The leaves and branches broke the fall of heavy rain, and the roots bound the soil together. When the hedges were removed, the soil was washed away by the rain, or blown by the wind.

Between 1945 and 1990 over 25% of Britain's hedges were removed – mainly to make fields bigger and to make it easier to use large machines. But removing them has meant losing habitats for wildlife.

Overproduction

Farmers used to be given subsidies which guaranteed them a minimum price for their produce. This meant they overproduced (produced food which wasn't needed). Since 1992, subsidies have been reduced, so this is no longer such a problem.

▼ *Soil erosion by wind in East Anglia.*

Use of chemicals

Farmers use a number of chemicals, including **pesticides** and **fertiliser**.

- Pesticides control pests, diseases and weeds in crops.
- Fertilisers replace nutrients removed from the soil. These need replacing for plants to grow well.

Pesticides, fertiliser, slurry (animal manure) and soil all end up in our water supply, and are a major cause of water pollution.

And there's more …

Hard up farmers quit the industry

More than 15 000 people left the farming industry in 2005, and the trend is likely to continue. Since 1999, 1 in 4 Scottish dairy farmers have gone out of business.

When a farm is put up for sale it's more likely to be snapped up by a city worker than taken on by a new farmer.

Activities

1 Find out where the food eaten in your home over a weekend is grown. List as many items as you can, particularly fresh food. Then describe what your survey tells you. How much of the food produced abroad is also grown in the UK?

2 Why could farmers in the UK have difficulty in competing with farmers abroad who wish to sell their produce here?

3 How far have environmental, economic, and social factors caused problems for UK farmers?

4 Find out about the problems caused for farming in the UK by *either* BSE in the mid-1990s, or the outbreak of foot and mouth disease in 2001.

All change for farming

In this unit you'll find out about changes in farming in the UK.

EU changes farm payments

EU agriculture ministers have agreed to change the money paid to farmers. The deal has been described as a 'historic agreement'. It has altered the Common Agricultural Policy (CAP) and will shape Europe's farming for the next 10 years.

What is the CAP?

The CAP was created in 1962 to:
◆ guarantee regular food supplies at affordable prices
◆ ensure a fair standard of living for farmers.

Under the CAP, Europe's farmers received £31 billion worth of **subsidies** a year. This was up to 70% of the whole EU budget. The subsidies meant farmers produced as much food as they could. This led to huge surpluses of food products (called 'mountains' and 'lakes') in the 1980s.

When the EU expanded in 2004, an extra 10 mainly poor, rural, countries joined. The EU couldn't afford to keep paying all those subsidies – something had to be done.

What's changed?

CAP reform began in 1992. Further changes were introduced in 2005. The main change is that farmers don't get several different subsidy payments. Instead they get one single payment a year. This is called the **Single Payment System** (or SPS for short).

Farmers must meet certain standards of animal welfare and land management to get the payment.

The new system means that farmers:
◆ spend less time filling in forms
◆ don't have to keep a particular number of animals
◆ will be paid depending on how much land they have.

Some things stay the same

◆ Dairy farmers have a **quota**. They are told how much milk they can produce, and can't produce more than this.
◆ Arable farmers must **set-aside** part of their land – so that it *isn't* used for growing crops or keeping animals on. There are strict rules about how much, and what type of land can be set-aside, and also about how it should be managed so that farmers get their payment under the SPS.

Did you know?

The SPS will break the link between CAP subsidies and the amount that farmers produce. They will not have to produce lots to get a subsidy. They can produce what the market wants.

▲ Kath Toward from Herdship Farm (centre) said 'For the new system the moorland that we use has been added to our farmland. So, for the SPS our farm doubled in size overnight and we get paid more!'

▲ Farmers can set-aside land at the edge of fields. This will encourage greater biodiversity on the farm.

Other changes in farming

Animal welfare

More people are concerned about the way animals are treated. The EU and UK introduced laws about animal welfare. Other organisations have set up their own schemes to improve conditions, e.g. the RSPCA Freedom Food Scheme.

Farms get bigger

Agribusiness is large-scale, capital-intensive farming. It happens when small farms are merged into one large farm, and a lot of money is invested. Agribusiness farms tend to:

◆ have large fields, because hedgerows have been removed. (This makes it easier for machines to operate.)
◆ specialise in growing 1 or 2 types of crop, or rearing 1 or 2 types of animal.
◆ be owned by large companies or landlords.
◆ use the latest machinery.
◆ have high inputs of pesticides and fertiliser to get high outputs.

Agribusiness is popular in East Anglia, where there's a lot of fertile arable land.

> **Did you know?**
> Farmers plant more hedges than they remove.

> **Did you know?**
> Scientists are developing insect-like robots that could be used for crop pollination.

Mechanisation and the loss of jobs

Remember Robert and Charles Sears who run Lynford House Farm in East Anglia? They said 'On our farm we have gradually reduced the labour force. Larger machinery means the same work can be carried out by fewer people.'

Although machines such as tractors, combine harvesters and seed drills are expensive to buy, they do save time and money. The number of people working in farming continues to go down.

2001	2002	2003	2004
82 000	76 000	70 000	68 000

▲ The number of people employed full-time in farming. (There are others who work part-time or seasonally, who add to the numbers.)

Activities

1 Explain why the CAP led to food 'mountains' and 'lakes'.
2 How is the 'Single Payment System' different from CAP subsidies?
3 Do you think all farmers will benefit from changes to the system? Explain your answer.
4 Why do you think farmers are paid to 'set-aside' some of their land? Do you agree with this policy?
5 What are the benefits of 'agribusiness'? What are the disadvantages of this type of farming?
6 Why is increased mechanisation likely to benefit larger, more profitable farms? Which parts of the UK do you think are unlikely to be affected by increased mechanisation?

Making farming sustainable

In this unit you'll find out about some ways of making UK farming more sustainable.

What does 'making farming sustainable' mean?

The last few pages showed you some of the problems and challenges farmers in the UK have faced recently. Making farming sustainable means it needs to change and develop so that it meets people's needs today and can continue without harming the environment. There are a number of ways this can happen. Here are a few.

Old methods help wildlife

Who'd have thought we'd see a scene like the one on the right in the twenty-first century?

Ty Brith farm near Welshpool is farmed using traditional methods. The farm is run by Jonathan and Anna Khan. They use horses to cut the hay, as the small steep fields are surrounded by hedges. They would need to be removed if the Khans wanted to use modern machinery. Using traditional methods has helped to increase the numbers of bullfinches and thrushes. Ty Brith operates under the Tir Gofal Scheme.

Tir Gofal and Environmental Stewardship

These are **agri-environment** schemes for Wales and England (Tir Gofal is the Welsh one). They have similar aims. Farmers are encouraged to:
♦ maintain and improve the landscape
♦ conserve wildlife
♦ provide opportunities for people to visit the countryside.

Rural Stewardship Scheme

This is a Scottish scheme which provides help to encourage farmers and crofters to:
♦ farm in an environmentally-friendly way
♦ improve habitats and landscape features.

What else?

As well as schemes like Tir Gofal and the Rural Stewardship Scheme, there are other ways that farming can become more sustainable.

◆ Go **organic**. Organic farms don't use artificial fertilisers, herbicides or pesticides. Organic farms and those converting to become organic made up 4% of the UK's farmland in 2005.
◆ **Diversify**. That means do other things as well as farming.

Herdship Farm

Remember Maurice and Kath Toward who run Herdship Farm in Teesdale? Look back at Unit 6.3 to remind yourself what else they're paid to do besides keeping all those sheep.

They, and other farmers in their area, work with other organisations to maintain and improve the environment, including:

◆ English Nature
◆ RSPB
◆ local authorities
◆ DEFRA (Department for Environment, Food and Rural Affairs)

Like many farmers, Maurice and Kath have had to diversify. They have a self-catering cottage called 'Frog Hall' which they let out for holidays.

The chipping news

Offering holiday cottages is a fairly common way of diversifying. Other farmers do things differently.

William Chase was an arable farmer in Herefordshire, growing potatoes on Tyrrells Court Farm. He supplied supermarkets with what they wanted – smooth-skinned potatoes, all about the same size. But he got fed up with dealing with the supermarkets' demands.

He wanted to use his potatoes in a different way. 'I decided to produce high-quality, pedigree potato chips – not mere crisps.' William said.

He uses old-fashioned varieties of potatoes grown without pesticides, and buys other vegetables from a neighbouring farm. 'We get the carrots that are too big or funny-shaped to sell.' William produces 160 000 packets of Tyrrells chips a week on the farm.

▲ Who's a pretty boy? This Black Grouse is just one of many species of birds found on Herdship Farm.

Did you know?
Grants worth £3.3 million have been given to 200 farm projects in central and southern Scotland. The money is to help farming families diversify and support rural communities.

Activities

1 Why is it important to make farming in the UK sustainable?
2 a Explain why farmers might be attracted to agri-environment schemes.
  b What do you think might be the disadvantages of these schemes?
3 Find out about some of the ways farmers diversify. Explain one type of diversification in detail.
4 Sustainable farming includes looking after the countryside. Do you think farmers should be paid to do this, even if they don't produce any food on their farms? Justify your opinion.

The big picture

This chapter is all about industry and change. These are the big ideas behind the chapter:

◆ Industry and employment is classified as primary, secondary, tertiary and quaternary.

◆ As industry changes different location factors become more important, so industry locates in different places, and employment structures change.

◆ Some areas of traditional heavy industry, like South Wales, the Ruhr and West Lothian declined, but have now attracted new industries and jobs.

◆ Economic change affects people, jobs, communities and the environment.

Your goals for this chapter

By the end of this chapter you should be able to answer these questions:

◆ What do these terms mean, and can I give an example of each?
primary industry, secondary industry, tertiary industry, quaternary industry, inputs, processes, outputs, feedback

◆ Give an example of the location of one industry in the UK, and list the factors affecting its location.

◆ Why has the location of industry changed in the UK? Where is industry located now? And how has employment structure changed in the UK?

◆ Name an area where traditional heavy industry located and say why it declined. How has this area changed?

◆ What do these terms mean?
high-tech, footloose, deindustrialisation, employment structure

◆ Where can you find high-tech footloose industries, and why?

◆ How has industry changed in West Lothian?

◆ How does economic change affect people, jobs, communities and the environment? Give examples.

And then . . .

When you finish the chapter, come back here and see if you've met your goals!

> **Did you know?**
> ◆ Computer games is a fast-growing industry.
> ◆ From 1995 to 2003 over 25 million gaming devices were sold in the UK – enough for every household in the country to have one.

> **Did you know?**
> The UK is the third-largest market in the world for computer games, after the USA and Japan.

> **Did you know?**
> About 60 million cars and trucks are made around the world each year, and the industry employs millions of people.

> **Did you know?**
> This book is a product of the publishing industry.

Your chapter starter

Look at the photo on page 118.
What is this man doing?
What are the white things in the photo? What are they for?
Where do you think these things have been made? Why?
What effect will making them have on the environment?

Scalpel please, nurse.

Industry, jobs and systems

In this unit you'll find out about different types of industries and jobs, and how industry works as a system.

Industry – what's it all about?

Making things? Partly – but it's about other things as well.

Industry provides jobs, or **employment**. There's different types of industry and different types of jobs. Think about these: baby-sitting, paper-round, hairdresser, teacher, carpenter, farmer, magician, mechanic, IT consultant – the list is endless. They're all types of jobs and someone's got to do them (even you)! We all need to work to earn enough money to live on.

But the world of work is changing. The job you do in 10 years time might not be the same as the one you do 10 years from then.

Classifying industry

Geographers (that's you reading this book, and me writing it) find it helpful to sort things into groups. The word for this is **classifying**. Industry and jobs can be classified in four ways.

Primary industry – people extract **raw materials** from the land or sea. Farming, fishing and mining are examples.

Secondary industry – this is where people make (or **manufacture**) things. Like turning iron ore into steel, making cars, building houses – and hard drives (like in this picture).

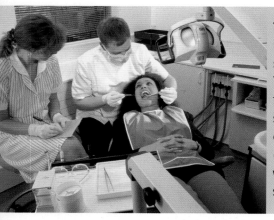

Tertiary industry. These industries provide a **service** for people. There are lots of them, for example the health service (doctors, nurses, dentists) and education (your teachers). Shop workers provide a service too.

Quaternary industries provide information and expert help. IT consultants and researchers work in these industries.

The names primary, secondary, tertiary and quaternary just mean, first, second, third and fourth. They refer to the order in which the industries developed.

The four types of industry aren't separate. They're linked together. Look at this example of car manufacturing.

| Mining for iron ore. | → | Making steel to turn into cars. | → | Car sales person orders cars using a computer. | → | IT expert fixes the sales person's computer when it goes wrong. |

In . . . out

In geography we say industry, or a factory where something is made, is a **system**. This is a technical way of saying there are:

◆ **Inputs** – things that go into the system
◆ **Outputs** – things that come out of the system
◆ **Processes** – things that happen in the middle

There might be some **feedback**, for example where some of the profits (if there are any) are put back into the system. The profits will buy more raw materials, new machinery and pay the workers. If there isn't any profit, the factory or industry will go bust!

The system diagram below shows how inputs, processes and outputs fit together. Inputs can also be called **factors**. These are the things which affect where an industry, or factory, will locate. Systems can be applied to any industry, or factory, anywhere in the world.

Physical inputs
• Raw materials
• Energy supply
• Site and land
Human and economic inputs
• Labour (workers)
• Transport
• Capital (money)
• Markets
• Government policies
• Environment

Processes
• Processing
• Assembling
• Packaging
• Administration

Outputs
• Finished product
• Profit
• Waste

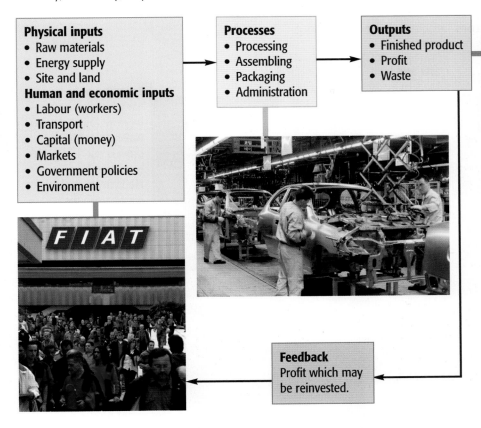

Feedback
Profit which may be reinvested.

One of the outputs from the system isn't really wanted – **waste**. It can be a real headache. It can cause pollution, and can be difficult and expensive to get rid of.

Industry – deciding where to put it

In this unit you'll learn how industry decides where to locate, and how location changes.

Burnaston

Cars – love them, or hate them?

Most of us use them. They've all got to be made somewhere – but where? How do people decide? Read this. It's adapted from the Toyota UK website and explains why Toyota decided to build their car assembly plant at Burnaston, in Derbyshire (that's the Toyota plant in the photo).

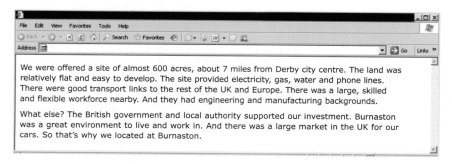

We were offered a site of almost 600 acres, about 7 miles from Derby city centre. The land was relatively flat and easy to develop. The site provided electricity, gas, water and phone lines. There were good transport links to the rest of the UK and Europe. There was a large, skilled and flexible workforce nearby. And they had engineering and manufacturing backgrounds.

What else? The British government and local authority supported our investment. Burnaston was a great environment to live and work in. And there was a large market in the UK for our cars. So that's why we located at Burnaston.

Industrial location factors

Toyota and Burnaston is a real-life example of how people decide where to **locate** their industry or factory. The photo and text boxes below break it down to show *exactly* what location **factors** people have to think about.

Did you know?
Toyota have another site in north Wales where they produce engines. They employ over 5500 people at their two UK sites.

Did you know?
Toyota is the third biggest car manufacturer in the world.

Raw materials
If these are heavy and bulky to transport – like coal and iron ore – the factory needs to be close to them. This is less important than it used to be.

Site and land
Modern industry needs large, flat sites with space to expand.

Energy supply
Early factories had to be close to fast-flowing water or coal fields to provide energy to work machines. Now electricity is available anywhere in the UK.

Labour (workers)
Some industries need lots of workers, others need workers with special skills.

Environment
A good environment – nice surroundings with lots of things to do – will attract workers.

Transport
A good transport network (road, rail, air and sea) is important to get the finished product to the market.

Capital (money)
Industry needs money to set up factories and produce things. Banks, governments and local authorities can provide money.

Markets
This is where the finished product is sold. It might be nearby in the UK, or abroad.

Government policy
The UK government can attract industry to some parts of the country by giving grants and subsidies.

Changing industries and changing locations

Nothing stays the same forever, and that includes industry. As industry changes, different location factors become more important.

Many of the old traditional industries in the UK – things like coal mining, ship building and textiles – began in the 19th century in the Industrial Revolution. They needed:

◆ raw materials – often heavy and bulky
◆ energy – provided by coal

So, they were usually found near coal fields, or ports (so raw materials like cotton could be imported, and finished products like cloth could be exported). The maps show where the traditional industries used to be found in the UK before 1970 (top map) and where industry is now (bottom map). What's happened?

◆ During the 20th century coal mines, textile mills, shipyards and steelworks all closed.
◆ New industries, many to do with electronics and computers, have developed.

For newer industries, being in a good environment with a trained workforce, close to large markets and with good transport links is important.

Changes to the type of industry, the way it works, or where it locates, can mean that businesses and factories close. People lose their jobs and way of earning a living. And that can affect families and the whole community.

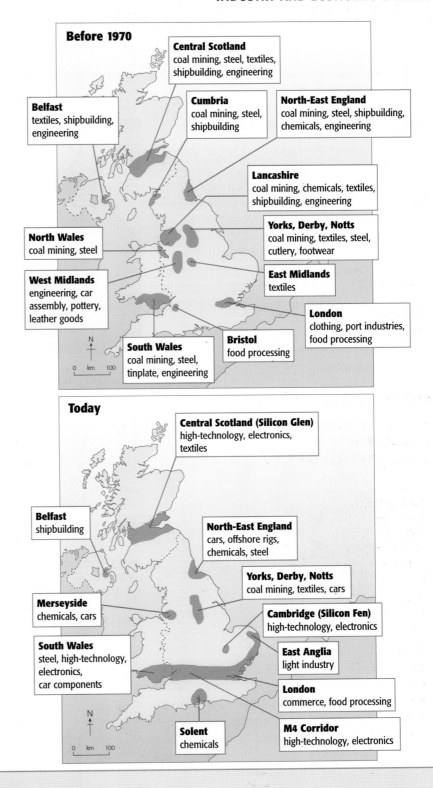

Before 1970

Central Scotland
coal mining, steel, textiles, shipbuilding, engineering

Belfast
textiles, shipbuilding, engineering

Cumbria
coal mining, steel, shipbuilding

North-East England
coal mining, steel, shipbuilding, chemicals, engineering

Lancashire
coal mining, chemicals, textiles, shipbuilding, engineering

North Wales
coal mining, steel

Yorks, Derby, Notts
coal mining, textiles, steel, cutlery, footwear

West Midlands
engineering, car assembly, pottery, leather goods

East Midlands
textiles

London
clothing, port industries, food processing

South Wales
coal mining, steel, tinplate, engineering

Bristol
food processing

Today

Central Scotland (Silicon Glen)
high-technology, electronics, textiles

Belfast
shipbuilding

North-East England
cars, offshore rigs, chemicals, steel

Yorks, Derby, Notts
coal mining, textiles, cars

Merseyside
chemicals, cars

Cambridge (Silicon Fen)
high-technology, electronics

South Wales
steel, high-technology, electronics, car components

East Anglia
light industry

London
commerce, food processing

Solent
chemicals

M4 Corridor
high-technology, electronics

Activities

1 Describe the distribution of industry before 1970, as shown by the first map.
2 Explain why the location of industry in the UK has changed since 1970.
3 During the 20th century, industries such as coal mining and textiles closed down. Why?
4 Explain why the factors important for locating an industry are different now compared to the 19th century. How important was the natural environment, then and now?
5 Do you think that companies such as Toyota would choose to locate in the UK without help from the government? Give reasons for your answer.

Industry – traditional and heavy

Did you know?

The iron and steel industry is called a **heavy industry**. This is because it needs lots of heavy and bulky raw materials.

In this unit you'll find out why traditional heavy industry located in South Wales, and in the Ruhr in Germany.

Iron and steel in South Wales

This is my job – my life. Tower Colliery is the only deep coalmine left in South Wales. My dad was a miner, and his dad before him. Our communities were built around the mining and steel industry. And that's almost disappeared now.

Q What do you need to make iron and steel?

A Iron ore, coal and limestone. Coke from the coal is used to smelt the iron ore. Limestone is added to help separate the pure iron from what isn't pure.

South Wales

In the nineteenth century, South Wales became important for producing iron and steel. The three raw materials needed to make iron and steel were all found locally. The steep valleys with fast-flowing rivers provided power to begin with, and also transport. The iron industry developed in places like Ebbw Vale and Merthyr Tydfil.

After 1860, steelworks began to replace ironworks. Fast forward to the 20th century. The local raw materials had run out, and only Tower Colliery remained working. By the 1990s, all the steelworks had closed – except two. These were Port Talbot and Llanwern, both on the coast. They were **integrated steelworks**. All the stages in the steel-making industry happened on one site. They imported raw materials and exported steel. Llanwern closed in 2001, and 3000 jobs were lost.

But these days it's not all doom and gloom in South Wales. Read Unit 7.6 to find out what's happening there now.

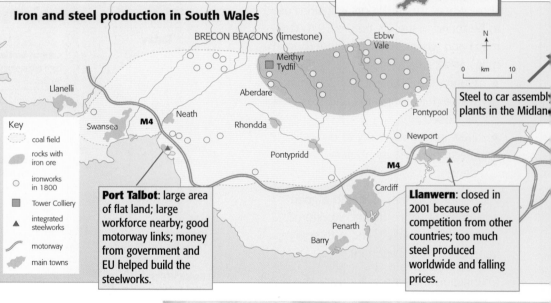

Iron and steel production in South Wales

BRECON BEACONS (limestone)

Ebbw Vale

Merthyr Tydfil

Aberdare

Llanelli

Swansea

M4

Neath

Rhondda

Pontypool

Newport

Pontypridd

M4

Cardiff

Penarth

Barry

N

0   km   10

Steel to car assembly plants in the Midlands

Key

- coal field
- rocks with iron ore
- ironworks in 1800
- Tower Colliery
- integrated steelworks
- motorway
- main towns

Port Talbot: large area of flat land; large workforce nearby; good motorway links; money from government and EU helped build the steelworks.

Llanwern: closed in 2001 because of competition from other countries; too much steel produced worldwide and falling prices.

When industry declines, people lose their jobs. It affects the whole community. People leave. Shops close. Crime goes up. ▶

The Ruhr industrial region – Germany

Factfile

◆ The Ruhr coal field is Europe's largest energy supply. There's a huge amount of coal and it won't run out in the near future.

◆ Local supplies of iron ore meant that the iron and steel industries developed.

◆ There was an excellent system of rivers and canals. They were used for power (the rivers) and transport.

◆ Other industries were attracted to the area, like the chemical industry (used coal as one of its raw materials); engineering (used the iron and steel); textiles (used some of the machines produced by engineering).

◆ In 1956, nearly half a million people had jobs in coal mining.

But, like South Wales, this area has suffered too.

◆ Since the 1970s, coalmines, steelworks and other heavy industries have closed.

◆ By 1999, there were only 53 000 jobs left in coal mining.

◆ Half a million people have left the area since the mid-1980s.

◆ Lots of people have no jobs. In 2001, 12.5% of workers were unemployed – far more than in the rest of Germany.

◆ The environment was ruined. Slag and waste heaps were left by coal mining and other industries. And both air and water were massively polluted.

◆ There is still a large local population – 5.4 million people live in the Ruhr region. This means there is a big workforce, and big market for goods produced here.

Did you know?
One-third of the EU's coal is still produced in the Ruhr.

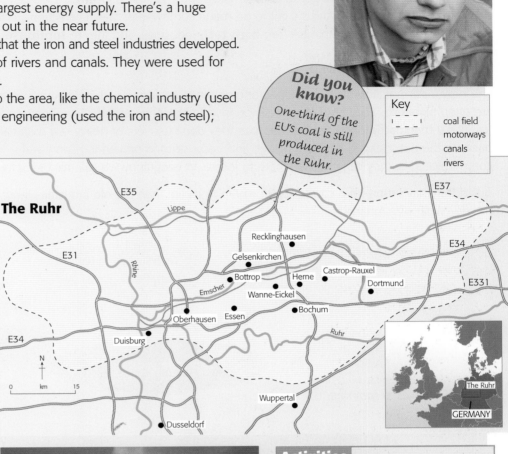

Key
- - - coal field
motorways
canals
rivers

The Ruhr

E35
Lippe
Recklinghausen
E37
E31
Gelsenkirchen
E34
Rhine
Bottrop
Herne
Castrop-Rauxel
Emscher
Wanne-Eickel
Dortmund
E331
Oberhausen
Essen
Bochum
E34
Ruhr
Duisburg
N
0   km   15
Wuppertal
Dusseldorf

The Ruhr
GERMANY

Industry can be bad for the environment. This is Duisburg. ▶

Activities

1 The natural environment – through raw materials – helped industry to develop in South Wales. What are the disadvantages of the South Wales natural environment?

2 Why do you think the steelworks at Port Talbot and Llanwern remained open while others closed?

3 Why do you think that competition from other countries would be a reason for the Llanwern steelworks closing?

4 Draw a 'consequences map' to show how people in South Wales have been affected by the decline of traditional industries.

5 Why do you think industry has declined in the Ruhr, even though there's still plenty of coal?

6 What are the similarities and differences between the examples of South Wales and the Ruhr?

Industry – footloose (and fancy free)

In this unit you'll learn about high-tech and footloose industries.

What's the photo on the right got to do with geography? At first glance not a lot. But someone's got to make the computer. And it's got to be made somewhere. Making electronic equipment, computers – those sorts of things – are **high-tech** industries, and they're **footloose**.

High-tech and footloose

The new industries that have developed and begun to replace traditional heavy industries are often high-tech. They tend to make expensive things. They employ fewer people than traditional manufacturing industries. Because they don't use lots of heavy raw materials, because the national grid provides power, and because of improved transport and communications, they can choose where to locate. In geography we call this being footloose.

But, if they have more of a choice about where to locate than the old industries, how *do* they decide? What's important?

Locate in areas with good transport links – close to motorways, railways and with good access to airports.

Need workers with special skills close by.

Use small, light parts to make products.

Don't cause pollution like traditional industries do.

Footloose industries

Final products are small, and easy to transport to markets.

Locate in a nice environment.

Power is provided by electricity (just plug into a socket).

Are close to other industries so they can swap ideas and information.

Need cheap land with large sites to expand.

Footloose industries are often found on the edges of towns and cities, in specially built 'parks', or estates. These might be:

Science parks

These have links with universities. Businesses are high-tech and might concentrate on R and D. A lot of land isn't developed. Instead it's landscaped with lots of trees and grass to make a good environment for people to work in.

Business parks

These are like science parks – but they don't have a link with a university. They have high-tech industries, as well as offices, hypermarkets and leisure facilities. And, like science parks, they're landscaped.

Industrial estates

These can be found towards a city centre, as well as on the edges of towns and cities. Some businesses are high-tech, but more are likely to be involved in manufacturing. There are more buildings and less trees and grass than in science and business parks.

Did you know?

Many high-tech companies have two parts. One involves lots of R and D (research and development) and is to do with developing new products. The other is to do with making things. They put together parts made somewhere else.

Areas where footloose industries have located include:

◆ the M4 corridor (aka 'Sunrise Strip')
◆ Silicon Glen in central Scotland
◆ Silicon Valley in California.

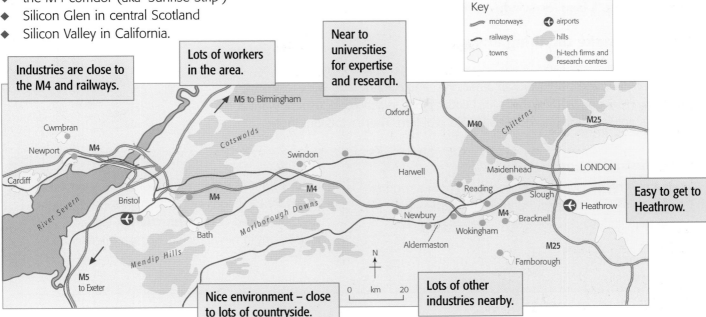

Industries are close to the M4 and railways.

Lots of workers in the area.

Near to universities for expertise and research.

Easy to get to Heathrow.

Nice environment – close to lots of countryside.

Lots of other industries nearby.

▲ Advantages of the M4 corridor

Heriot-Watt Research Park

The research park opened in 1971 and was one of the first science parks in Europe. The park was created by Heriot-Watt University. The emphasis is on research, development, design, engineering and training. Companies locating there have access to all the University's staff and facilities.

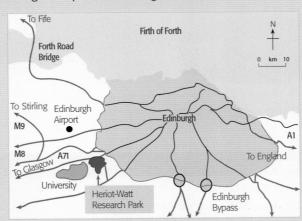

The research park is set in native gardens and woodland on the western edge of Edinburgh, and has excellent access to road, rail and air services.

There are over 40 companies at the research park.
These are just a few of them:

◆ The Centre for Maritime and Industrial Safety Technology
◆ Computer Application Services
◆ Inveresk Clinical Research
◆ Scotch Whisky Research Institute
◆ Scottish Environmental Protection Agency
◆ Scottish Road Safety Campaign.

Activities

1 Make a list of ten high-tech products. Find out where each of them is manufactured. Comment on what you find.

2 There is no perfect location for an industry. Look at the spider diagram and choose the three factors which you think would be most important for a company manufacturing high-tech products. Justify your choices.

3 Name three industries that would be able to locate virtually anywhere. Now choose two that are tied to a certain location. Explain why you have chosen each industry.

4 If footloose industries can locate almost anywhere, what problems could this bring to the UK economy?

5 Do the businesses or organisations which are located at the Heriot-Watt Research Park have offices anywhere else? Are the reasons the same for all locations?

All change for industry

In this unit you'll learn how industry has changed in the UK.

Don't we make anything any more?

Leaving school soon? Fancy a job? How about manufacturing? You'll be lucky. It's in decline in the UK. Over half a million manufacturing jobs were lost between 1997 and 2004. What's left? Lots of jobs in service industries. Want a job that's got something to do with IT? No problem. There's lots out there.

Did you know?
In 1950, nobody in the UK worked in IT. In 2000, 855 000 people had IT-related jobs.

Deindustrialisation

This is the name given to the decline in manufacturing (secondary) industry, and the growth in tertiary and quaternary industry. In the UK, this has happened because:

◆ machines replaced people in most manufacturing industries

◆ other countries produced goods more cheaply
◆ prices for UK goods were too high – not enough were produced (low **productivity**), lack of investment in new machinery, high interest rates.

Changing industry in the UK

What's happened? Before 1800, most people worked in farming, or things to do with farming. The Industrial Revolution in the 19th century changed all that. Lots of people moved to the towns for work – making steel, ships or textiles. Others worked in mines.

In the 20th century it all changed again (but not overnight). There was a shift to jobs in service industries, and more recently to quaternary industries.

▼ *Changing employment structure in the UK.*

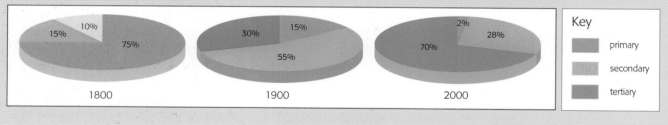

		Key
1800: 10%, 15%, 75%	1900: 15%, 30%, 55%	primary
2000: 2%, 28%, 70%		secondary
		tertiary

Where are the 'new' jobs?

In Unit 7.4 we looked at high-tech and footloose industries. Lots of these are found on the edges of towns and cities. (In geography we call that the **rural-urban fringe**.) They're found on specially built 'parks' or estates. And shops have moved to out-of-town shopping centres on the rural-urban fringe.

Why build there, and what are the consequences? Look at the table.

Did you know?
A **greenbelt** is an area of land around a town or city where development is restricted.

Why?	Consequences
◆ Land is cheaper ◆ Big sites with space to expand ◆ Less traffic and pollution ◆ Close to good transport links ◆ Close to workers ◆ Nice environment with open space	◆ Urban sprawl (towns keep growing) ◆ Nearby villages become **suburbanised** (and more like towns) ◆ **Greenbelts** disappear ◆ People often need to travel by car to get there – so pollution increases ◆ Traffic congestion – especially at out-of-town shopping centres ◆ Town and city centres have become 'urban deserts', with fewer businesses and shops.

What does the government do?

Car parts manufacturer cuts jobs

More than 150 jobs are being lost at a factory making brake and steering parts in Pontypool, South Wales.

The company blamed a drop in business caused partly by the closure of Rover.

A councillor blamed competition from Eastern Europe and Asia for the job losses.

August 2005

Assisted areas in the UK

Key

Development areas

Intermediate areas

Special status for Northern Ireland

N

0   km   100

The example above is from 2005, but it's in places like South Wales where lots of people have lost jobs over the years that the government has tried to help. They have encouraged industry to move to areas of high unemployment to create new jobs, for example by providing government grants and subsidies, and have tried to protect existing jobs.

The map shows the places that most needed help in the late 1990s.

But the way the government helps is going to change. The EU is changing the rules. From 2007 they want there to be less aid. And they want it to be better targeted.

Cleaning up industry

The oil and chemical leak in the article opposite might have been an accident, but industry causes all types of pollution in its normal day-to-day business. Air pollution can result in global warming and acid rain. Water pollution can upset ecosystems, kill fish and affect our health. There's masses of legislation (laws) which are intended to help industry clean up its act and reduce pollution.

The Environment Agency is responsible for maintaining and improving water quality in England and Wales. In Scotland the Scottish Environment Protection Agency (SEPA) is responsible for controlling pollution. SEPA works with others to protect and improve the environment.

Firm fined over water pollution

A firm in Rugby was fined £6000 after oil and chemicals leaked from drums and entered Sow Brook. The charges were brought by the Environment Agency.

Activities

1 Look back to the list of jobs you wrote for activity 1 in Unit 7.1.
   a Does your list suggest that deindustrialisation is taking place?
   b How many of your jobs are in some way connected with IT? Does this fit in with your answer to a above?
2 Explain why deindustrialisation has happened in the UK.
3 Look back to the maps in Unit 7.2. What is the relationship between the changing location of industry and the information shown in the pie charts opposite?
4 The table opposite shows the negative effects of industry setting up on the edges of towns. Can you think of any positive impacts?
5 Why do you think the government should help industries that are declining or struggling?

Industry – about turn

Did you know?

Reindustrialisation is where new industries are established in areas where traditional industries have declined.

In this unit you'll find out how two declining areas have changed.

The new South Wales

We've looked at declining heavy industries in South Wales and the Ruhr. Industry in decline is bad news. But things can get better.

Attracting new industry to South Wales

◆ The Welsh Development Agency was set up in 1976 to attract industry to Wales, and to encourage people to set up businesses.

◆ Urban Development Corporations were set up, for example Cardiff Bay.

◆ The region became a Development Area and had help from the government and the EU.

Did it work?

◆ In the 1980s, lots of companies came to South Wales, including 130 American and 130 European ones, as well as over 20 from Japan.

◆ New industry attracted to South Wales included biotechnology, IT, electronics, and financial services.

◆ Most urban areas in South Wales now have modern business parks.

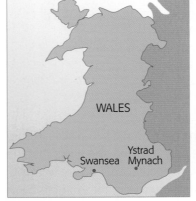

WALES

Swansea Ystrad Mynach

Valleys town to receive facelift

A five-year regeneration project in Ystrad Mynach (a South Wales valley town) will include:

◆ The transformation of the Penallta colliery (which closed in 1991) into a new 'urban village'.

◆ Improvements to recreation facilities at Penallta Country Park.

◆ Better public transport.

◆ New business developments at Tredomen Business Park.

Swansea

Swansea Waterfront has had a makeover. The latest news is:

'Insurance group Admiral will create 250 jobs in Swansea over the next 3 years. The company will move to purpose-built offices in the city's waterfront area.'

Admiral's move was helped by a £1.9 million grant from the Welsh Assembly.

One of the aims of developing the waterfront is to attract jobs in the tertiary and quaternary sectors.

But not everyone is happy. Swansea's city centre has been in decline for 20 years. Businesses and shops have left. People think the city centre won't benefit from the development. A member of the city's civic society said:

'The projects on the waterfront might split the city. Development will concentrate things there and everyone else will lose out.'

▲ *New building at Swansea Waterfront*

Cycles

You can look at what's happened in South Wales like this:

Market declines
↓
Industries close
↓
People lose jobs
↓
Less money to spend in local shops/services
↓
Local economy declines
↑
No new investment
↑
Industries close

▲ *Cycle of decline*

But if someone helps – like the government – things can get better.

Government help
↓
New industries encouraged to locate in the area
↓
Jobs created
↓
People have more money to spend in local shops/services
↓
Local economy grows
↑
More people move to the region

▲ *Cycle of growth*

Much the same has happened in the Ruhr.

What's new in the Ruhr?

The Ruhr – heavy industry was in decline, and it had an image problem. Rivers and the atmosphere were polluted, the landscape was ruined. Something had to be done. The state and central government wanted to encourage new types of employment and improve the environment. Work began in the 1960s.

◆ Now 65% of the Ruhr's workers are employed in the tertiary sector. Jobs range from those in shops, health and veterinary services, to transport, legal and business consultants and telecommunications.
◆ New universities and colleges were set up to educate workers with new qualifications and skills.
◆ Business parks were developed for light and high-tech industries.
◆ The environment has been cleaned up.

Activities

1 Do you think new industries would have located in South Wales without government help? Explain your answer.
2 Most industries that have chosen to locate in South Wales are from outside the UK. Why do you think this is?
3 What do you think might be the advantages and disadvantages of large foreign companies locating in South Wales?
4 Compare the changes that have taken place in South Wales and the Ruhr. What are the main similarities and differences?
5 Find out about one other area in the UK where new industries have chosen to locate. Are the factors causing the decline, and the reasons for re-growth, the same as in South Wales, or are they different?

Emscher Landscape Park

A whole area along the River Emscher has been transformed to create Europe's largest regional park. It stretches 70 km from east to west and covers 320 sq. km. The aim was to improve the working and living environment for the 2 million people who live in the region.

Lots of work has been done, ranging from developing large areas of derelict land to planting trees. Old industrial buildings have been deliberately included in the park. The park includes 230 km of cycle tracks and 130 km of footpaths, and a golf course.

Work began on the park in 1989, but it's still not finished. It'll continue until 2020.

▲ *Where's that gone?*

Industrial change – West Lothian

In this unit you will find out about the changing fortunes of one region.

Embracing change

Some parts of Scotland's Central Belt have really struggled to cope with the decline of the traditional heavy industries like coal mining, heavy engineering, and steel.

But West Lothian has embraced change and is now one of Scotland's fastest-growing local economies in terms of population and job creation.

The decline of coal mining and the steel industry dates back to the mid-1950s.

Bathgate no more …

In the early 1960s, the government used its regional development policy to persuade British Leyland to locate its new truck and tractor plant in Bathgate. This created 7000 jobs. Due to the huge distance between the plant and its main markets, poor management and damaging labour disputes, and cheaper imports, it closed in 1986. In the same year Plessey, an electronics factory, also closed. This left Bathgate with one of the highest unemployment rates in the UK.

Bathgate no more … again!

With a lot of effort and local authority funding, several international companies were persuaded to build new plants on greenfield sites in Bathgate and 2 km away in Livingston.

They concentrated on electronics firms. Bathgate became one of the growth points in 'Silicon Glen', the zone of high-tech industries across Central Scotland. One of the plants was the American electronics giant Motorola, which at its peak employed 3400 workers in its state-of-the-art £300 million mobile phone facility. Just over 1 km to the east, the Japanese electronics firm NEC built a huge factory to produce semi-conductor chips for the computer industry. It employed 1500 workers. But due to a global downturn in the electronics industry both plants closed in 2002.

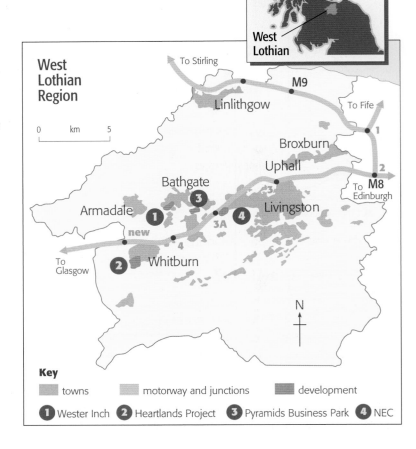

West Lothian

The NEC factory no more … ▶

So, what's happening now?

Distribution

The NEC site was sold, and the factory was demolished by June 2005. The site was cleared to house Tesco's new national distribution centre.

The West Lothian area is being marketed as ideal for distribution centres. It's within an hour's drive of 60% of Scotland's population, 20 minutes from the Eurocentral rail terminal, 30 minutes from the ferry terminal at Rosyth connecting to Zeebrugge in Belgium and the continent, and 20 minutes from the Grangemouth container terminal.

Already over 100 distribution centres have located in West Lothian, including Aldi, Morrisons supermarkets, Scottish Courage Brewers, and major logistics companies Exel and Wincanton.

The Pyramids Business Park

The Motorola phone factory has been re-branded as the Pyramids Business Park. Most of the old factory has been turned into a call centre for the Inland Revenue tax credits organisation.

The Heartlands Regeneration Project

The Heartlands Regeneration Project is centred on the former site of the Polkemmet Colliery. Polkemmet, in Whitburn, closed in 1986. The mine area and the surrounding bings (spoil heaps), covering 600 hectares, is now one of the largest industrial regeneration schemes in the UK. The lead company is Ecosse Regeneration.

Existing coal reserves close to the surface will be mined using open cast methods and then the whole area will be redeveloped, in stages. A 14-hectare business park for small to medium enterprises will hopefully create up to 4000 new jobs. 2000 new homes will be built, alongside a 150-bedroom luxury hotel with conference centre and two championship golf courses. A new motorway junction on the M8 will be built.

▲ The Heartlands Regeneration Project.

Wester Inch

West Lothian Council finally gave up trying to sell the British Leyland site for industrial use and tried a different tack. The planners decided to help create jobs in the construction industry by allowing the building of houses. The developers have been given permission to build 1960 houses on the site, now re-named Wester Inch. As part of the agreement, they will also build a primary school and community sports facilities. Nine hectares have been set aside for industrial use and the hope is that the good transport links, high-quality housing, and high-quality environment will attract companies.

Activities

1 What were the reasons for the closure of the Bathgate tractor plant in 1986?
2 How successful were the authorities in replacing the 7000 jobs lost due to the closure of the tractor plant?
3 Devise a graphic timeline showing the major job losses and gains over the last 20 years in West Lothian.
4 Explain why distribution companies are being encouraged to locate in West Lothian.
5 Describe how the Heartlands Regeneration Project will help to regenerate not only the landscape but also the economy of the Whitburn area?

▼ Wester Inch.

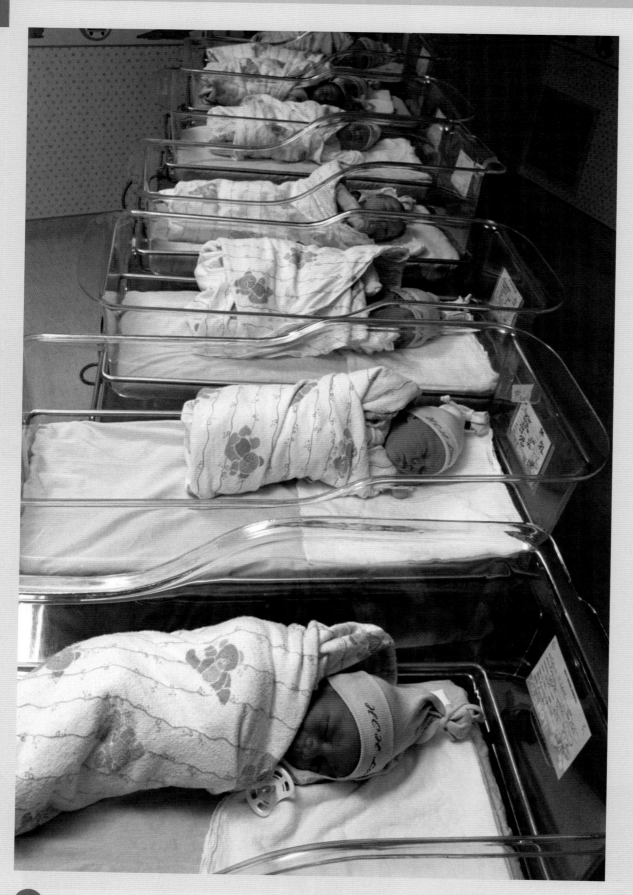

The big picture

This chapter is about people – all of us. These are the big ideas behind the chapter:

◆ There's a lot of people in the world – 6.5 billion and rising – but we're not evenly spread out.

◆ Population is increasing fastest in LEDCs.

◆ Migration is the movement of people from one place to another. It affects population sizes and structures – but most of all it affects people themselves.

◆ Countries need to know the size of their population so they can plan for the future.

◆ Population change can cause problems – too many people, especially young ones in LEDCs, too many older people in MEDCs.

◆ Immigration might help to sort out some of the problems in the UK, population control and family planning can help in LEDCs.

Your goals for this chapter

By the end of this chapter you should be able to answer these questions:

◆ What factors affect population density? How many can you name?

◆ What does the demographic transition model show us (and can you draw it)?

◆ Where is population growing fastest, and slowest?

◆ What do population pyramids show, and why are they useful?

◆ List four types of migration, four push factors and four pull factors.

◆ How does migration affect the UK? (Think about international and internal migration.)

◆ Give an example of international refugees. Why are they refugees? What's happened to them? What's being done to help?

◆ What is a census? Why do countries have them? What problems does an LEDC like Sudan have carrying out a census?

◆ What's the problem of population change in an MEDC like the UK? How will we cope?

◆ What are the problems of population change in an LEDC like India? What are they doing about it?

◆ What do these terms mean?
population density, birth rate, death rate, natural increase, population growth rate, fertility rate, infant mortality, life expectancy, refugee, economic migrant

And then . . .

When you finish the chapter, come back here and see if you've met your goals!

Did you know?
◆ The world's population hit 6.5 billion in the spring of 2006.
◆ It's increasing by 201 331 people every day.

Did you know?
◆ The UK's population reached 60 million in 2005.
◆ It's expected to peak at 67 million in 2050 and then start falling.

Did you know?
The UK's birth rate has fallen to an all-time low.

Did you know?
The average age of the UK population was 34 years in 1971 – it rose to 38 in 2002 and will be 43 by 2031.

Your chapter starter

Look at the photo on page 134.
Where do you think these babies are?
What will their lives be like?
How many children will they have?
How long might they live?

Which one's ours?

Where in the world is everyone?

In this unit you will learn why the world's population is unevenly distributed.

A lot here, a few there

The first humans left Africa about 70 000 years ago. Since then, people have spread all over the world. We're capable of living almost anywhere!

But the world's population certainly isn't evenly distributed. Some places are **densely** populated – they have lots of people. Other places are **sparsely** populated. Look at this map:

> **Population density explained**
>
> The **population density** of an area or place is the average number of people per square kilometre. It is calculated like this:
>
> Population density = population ÷ area (km^2)
>
> You will come across population density figures for all sorts of areas: continents, countries, regions, and even parts of cities.

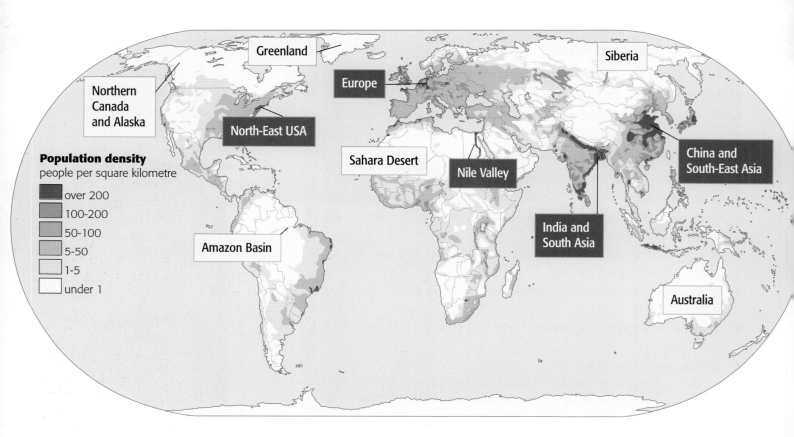

Population density
people per square kilometre

- over 200
- 100-200
- 50-100
- 5-50
- 1-5
- under 1

Map labels: Greenland, Siberia, Northern Canada and Alaska, Europe, North-East USA, China and South-East Asia, Sahara Desert, Nile Valley, India and South Asia, Amazon Basin, Australia

Why aren't we spread more evenly?

The more densely populated areas are generally easier for people to live in. These factors combine to make an area easier or harder for people to live in:

- **physical** factors, like relief, climate, and water supply.
- **human** factors, like industry and transport.

So flat lowlands, areas with a moderate or temperate climate, and areas with a reliable water supply are usually densely populated. The extreme environments – the polar regions, the high mountains, the deserts, and the rainforests – are usually sparsely populated.

Transport and trade mean that dense populations can be found at major ports, or where transport networks like roads and rail lines come together.

> **Did you know?**
> ◆ Monaco has a population of 32 409 and an area of just 1.95 sq. km – giving it a population density of 16 620 people per sq. km.
> ◆ It is one of the most crowded places in the world.

Western Europe is an area of high population density. It has a temperate climate, with reliable rainfall. The land is low and fairly flat. Transport networks have been easy to develop. Resources like coal encouraged industries, making it even more attractive. Scandinavia has a much lower population density. It has a rugged landscape, a cold climate, and some dense coniferous forests.

In North Africa, the Nile Valley is much more densely populated than the **Sahara Desert**. In the Nile Valley there's a reliable water supply, so the land can be irrigated, and crops can be grown in fertile soils. Contrast this attractive environment with that of the Sahara Desert. People have found living in the Sahara much harder. The climate is hot, with very little rainfall, so water for drinking and farming is in short supply.

You will often see population density figures for countries. But remember that there can be great variations in density within a country. Take the UK, for example. The population density for the country as a whole is 247 people per square kilometre. But within the UK the density varies widely – from over 500 people per square kilometre in the cities to under ten people per square kilometre in northern Scotland.

A Countries with highest population densities, 2005	People per sq. km
Bangladesh	1002
Taiwan	636
South Korea	492
Netherlands	395
Lebanon	368
Belgium	340
Japan	337
India	329
Rwanda	320
El Salvador	319

B Countries with lowest population densities, 2005	People per sq. km
Australia	2
Mongolia	2
Namibia	2
Botswana	3
Canada	3
Mauritania	3
Central African Rep.	6
Chad	6
Kazakhstan	6
Bolivia	8

C Ten other countries, for comparison, 2005	People per sq. km
UK	247
Germany	231
France	111
Spain	81
USA	31
Afghanistan	46
China	136
Brazil	21
Nigeria	141
Iraq	60

Activities

1 Using the map:
  a Describe the distribution of the most densely populated parts of the world.
  b Explain why population density is low in any two named locations.
2 Explain why population density is low in any two of the countries in table B.
3 Explain why population density varies so much within the United Kingdom.
4 Which sparsely populated environments do you think will be least likely to gain population in the future? Why is this?
5 'Low population density is because of physical factors, high density is due to human factors'. To what extent do you agree with this statement?

World population increase

In this unit you'll find out how quickly and how evenly the world's population is increasing.

The population explosion

In the next two seconds, ten babies will be born around the world.

Of course, some people will have died. But overall, it adds up to 200 000 extra people every day. That's just over 70 million a year.

The graph below and the tables on the next page tell the story.

> **Birth rate:** the number of births in a country in a year, per 1000 people.
>
> **Death rate:** the number of deaths in a country in a year, per 1000 people.
>
> **Natural increase:** the birth rate minus the death rate, often given as a percentage. Don't confuse this with 'population growth rate'.

Did you know?
96 100 000 000 people have lived on the Earth.

Did you know?
- At a growth rate of 1%, the population of a country will double in 70 years.
- At 2%, it will double in 36 years.
- At 3%, 24 years.
- At 4%, 18 years.

Did you know?
- About 6% of all the people ever born are alive today.
- That's actually a fairly large percentage, when you think about it!

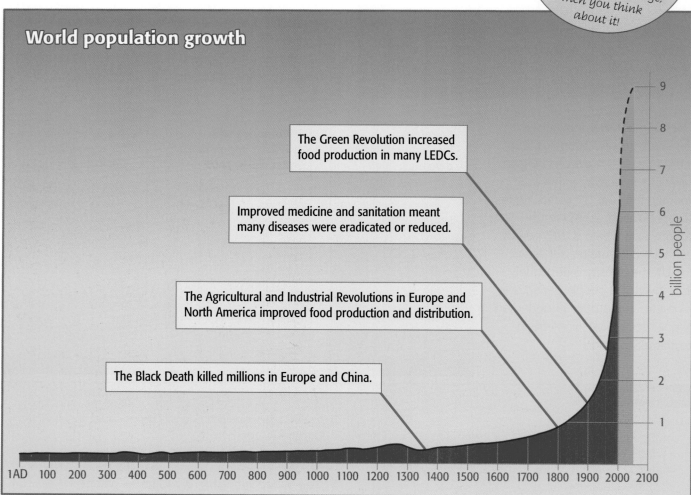

World population growth

The Green Revolution increased food production in many LEDCs.

Improved medicine and sanitation meant many diseases were eradicated or reduced.

The Agricultural and Industrial Revolutions in Europe and North America improved food production and distribution.

The Black Death killed millions in Europe and China.

billion people

1AD 100 200 300 400 500 600 700 800 900 1000 1100 1200 1300 1400 1500 1600 1700 1800 1900 2000 2100

World population increase

	total population (billions)	natural increase (%)	annual increase (millions)
1950	2.56	1.47	37.8
1955	2.78	1.89	52.9
1960	3.04	1.33	40.8
1965	3.35	2.08	70.2
1970	3.71	2.07	77.6
1975	4.09	1.75	72.2
1980	4.46	1.70	76.3
1985	4.85	1.70	83.0
1990	5.28	1.56	83.2
1995	5.69	1.36	77.7
2000	6.08	1.26	77.3
2005	6.46	1.14	73.8
2010 (est.)	6.82	1.03	70.8
2015 (est.)	7.17	0.97	69.6
2020 (est.)	7.52	0.88	66.4

The number of countries with a population over 50 million

1950	8
2000	22
2050	33

When did/will we reach the next billion?

year (estimate/projected)	amount	years in-between
1804	1 billion	-
1927	2 billion	123
1960	3 billion	33
1974	4 billion	14
1987	5 billion	13
1999	6 billion	12
2013	7 billion	14
2028	8 billion	15
2054	9 billion	26

Population increase for selected countries, 2005

	birth rate (per 1000)	death rate (per 1000)	natural increase
Afghanistan	47.02	20.75	2.68%
Nigeria	40.65	17.18	2.35%
Angola	44.64	25.90	1.87%
India	22.32	8.28	1.40%
Brazil	16.83	6.15	1.07%
China	13.14	6.94	0.62%
USA	14.14	8.25	0.59%
UK	10.78	10.18	0.06%
Germany	8.33	10.55	−0.22%
Bulgaria	9.66	14.26	−0.46%

Is population increase spread evenly?

No – there are big differences from country to country.

◆ India has a natural increase of 1.4% and, because it has such a large population, this adds about 15 million people a year.

◆ Afghanistan has a natural increase of 2.68%, one of the fastest in the world in 2005 – but because it has a smaller population than India, this adds just 800 000 people.

◆ The UK's natural increase is 0.06%, and this adds about 36 000 people a year.

◆ A few countries have a falling population. We'll look at these differences in Unit 8.9.

Overall, the rate of world population increase is slowing down a bit. But people are still worried that we won't have the resources to support everyone.

Activities

1 Use this writing frame to make notes about world population increase.

> Birth rate is …
> Death rate is …
> Natural increase is …
> The world's population is currently increasing by …
> Overall, the rate of increase is …

2 **a** When was the world's population increasing most quickly in percentage terms?
   b When was it increasing quickest in terms of millions added each year?

3 When would you say the world's population explosion began?

4 Look at the table of population increase for selected countries.
   a Both Afghanistan and Angola have a high death rate – but their natural increase is still high. Why?
   b What's happening to the population in Germany and Bulgaria?
   c Why do you think Brazil and China have lower death rates than the UK and Germany?

5 Do you think the 'population explosion' was due mainly to high birth rates or decreasing death rates?

6 To what extent do you think it's correct to say that the population explosion is a problem caused by population change in LEDCs?

The demographic transition model

In this unit you'll find out **why** the world's population is increasing.

Many countries have had a similar pattern of population increase over time. Geographers have devised a model to show and explain this.

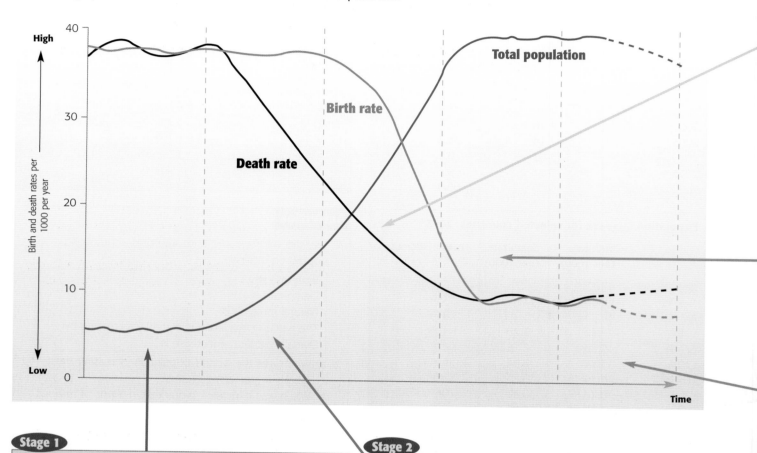

Stage 1

High stationary

The death rate is high due to diseases, famines, a lack of clean water, and a lack of medical care.

But the birth rate is also high due to a lack of birth control, a low age of marriage for women, and the fact that children work so they can add to the family income.

So the natural increase is low – the population doesn't increase much.

The UK was in Stage 1 before 1760.

Few places are in this stage today – perhaps a few remote tribes in the tropical rainforests.

Stage 2

Early expanding

The death rate is starting to fall due to improved medicine, cleaner water, more and better food, and improved sanitation.

But the birth rate is still high, for the same reasons as before.

So the natural increase is high – the population increases quickly.

The UK was in Stage 2 between 1760 and about 1900, during the Industrial Revolution.

Today some LEDCs are in this stage – for example, Bangladesh and Nigeria.

Stage 3

Late expanding

The death rate is still falling, for the same reasons as before.	But now the birth rate is starting to fall because there are fewer farmers needing children to work the family land, birth control is available, infant deaths are falling, and women are staying in education and marrying later.	So there's still some natural increase, but it's lower than it was – population increase is slowing down. The UK was in Stage 3 between 1900 and about 1950. Today many LEDCs are in this stage – for example, India, Brazil, and Mexico.

Stage 4

Low stationary

The death rate remains low.	And the birth rate is low – through birth control, people are now having the number of children they want.	So there's little or no natural increase – the population doesn't increase much. The UK has been in Stage 4 since about 1950. Many other MEDCs are currently in this stage, such as the USA, France, and Japan. Few LEDCs have reached this stage.

Stage 5

Declining

The death rate could go up because a greater proportion of the population is elderly.	The birth rate remains low and could get lower – lifestyle changes mean people have children later in life, and have fewer of them.	If more people die than are being born, there's negative natural increase – so the population falls. This stage wasn't on the model when it was first devised – it has been added to show recent developments in population change. The UK could enter Stage 5 soon. Other MEDCs are already there – Germany, Sweden, and Italy.

The demographic transition model works quite well for countries that have gone from a rural, poorly educated society to an urban, industrial, well educated one. So it fits what has happened in the UK, the rest of Europe, and other MEDCs. But LEDCs might not follow the same transition.

Activities

1 a Which stage of the demographic transition model has a high birth rate and a high death rate?
  b Which stages are MEDCs in?
  c Which stages are LEDCs in?
  d In which two stages will population increase? Why?

2 Could there be a 'stage 6' of the demographic transition model at some time in the future? If so, what might it look like?

3 Why might some LEDCs not follow the stages of the model?

Population contrasts

In this unit you'll learn how population increase varies between MEDCs and LEDCs, and how to use population pyramids.

Where's the increase?

Population increase isn't happening everywhere at the same rate.

◆ Six countries account for about half the world's current increase in population.

◆ India, on its own, accounts for about 20% and China about 10%.

◆ Over 90% of the world's increase is in the LEDCs.

◆ In many MEDCs, population increase is slowing down – and in some, in Europe, populations are declining.

Daily increase in population

1	India	41 435
2	China	20 758
3	Indonesia	9 613
4	Pakistan	9 033
5	Nigeria	8 361
6	Bangladesh	8 264
	World	**201 331**

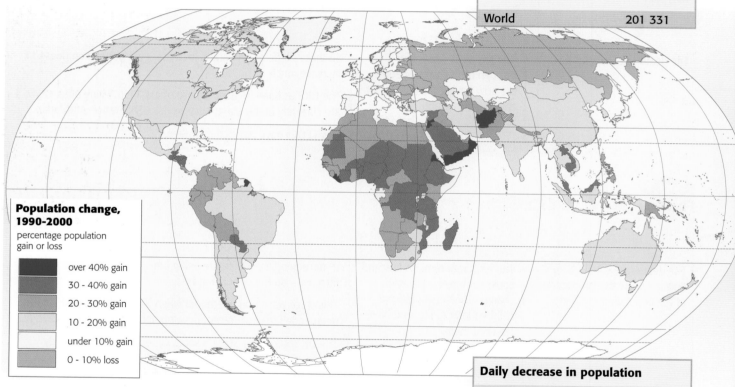

Population change, 1990–2000

percentage population gain or loss

- over 40% gain
- 30 – 40% gain
- 20 – 30% gain
- 10 – 20% gain
- under 10% gain
- 0 – 10% loss

Daily decrease in population

1	Russia	1 454
2	Ukraine	819
3	South Africa	377
4	Bulgaria	182
5	Romania	73
6	Hungary	71

So, in many LEDCs, rapid population increase is the problem. But in the MEDCs, people are starting to get worried about ageing populations and population decline. We'll look at these problems more closely in Unit 8.9.

The last 50 years

The world's population has increased from 2.5 billion to 6.5 billion. Much of this increase has been in China, India, and other countries in Asia, Africa, and South America. This is because they have had high birth rates and a dramatic fall in death rates – especially infant mortality – due to improvements in health and the availability of food.

Population pyramids

These are a type of graph that shows the age structure of a country's population. They show the percentage or number of males and females in each age group – the number aged 0-4 years, 5-9 years, 10-14 years and so on.

The trick is to know how to 'read' the pyramid.

◆ First, look at the overall shape, to see what that tells you. For example, if the pyramid is wide at the bottom, it means there are lots of young people in the population – we say the country has a young population.

◆ Then look for details, like bars that are longer or shorter than those above and below them. For example, shorter bars could indicate high death rates in those age groups, perhaps through war or famine.

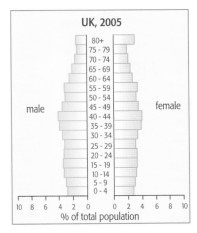

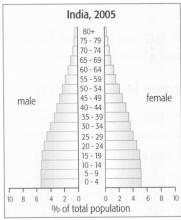

Why are they useful?

They tell us how the population might develop, and this can help us plan for the future needs of that population. If the country has a very young population, it will need more schools and more teachers. If the country's population is ageing, it will need more old people's homes and more money for pensions. Population pyramids also help us to compare the populations of countries.

Population pyramids and the DTM

The stages of the demographic transition model (Unit 8.3) produce different-shaped population pyramids. So, by recognising the shapes, and understanding what they show, you can tell which stage of the model the country is at.

Activities

1 Explain the causes of population increase in LEDCs.
2 Why do you think birth rates remain high in many LEDCs, despite a decrease in death rates?
3 Why do many MEDCs have an ageing population?
4 Compare and contrast the population pyramids for India and the UK.
5 Look back to the demographic transition model in Unit 8.3. How do the population pyramids for India and the UK help to explain their positions on the model?
6 A fifth stage to the demographic transition model is where a country has a continued decline in birth rate, together with a further increase in life expectancy. Draw an outline population pyramid to show this stage. Which countries do you think might reach stage 5?

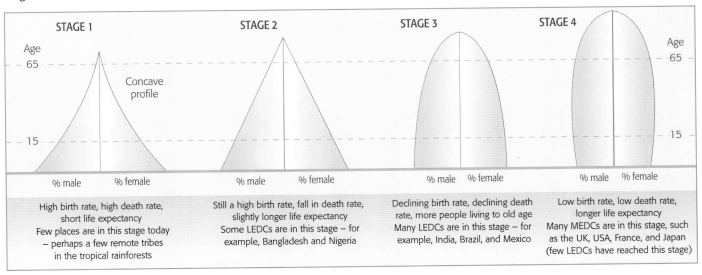

Migration

In this unit you'll learn what migration is, what causes it, and about population change due to migration.

What is migration?

Simple - **migration** is the movement of people from one place to another.

It has always gone on – people have always moved around. As geographers, we get interested when a migration involves a lot of people. We do two things:

1   We identify the reasons for the migration, and say what type of migration it is.
2   We analyse the effect of the migration – on the place sending people, on the place receiving people, and on the people themselves.

Four types of migration

Voluntary migration

This is when people move of their own free will – they're usually trying to find a better standard of living. For example, many people from Eastern European countries, like the Poles on the right, are moving to Western European countries for jobs and higher wages. They are called **economic migrants**.

Forced migration

This is when people have no choice – they either move, or face extreme hardship or even death. This often happens when there's a natural disaster or war. These migrants are called **refugees**. For example, by the end of 2005, 200 000 people had fled Sudan for Chad after two years of civil war (there's more about this in Unit 8.7). The picture on the right shows Afghan refugees fleeing to Pakistan during the recent war.

Permanent migration

This is when people move forever, to find a new place to live. An example from history would be the millions of people who left Ireland during the 19th century, largely due to famine, and settled in the USA.

Temporary migration

This is when people don't move forever – they always intend to go home at some point in the future. For example, each summer many workers come to the UK from Eastern Europe to pick fruit and vegetables and, when the season's over, they go home (see Unit 8.10).

The United Nations says there should be a new term: environmental refugee. It calculates that drought, flooding, deforestation, and falling soil fertility now cause more refugees than wars. It says there will be up to 50 million environmental refugees in the world by 2010.

Migration between countries

This is **international migration**. It takes place because of **push and pull factors**. It's important because it can affect the population size and structure of the countries involved.

How does migration affect population size?

People leave one country, and go to another – this obviously affects the number of people living in each country. In many cases, a country loses some and gains some – the balance is called **net migration**. So, migration plays an important part in the **population growth rate**.

> **Population growth rate explained**
>
> The **population growth rate** is the number of people added to a population each year due to natural increase and net migration. It is given as a percentage, and is calculated like this:
>
> Population growth rate (%) = the number of extra people ÷ the total number of people before x 100

How does migration affect population structure?

This is a bit harder to understand. You need to think about who's migrating.

In some migrations – like those forced by war or starvation – whole families leave. But in other migrations – such as when people go looking for work – it's often a certain group that leaves. This might be the young men, or young couples. So a country loses people from just a few age groups in its population pyramid. The country these people go to receives extra young people – and in time, it also gets their children.

Migration inside a country

This is called **internal migration**. It's important because it affects the distribution of the country's population.

A good example is the migration of people from the country to the towns and cities. This is called **rural-urban migration**.

It happened in the UK and many other MEDCs during the Industrial Revolution in the 19th century.

Today it's happening on a massive scale in the LEDCs. Again, it takes place because of push and pull factors:

◆ People are pushed to leave the rural areas. They are trying to escape the population pressure and environmental deterioration that are making it more and more difficult to survive there.

◆ The urban areas act like magnets. They are pulling people from rural areas and small towns. The cities offer more hope of jobs, education, and better living standards.

Push and pull factors for migration between countries

Push factors encourage people to leave their own country:

◆ not enough jobs
◆ low wages
◆ poor educational opportunities
◆ war with another country
◆ civil war
◆ drought and famine

Pull factors attract people to a new country:

◆ hope of finding a job, or a better job
◆ higher wages
◆ better health care
◆ chance of a better education
◆ better all-round standard of living
◆ family or friends may have already moved
◆ safety

Other factors

Barriers to international migration are important:

◆ cost of travel can be high
◆ there are legal restrictions *
◆ cultural differences – language, way of life

Most people prefer their own country:

◆ existing job and work contacts
◆ family and friends are near
◆ familiar surroundings and culture
◆ living costs may be lower

Migrants may return home:

◆ with capital to start a business
◆ with new skills and qualifications
◆ if they have difficulty in settling overseas
◆ when they retire
◆ if they are forced to return for legal reasons

* Most countries have restrictions on migration. They are willing to take those who have been well educated and have valuable work skills, and are in good health. Family members are often allowed to follow. Migrants with a criminal record aren't wanted.

Activities

1 What effects is economic migration likely to have on the countries from which people have migrated?

2 How might push and pull factors be different for internal and international migration?

3 'Push factors are more important for international migration, while pull factors are more important for internal migration.' To what extent do you agree?

Migration and the UK

In this unit you'll learn how migration is affecting the UK.

International migration

Just over half the UK's population growth in the last ten years has been due to immigration. It now accounts for about 80% of the country's population growth.

Looking ahead, the UK's population is expected to increase from 60 million to 67 million in the twenty-five years from 2006 to 2031. This means a population growth rate of about 0.4% per year. But the rate of natural increase is only 0.06%. It's immigration that will make up the difference.

Of the 7 million growth, about 4 million – 57% – is expected to come from immigration. A further 1.8 million is expected to be the children of the immigrants. If it was left to natural increase, the population would go up by just 1.2 million.

50% of immigrants settle in South-East England, mostly in London. But immigration is now affecting almost every area of the country. The North-East and North-West would have had population declines without the current rate of immigration.

There's a big reason why migrants head to the UK: jobs. The people coming are mainly **economic migrants**.

Where the migrants come from

The graph on the bottom right shows the most common countries of origin. A new trend in migration to the UK has been the arrival of workers from the EU's new eastern countries.

The UK is the favourite destination for workers from these countries. This is because the government has introduced generous employment rules for workers from the EU to plug what it says are labour shortages in a strong economy.

About 130 000 new EU workers came to the UK in the first year after EU enlargement in May 2004.

What about illegal immigrants?

The government's official guess is that in 2005 there were between 310 000 and 570 000 illegal immigrants. No one can tell if that's accurate.

| 1973-1982 net migration **out** 430 000 |
| 1983-1992 net migration **in** 240 000 |
| 1993-2002 net migration **in** 1 million |

Did you know?
- In 2004, a record 582 000 people migrated to the UK.
- Of course, others left – 360 000 emigrated.
- That meant an extra 222 000 people living here.

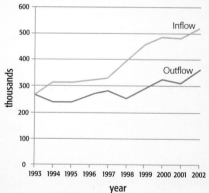
International migration into and out of the UK

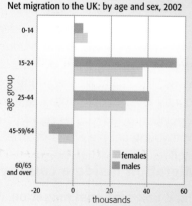
Net migration to the UK: by age and sex, 2002

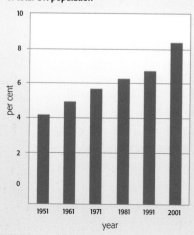
Overseas-born population as a percentage of total UK population

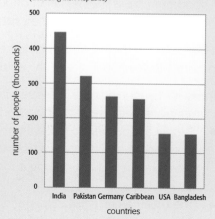
Most common countries of origin, 2001
(excluding Irish Republic)

Internal migration

There's a lot of internal migration in the UK. People are moving to and from every part of the country, but there are two clear trends:

◆ There's a general movement of people from the North to the South – people are moving away from the old industrial areas of the North to southern England, especially the South-East.

◆ At the same time, there's a movement of people out of the cities, especially the inner cities.

Around one in ten people moved within the UK in the year before the 2001 Census. Many were workers who moved south to find jobs. The northern regions of England, the Midlands, Wales, Scotland, and Northern Ireland all had a loss of full-time workers. The South-East had the largest net gain. London, the South-West, and the Eastern regions of England also had a net gain of full-time workers.

London's a special case

More people leave London for other parts of the UK than move there. But London's population is increasing because it's where most international migrants head for.

We're leaving the cities

People are moving from the big cities and conurbations to smaller towns and villages, often quite nearby. This is called **counter-urbanisation**. They're usually looking for bigger houses in quieter, less-polluted places.

Why does all this matter?

Knowing about internal migration matters because we need to know how the distribution of our population is changing – so that we can build houses, schools, hospitals, sports centres, and so on in the right places. For example, there are 850 000 empty homes in the UK, but the government says we need to build 4 million new homes across the UK, mostly in the South and South-East.

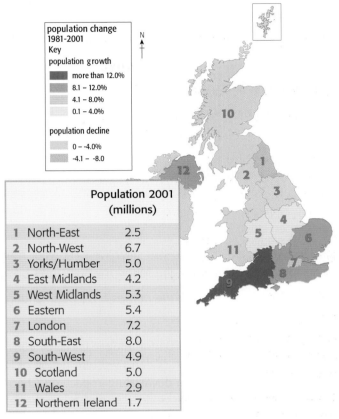

population change 1981-2001
Key
population growth

■	more than 12.0%
■	8.1 – 12.0%
■	4.1 – 8.0%
■	0.1 – 4.0%

population decline

■	0 – -4.0%
■	-4.1 – -8.0

	Population 2001 (millions)	
1	North-East	2.5
2	North-West	6.7
3	Yorks/Humber	5.0
4	East Midlands	4.2
5	West Midlands	5.3
6	Eastern	5.4
7	London	7.2
8	South-East	8.0
9	South-West	4.9
10	Scotland	5.0
11	Wales	2.9
12	Northern Ireland	1.7

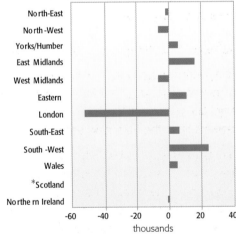

Net migration with the rest of the UK in the year to April 2001: by region (* In Scotland the number of people who moved out was balanced by the number moving in)

Activities

1 Describe how international migration patterns to and from the UK have changed since 1973.

2 What effect has international migration had on the total population of the UK?

3 What impact has the expansion of the European Union had on migration into the UK?

4 What do you think might be some of the consequences of large-scale migration from other countries?

5 Why do you think that government estimates of the number of illegal immigrants are likely to be inaccurate?

6 Describe and explain the pattern of internal migration within the UK.

7 Why is London 'a special case?'

8 Do you think it's right for the government to propose the building of 4 million new homes, when there are so many empty? Justify your answer.

Darfur refugee emergency

In this unit you'll find out about an example of international refugees.

Aisha's story, from a refugee camp in Chad

I'm 27. My three children have diarrhoea. We live in one hut with my sisters, Neimad and Mona. My husband is dead. Neimad's husband was taken away. We haven't seen him for months.

We had to leave our village when the Janjaweed attacked us. The village had 7000 goats, 1000 donkeys, 2000 camels, 3000 horses and many thousands of chickens. They took the men away, and then we heard shots. The women stayed.

The Janjaweed said: "Why do you stay? We killed your men." Later I went to where the shots came from and found my husband's body.

This is a real story – though the names have been changed.

Aisha is just one victim of the Darfur refugee crisis. By early 2006, there had been three years of civil war in Sudan's western region of Darfur. The UN said events in Darfur could have 'a devastating impact' on Chad and Sudan – two of the poorest countries in the world – as well as on the refugees.

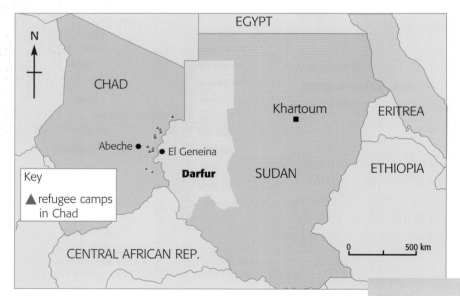

The two sides

Sudan's government, and the Arab militias that support it, especially the Janjaweed. They're accused of war crimes against Darfur's black African population.

Black African Darfuris. There are two main rebel groups – the Sudan Liberation Army (SLA), the biggest, and the Justice and Equality Movement (Jem). The SLA was formed in 2002 to defend black African farmers against the Arab militias.

Details of the crisis

- 180 000 Darfuris have been killed.
- 200 000 have fled to next-door Chad, and live in refugee camps.
- Up to 1.8 million live in camps within Darfur.
- News reports say militias have killed, raped, and forced hundreds of thousands from their homes.
- Hundreds of villages have been burnt (see right).

What's the fighting about?

The black African Darfuris say that Sudan's government favours the ruling Arab elite in the north of the country. Both groups are Muslims, but the Darfuris say that as non-Arabs they suffer discrimination.

There has been tension in Darfur for many years over land and grazing rights. In 2003, rebels started attacking government targets. The government struck back. It admits supporting 'self-defence' militias, but says it doesn't support the Janjaweed.

Refugees from Darfur say that following air raids by government aircraft, the Janjaweed ride into villages on horses and camels, slaughtering men, raping women, and stealing or burning whatever they can find.

Refugees in Chad

Refugees fled to Chad, seeking safety. They arrived in a remote, desert region where water is in short supply. They made rough shelters, often just yards from the border – still within reach of raiding militias. In 2004, The United Nations High Commission for Refugees (UNHCR) moved most of the refugees to camps a safe distance from the border.

The UNHCR and other aid agencies built the camps to provide everything from family shelters to wells, toilets, clinics, and schools. Twelve camps were built by the summer of 2005. Emergency airlifts flew thousands of tonnes of tents, blankets, plastic sheeting, soap and other relief items.

Many refugees remain camped along a 600-km stretch of the border and are still vulnerable to attacks from Sudan.

No one knows if or when the refugees will be able to go home.

▲ *Fleeing to Chad.*

▲ *Safe at last?*

What's being done in Darfur?

Lots of aid agencies are working in Darfur, but they can't get access to wide areas. They say the government blocks their movements by demanding visas. Aid workers have warned that many thousands are at risk of starvation and disease in the camps, with 1 million children threatened by malnutrition.

Peace talks keep failing. The lives of thousands of people are being ruined.

Did you know?

An all-star charity concert Voices for Darfur was held to raise money for the refugees.

Activities

1 Describe the background to the conflict in Darfur.
2 Why do you think the conflict has gone on for so long without being resolved?
3 Why did the UNHCR move the refugees who had fled into Chad?
4 Why do you think the government of Chad relied upon the UNHCR for emergency relief and aid?

5 What do you think might be some of the effects on Chad of such a large number of refugees?
6 Find out about another example of international refugees. Compare and contrast this example with the situation in Darfur and Chad.

Population census – count me in!

In this unit you will learn why countries carry out population censuses – and about some of the problems they face.

Why bother with a census?

Governments need to know:
- how many people there are in the country
- where they live
- how many are school age
- what jobs they do.

This information helps in the planning of services like health and education, and in planning for housing needs.

Most countries hold a census every 10 years to count their population.

The UK Census

The last census was on 9 April 2001. Forms were filled in giving details of every person in each house, including their ages, how they were related to each other, what jobs they had, how they travelled to work, their educational qualifications, the kind of house they lived in, and so on.

The Scottish Executive spends more than £500 every second on providing hospitals, roads, schools, and many other services, and supporting industry and transport. To make the best use of its £18 billion budget, the Scottish Executive must know where money is most needed. The census provides vital information. The details gathered by the census are set out in tables, graphs, and charts which give a picture of life in the UK in a way which lets councils see where there is need and businesses see where there are opportunities.

Interesting facts

	Glasgow City	Scotland
Average age of a person with good health	30.14	32.86
Average age of a person with a limiting long-term illness	55.68	57.94
Average age of carer	45.09	47.83
% of economically inactive people who are permanently sick/disabled	28.02	21.25
% of households with one or more carers resident	16.69	16.84

The UK has held a census every ten years since 1801. Since devolution of the Scottish Parliament, Scotland has had a separate census organisation and a different census. The census in Scotland, England, Wales, and Northern Ireland takes place at the same time and all the statistics are collated for the whole of the UK. The Scottish census data is available online at www.scrol.gov.uk

Problems faced by some LEDCs

- **A large population.** Imagine trying to count one-sixth of the world's population in a fortnight! That's what India has to do.
- **Cost.** Carrying out an accurate census costs millions – poor countries could use the money for some other national priority.
- **A difficult landscape.** Some countries have huge areas of rainforest, or high mountains, or areas with no roads – all of which can make carrying out the census very difficult.
- **Different languages.** Some countries have a number of different languages – if the census needs to be printed in several languages, this adds to the cost. Mexico has more than 90 working languages.

Censuses in LEDCs

Many LEDCs face big problems collecting census data. These problems make it hard to guarantee the accuracy and quality of the census results. An accurate census is more useful than an inaccurate one.

Sudan

Sudan is one of the poorest countries in the world. Population growth is rapid. Many women have more than 5 children, and the birth rate of 39 people per 1000 per annum is one of the highest in the world. Life expectancy is just 56 years, compared to 78 in the UK. This is due to a poor diet in many parts of the country, where subsistence farmers struggle to feed their families, especially in periods of drought or civil war.

Why hold a census?

Sudan's government and relief agencies need information about where the population is growing fastest, where people are moving to, and what jobs they are doing. For example, if the government introduced a family planning project or community health programme in an area, a census would help them to see if the project is working.

Problems in carrying out a census

Sudan is huge – it's one of the largest countries in Africa, covering an area half the size of Europe. It's 1900 km from north to south.

It has mountain ranges in the south, and inhospitable deserts with nomadic groups in the north. This makes it difficult to keep track of, and count, the general population.

Parts of the country have a wet season that makes it difficult to move around because much of the limited road network becomes impassable.

A civil war in the south has forced thousands of people to move to other parts of the country. The government would find it difficult to persuade census workers to travel into dangerous areas controlled by anti-government rebels.

Sudan last held a census in 1993. The population was 25 million. There hasn't been a census since, mainly due to the civil war. In 2006 the population was estimated to be 37 million.

Did you know?
Scotland would fit into Sudan 32 times.

Activities

1 Why does a company like Tesco need to look at census data when planning new stores?
2 Describe some of the problems in collecting census information in an LEDC.
3 Why is it important for the Scottish Executive to have population information?
4 Explain why Scotland has a separate census from England and Wales.

e problems of population change

...nit you'll learn about the different problems
...used by population change in LEDCs and MEDCs.

Population growth in LEDCs

◆ Over 90% of the world's population increase is in
LEDCs.
◆ They have falling death rates and high birth rates –
which means their natural increase is high.
◆ Most are at Stages 2 and 3 of the Demographic
Transition Model (see Unit 8.3).
◆ They have population pyramids that are wide at
the base.

Death rates are falling due to better sanitation and health
care. Birth rates are high for a number of reasons:
◆ lack of **family planning** education or contraceptives
◆ in rural areas children are needed to work on farms; in
urban areas they're needed to work to earn money for
their families
◆ **fertility rates** are high – women have a large
number of children as there's a high level of **infant
mortality**
◆ culture or religion often mean it's unacceptable to use
contraception.

The problem

Many LEDCs are being held back by rapid population
growth – it's slowing down their development. They're
struggling to earn enough money from farming and
industry to provide for more and more people. The
growing population puts too much pressure on resources.
◆ Some LEDCs find it difficult just feeding everyone –
but they're getting more and more mouths to feed.
The result: millions of people go hungry.
◆ LEDCs can't afford better schools and more teachers.
The result: millions of people aren't getting the
education and skills that would help them and their
countries to prosper.
◆ LEDCs can't afford the best health care, with more
hospitals, doctors, and nurses.
The result: millions of people are suffering from
illnesses and diseases that could be cured or
prevented.

So, having a young, rapidly growing population makes it
...d for any LEDC to improve the living standards of
...ple.

Fertility rate: the number of children,
on average, a woman will have in
her lifetime. If it's about two, the
population will replace itself each
generation. If it's more than two, the
population will increase, if it's less
than two, it will fall.

Infant mortality: the number of
babies dying before they reach the
age of one, per 1000 births.

Did you know?
Andorra has the longest
life expectancy in the
world – 83.5 years.
Botswana has
the shortest –
30.8 years.

Indicators of population change

	Population growth rate	Fertility rate	Life expectancy (years)	GDP per capita (US $ ppp)*
China	0.58%	1.69	72.0	5 600
India	1.40%	2.85	64.0	3 100
Bangladesh	2.09%	3.15	61.7	2 000
Sudan	2.60%	4.97	58.1	1 900
Chad	2.95%	6.38	48.2	1 600
Brazil	1.06%	1.97	71.4	8 100
UK	0.28%	1.66	78.3	29 600
France	0.37%	1.85	79.4	28 700
Germany	0.00%	1.38	78.5	28 700
Italy	0.07%	1.27	79.5	27 700
Bulgaria	−0.89%	1.37	71.8	8 200
Japan	0.05%	1.38	81.0	29 400
World	1.14%	2.62	64.1	8 800

* ppp = purchasing power parity

Population change in MEDCs

- Population growth in most MEDCs is slow – and some MEDCs even have a falling population.
- MEDCs have low birth rates and low death rates – which means their natural increase is low.
- They're in Stages 4 and 5 of the Demographic Transition Model (see Unit 8.3).
- They have population pyramids that are narrow at the base.

Birth rates are low. In some countries it has fallen below the rate needed to replace the people who die. Women are choosing to have children later in life, and they're having fewer of them. So there are fewer young people in the population.

Life expectancy, on the other hand, is increasing. People are living longer due to improvements in health care, diet, and lifestyle. So, there are more and more elderly people in the population.

> **Life expectancy:** how long people can expect to live, on average.

The problem

Fewer young people entering the population and more people living longer adds up to an **ageing population**. This means the proportion of older people in the population is going up.

This is a problem because it means there are fewer and fewer workers to pay for more and more old people. We say there will be a greater number of **elderly dependents**. We need to make sure the older people have:

- pensions to give them money to spend on food and housing and so on
- the right health care and hospital facilities, with doctors and nurses trained to deal with the illnesses that affect older people
- old people's homes and trained carers.

All these things cost a lot of money.

Fewer and fewer workers could also cause a problem for MEDC economies – there could be a shortage of labour. There could then be economic decline, and this would lead to falling living standards.

Activities

1. Why have birth rates remained high in many LEDCs, despite a fall in death rates?
2. What solutions do you think are most likely to reduce birth rates in LEDCs?
3. a Draw a scattergraph to show the relationship between life expectancy and GDP per capita for the countries shown in the table.
   b What does 'per capita' mean?
   c Describe and explain the pattern shown on your graph.
   d To what extent do you think that GDP per capita is a good indicator of development? Explain your answer with reference to information on your graph.
4. a Draw another scattergraph, this time to show the relationship between fertility rate and life expectancy (choose the scales for the axes carefully!).
   b Describe and explain the pattern shown on this graph.
5. Compare your two graphs. Explain the similarities and any differences between them.
6. Explain why ageing populations are a problem for many MEDCs.
7. Suggest ways in which MEDCs may attempt to solve some of these problems, and possible consequences if they do not.

he UK is coping

learn how the UK is coping with population change – and
s are coping.

UK

the first time ever, the UK has more people aged over 60 than under 16.
ere are five times more people aged over 85 than there were in 1951.

e age structure of the UK's population has been getting older – and this is
going to continue. This gives us two problems:

1   an increasing number of **elderly dependents**
2   an economy that could run short of workers.

How are we coping with these problems?

Save more, work longer

People working now pay for the pensions of people who have retired. (A
pension is the money we get to live on when we're no longer working). At the
moment, there are four workers to support a pensioner, but the increasing
number of pensioners means this will fall to two workers.

So the government thinks each of us will have to save more towards pensions.
We might also have to work longer – instead of retiring at 60 or 65, we might
have to work into our 70s.

The country will also need more old people's homes, and more trained carers
for elderly people. Higher taxes might be needed to pay for this.

Immigration

The number of people working in the UK is at a record high of 28.5 million,
but there are half a million job vacancies. There's a shortfall of 150 000 hotel
and catering workers, 25 000 lorry drivers, and 4000 dentists. The
construction industry will need 200 000 new workers over the next few years.

These labour and skills shortages in the economy are being filled by immigrants.

So immigration is beneficial:

◆   The UK gets highly motivated, well-educated workers who are keen
     to do well – they will play a vital part if our economy is to continue to
     be successful.

◆   The migrants get more money and a higher
      standard of living than they would at home.
      ligrants to the UK have always contributed
          in other ways as well – think food and
              for a start.

Did you know?
◆ In the UK life
expectancy for
women is 80.8 years.
◆ It's 75.8 years
for men.

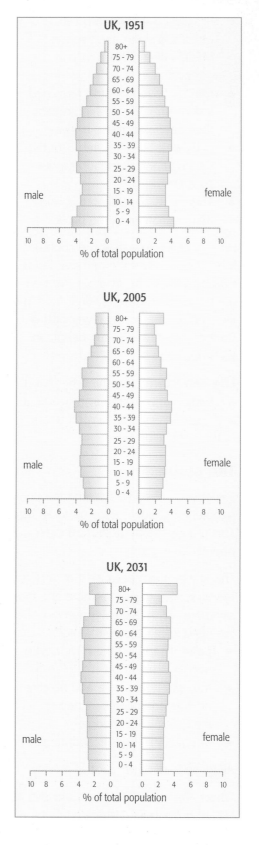

UK, 1951

80+
75 - 79
70 - 74
65 - 69
60 - 64
55 - 59
50 - 54
45 - 49
40 - 44
35 - 39
30 - 34
25 - 29
20 - 24
male   15 - 19   female
10 - 14
5 - 9
0 - 4

10 8 6 4 2 0   0 2 4 6 8 10
% of total population

UK, 2005

80+
75 - 79
70 - 74
65 - 69
60 - 64
55 - 59
50 - 54
45 - 49
40 - 44
35 - 39
30 - 34
25 - 29
20 - 24
male   15 - 19   female
10 - 14
5 - 9
0 - 4

10 8 6 4 2 0   0 2 4 6 8 10
% of total population

UK, 2031

80+
75 - 79
70 - 74
65 - 69
60 - 64
55 - 59
50 - 54
45 - 49
40 - 44
35 - 39
30 - 34
25 - 29
20 - 24
male   15 - 19   female
10 - 14
5 - 9
0 - 4

10 8 6 4 2 0   0 2 4 6 8 10
% of total population

Lucky to have them

Farmer Alan Dawes relies on workers from Eastern Europe to pick and pack fruit and flowers at his farm.

His old source of workers has gone. "Young mums have got jobs and students are going abroad" he said. "We're now employing Eastern European graduates. We're lucky to have them. There wouldn't be a fruit industry without them."

The workers like the UK because the pay is better than at home and they can improve their English. One worker from Poland said "I'm here to earn more money and get more experience. I've had good times here."

But . . .

New migrants are often treated with hostility. Some people think the migrants will take their jobs and swamp their way of life.

Many migrants find it hard to fit in. Some find it hard to learn English. Others can't get used to our customs. Many are exploited, working long hours for low pay in jobs that other people don't want to do. They end up in poor housing. They are attacked in some newspapers, and sometimes in the street. They face discrimination. They feel unwelcome.

Hidden army

Britain has a hidden army of foreign cleaners that most of us rarely see. While we sleep, they clean. Britain's economic strength pulls in people from around the world willing to mop our floors and clean our loos.

London alone now has an estimated 250 000 immigrant cleaners. The industry relies on cheap foreign labour. Much of the new immigration to Britain is to low-paid jobs from areas with no historic ties to Britain.

But according to cleaners it's an industry 'run on fear' as migrants find themselves exploited. Thomas, from Ghana, said he worked 75 hours a week on minimum wage to make money to send home to his family.

These are real opinions – though the names have been changed.

I was born in Somalia and came to the UK in 1990. I work in Essex as a civil engineer. Britain has welcomed many immigrant communities. This diversity has contributed to the economy. Look who your doctors, nurses, shopkeepers, bus drivers and street cleaners are. Abdi

I was born in Kenya and was brought up in Leicester. I consider myself British, not an immigrant. I pay taxes. Do I feel accepted as British? Sadly, no. Britain is paranoid about immigration, but without it we'd have no-one to earn money to contribute towards the NHS or schooling. More immigration is needed. Judy

We have water shortages, house shortages, traffic congestion, crowded schools and hospitals. There must be a limit to the number of people who can live on our small island. John

I was born in Serbia, and came to the UK in 2000 on a work permit. I'm applying for citizenship. I feel at home here. I think people who are against immigration don't understand that the diversity is one of the best things in this country. Savo

Activities

1 a Explain why the average age of people living in the UK is increasing.
   b Outline the problems that this trend may cause.
2 Explain why the UK is relying more and more on foreign workers.
3 Give your opinion of the comments made by each of the people shown on this page. Justify your opinions.
4 Draw a graph or graphs to show the information in this table. Explain the trends shown in your graph(s).

UK population – millions in each age group

	under 19	20-64	65+
1991	14.8	33.8	9.1
2005	14.7	36.2	9.5
2031	13.3	36.3	14.7
2050	12.5	35.0	16.4

How India is coping

In this unit you'll learn how india has tried to use family-planning to tackle population growth.

Some LEDCs are relying on economic development to bring higher living standards – which will in turn bring lower birth rates. These LEDCs would move into Stage 4 of the Demographic Transition Model (Unit 8.3).

But many LEDCs see **population control** as important. **Family planning** campaigns have worked better in some LEDCs than others, but overall the average number of children born per woman has been going down.

▲ *India's youthful population is typical of many LEDCs.*

India in the early 1950s

India's population was growing very quickly. The birth rate was over 45. The fertility rate (how many children a woman has in her lifetime) was 6.

India's government thought this would hold the country back. So 'population control' was seen as a way of helping the country to develop.

The government set two targets: to get the birth rate down to 21 and the fertility rate down to 2.1 (this is replacement fertility) by the year 2000.

Sterilisation and contraception

In 1952, the government started offering contraceptive advice and sterilisation. So India became the first country in the world with a population policy.

But the population continued to grow quickly. In the 1970s, the government declared a population 'state of emergency'. The government began forced sterilisations in the poorest areas. Medical workers who performed most operations were rewarded.

In 1976-77 a record 8.26 million sterilisations were performed, mostly on men. Many people were angry, and the government was brought down. The programme was changed to female sterilisations.

A policy to encourage just two children per family led to abortions and the killing of children, especially girls.

These policies were criticised because of the way they treated the poor, and women.

Did you know?
China's one-child policy is the best-known population policy in the world. It was introduced in the 1970s when China was afraid it couldn't continue to feed its rapidly growing population.

Did you know?
Kenya was the first African country to begin a national family-planning campaign. The average number of children per woman has fallen from around 8 in the 1980s to 3.3 in 2005.

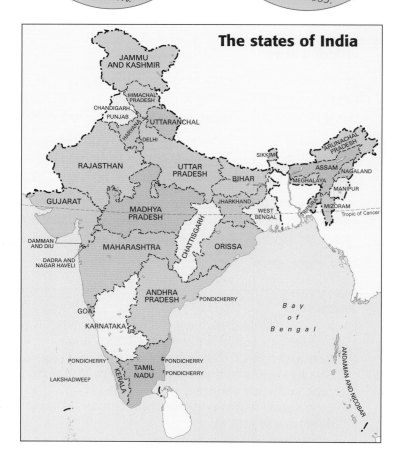

The states of India

India today

The population control policies did have an effect on India's rate of population increase. By 2005, the birth rate was down to 22.3, and the fertility rate was down to 2.8.

But the population has still trebled since 1952, from 0.36 billion to 1.1 billion at the start of 2006. This has been due to a big fall in infant mortality and a doubling of life expectancy, from 31 to 64.

The population is now growing by about 15 million per year. So India still faces population problems.

New population policies

Population control is now seen in the context of improving social and economic conditions, especially for women. In India, women have been the least powerful decision makers. Better health and welfare, including education, is now seen as a key part of controlling population growth – rather than relying on just contraception.

To reduce the rate of population growth, the Indian government has set targets to be met by 2010.

Small families are encouraged. Cash payments are on offer for the birth of girls (the first two children), for women who have their first child after the age of 19, and for couples getting sterilised after two children.

There are still controversial policies. In 2005, the Maharashtra state government announced a plan to cut off irrigation supplies to farmers who have more than two children.

But the Indian prime minister said forcing people to limit the size of their families was not the way to control population growth. He said people should be able to choose the number of children they have.

In some states in the south of the country, the fertility rate has fallen to low levels – in Kerala it's now 1.8. This is like many European countries (it's 1.6 in Germany, for example). But in the northern states of Uttar Pradesh, Bihar and Rajasthan the rates of population increase are still high. If the Indian government is to have any chance of meeting its population targets, it's in these states that the average fertility rate of 4.5 will need to fall.

Nearly one in five of the world's people live in India.

India is set to overtake China as the world's most populous country by 2050. By this time, 40% of the world's people will live in these two countries.

Family planning techniques and their advantages being explained. ▼

Targets for 2010

- All women, especially young women, should know about and be able to get contraception. It's predicted this would lower the fertility rate to 2.1.
- All births should be delivered by trained workers.
- All children should be immunised against common diseases such as polio, tetanus and measles.
- The infant mortality rate should be reduced to 30 per 1000 (in 2005 it was 56).
- The number of people affected by AIDs needs to be stabilised or reduced.
- All births, marriages and deaths should be registered.
- The law stating that women cannot marry before 18 should be properly enforced.
- All children should be entitled to primary education.

Activities

1 Explain why India's early attempts at population control were only partly successful.
2 Why do you think that population policies in China and India are important to the population of the whole world?
3 What is happening to the population in Kerala? Why is this?
4 Do you think the Indian government's new policies are likely to be more successful in controlling population growth? Explain your answer.

The big picture

This chapter and chapter 10 are about development – improving people's lives. These are the big ideas behind the chapter:

◆ Some countries are more developed than others, and there's a big gap in development between the most and least developed.

◆ Development can be measured in different ways.

◆ Resource use is increasing at a faster and faster rate due to population growth and economic development.

◆ Huge numbers of people around the world don't have enough food to eat, or access to clean water.

◆ International influence is the ability of a country, or group of countries, to control or affect other countries. It can be measured in different ways.

◆ Countries join together to increase their international influence – this is called an alliance.

Your goals for this chapter

By the end of this chapter you should be able to answer these questions:

◆ You can measure development using indicators. How many can you list?

◆ What does the UN's Human Development Index measure?

◆ What has helped to cause the gap in development between MEDCs and LEDCs?

◆ Name three MEDCs and three LEDCs.

◆ What's the link between population growth and resource use, and between economic development and resource use?

◆ Where in the world are people suffering from malnutrition? Why?

◆ Why does it matter if people don't have access to clean water? Give an example of a large-scale scheme, and a small-scale one to increase water supply – both in LEDCs.

◆ What does international influence mean? How can you measure it (give at least three examples)?

◆ Give an example of a trading alliance, a social alliance and a defence alliance.

◆ What do these terms mean:
GDP per capita (PPP), dietary energy supply, NGOs, appropriate technology, sustainable development

And then . . .

When you finish the chapter, come back here and see if you've met your goals!

Did you know?
If the world was a village of 100 people ...
◆ 14 wouldn't have enough to eat
◆ 31 wouldn't have electricity
◆ 17 wouldn't have clean safe water to drink
◆ 29 would be aged under 15.

Did you know?
During the 1990s, clean drinking water reached an extra 1 billion people in LEDCs – that's roughly one-sixth of the world's people.

Did you know?
◆ Deaths from diarrhoea have gone down by 60% in the last twenty years.
◆ But diarrhoea remains a leading killer in LEDCs, causing the deaths of 2 million people a year, mostly children.

Did you know?
Every five seconds a child dies because she, or he, is hungry.

Your chapter starter

Look at the photo on page 158.
What's this person doing?
Why is she doing it?
Where do you think this might be?
Would you want to do this job?

Careful ...

Development – a world of two halves

In this unit you'll learn what development means, and see how it is measured.

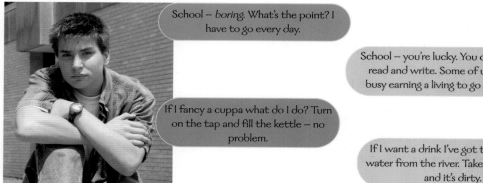

School – *boring*. What's the point? I have to go every day.

If I fancy a cuppa what do I do? Turn on the tap and fill the kettle – no problem.

School – you're lucky. You can learn to read and write. Some of us are too busy earning a living to go to school.

If I want a drink I've got to fetch the water from the river. Takes me hours – and it's dirty.

Development

It's about improving people's lives, so the Indian girl in the photo *can* go to school, and *can* have clean water to drink. Sounds simple? Read the rest of this chapter and you'll find it's not quite as easy as it sounds.

How **developed** a country is is affected by things like history, industry, politics, hazards, etc. – you'll find out more about these in Unit 9.2.

Can you measure it?

Yes, in all sorts of ways. One of the easiest is GDP per capita (PPP). This shows how wealthy a country is. Look at the map. It shows the world divided in two, according to levels of development.

- ◆ **GDP** stands for **Gross Domestic Product**. It's the total value of goods and services a country produces in a year.
- ◆ GDP is measured in dollars.
- ◆ GDP is divided by a country's population to give **GDP per capita**.
- ◆ **PPP** means **purchasing power parity**. GDP is adjusted because a dollar buys more in some countries than others.

The richer **More Economically Developed Countries (MEDCs)** are to the **north** of the line (though some, like Australia, are south of the equator).

We use labels like MEDCs, LEDCs, rich north, poor south, to describe countries.

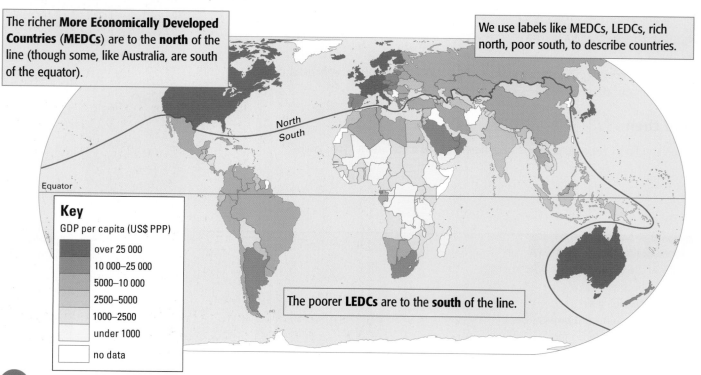

North
South

Equator

Key

GDP per capita (US$ PPP)

over 25 000
10 000–25 000
5000–10 000
2500–5000
1000–2500
under 1000
no data

The poorer **LEDCs** are to the **south** of the line.

How else can you measure development?

You measure development using **indicators** (that's the technical word). So, GDP per capita (PPP) is one indicator, but there's more.

◆ **Social indicators**. You can split these into population and health. The table below shows which is which.
◆ Then there's **others**. These can include all sorts of things, like the percentage of the adult population who can read and write (adult literacy), and so on.

Although these indicators aren't the same as wealth, a lot of them will depend on how wealthy a country is.

The table below shows some indicators for different countries. All those numbers look a bit baffling. But try looking at them one column at a time and compare the numbers for different countries and you'll see some patterns.

| Country | SOCIAL INDICATORS | | | | | | | | Others | | |
| | Population indicators | | | Health indicators | | | | | | | |
	GDP per capita (PPP) US$	Birth rate	Death rate	Natural increase	Infant mortality	Life expectancy	People per doctor	% adults with HIV/AIDS	% adult literacy	% in farming	% urban population
USA	40 100	14	8	6	7	78	182	0.6	97	0.7	80
UK	29 600	11	10	1	5	79	476	0.2	99	2	89
Japan	29 400	9	9	0	3	81	500	Less than 0.1	99	5	65
South Korea	19 200	10	6	4	7	77	714	Less than 0.1	98	8	80
Brazil	8100	16	6	10	30	72	476	0.7	86	20	83
China	5600	13	7	6	24	72	625	0.1	91	49	39
India	3100	22	8	14	56	64	2000	0.9	60	60	28
Kenya	1100	40	15	25	61	48	10 000	7	85	75	39

Spot the difference

The table shows you that:
◆ LEDCs like Kenya usually have higher birth, death and infant mortality rates than MEDCs like the UK.
◆ LEDCs like India have a lower level of literacy, and fewer doctors for the population than MEDCs like the UK.
◆ LEDCs like China have more jobs in the primary sector (for example farming) than MEDCs like Japan.

Activities

1 Look at the map. Describe the distribution of wealth shown. Explain any anomalies (countries that don't fit the general pattern).
2 Why do you think that GDP is measured in dollars? What doesn't a measure of wealth per person show (hint – think about people like yourself)?
3 List three indicators you think are good measures of development, and three you think aren't so good. Explain the reasons for your choices.
4 Look at the table. Describe, and explain, the main differences between
   a Kenya and the UK
   b Japan and China.
5 How far do you think it's possible to divide the countries in the table into MEDCs and LEDCs? Why is this?

Mind the gap

In this unit you'll find out why some countries are more developed than others. And about the Human Development Index.

What's caused the gap?

There's a gap in terms of levels of development between the LEDCs and the MEDCs. All sorts of things have caused it, and they're linked. Here's just a few for starters.

Did you know?
In Ethiopia some people are really poor. About half might only eat meat at feasts.

Did you know?
Less than 25% of the world's population live in MEDCs – that includes us – and we use over 75% of the world's energy. And over 75% of all the world's other resources.

History

Europeans began colonising large areas of the world from the 16th century onwards. The economies of the colonies were altered, and new country borders were created, so that raw materials could be sent from them to Europe. The development of the colonies was restricted, and they were left with economic and political problems.

Industry

The Industrial Revolution of the 19th century, meant that things started to change in countries like the UK. People changed from working in farming to working in manufacturing industry. In the 20th century, there was a shift to jobs in service industries.

Lots of LEDCs still have a lot of people working in primary industries, like farming. As they develop, more people will work in secondary and tertiary industries.

Debt

LEDCs have often borrowed lots of money to try to develop, and it has to be repaid (plus interest). If they can't repay the money, they get into debt. Add on the interest and the debt grows, leaving less and less money for things like schools, developing industry, and improving people's standard of living.

Politics

Political instability, poor management of the economy, and inefficient government haven't helped some LEDCs. For example, Nigeria changed from military rule to a civilian government in 1999. The country's economy is based on oil. It was mismanaged and now needs rebuilding.

Other countries have planned their economic development. South Korea has gone from being an LEDC to an NIC in 40 years.

Environment and hazards

Natural hazards affect both MEDCs and LEDCs, but their overall impact can be different – depending where they occur. For example, if we have too much or too little rain in the UK, we can cope. But it's different in LEDCs. They lack the money and technology to cope with major hazards.

Tropical storms, earthquakes and volcanic eruptions hit both MEDCs and LEDCs. For instance, Hurricane Katrina left about 1000 people dead and caused $125 billion of damage in the USA in 2005, which the US economy could cope with. However, in the same year, an earthquake in Pakistan had a much greater human cost – it killed nearly 80 000 people. And the country struggled to cope with helping the survivors without major international support.

How else can you measure development?

In Unit 9.1 we looked at how you could measure development by wealth. But development is about more than that. The UN measures **quality of life**. They produce the **Human Development Index** (**HDI** for short) which combines three aspects of human development:

- A long and healthy life – measured by life expectancy.
- Knowledge – measured by the adult literacy rate combined with the number of years spent at school.
- Standard of living – measured by GDP per capita (PPP).

Each of the three aspects is given a score. 1.000 is the best. 0.000 is the worst. The HDI is the average of the three scores. Countries are ranked according to their overall score.

Did you know?
The HDI was developed in 1990 and has been used by the UN since 1993.

The HDI 2005 factfile

Country	Rank	HDI
USA	10	0.944
Japan	11	0.943
UK	15	0.939
South Korea	28	0.901
Brazil	63	0.792
China	85	0.755
India	127	0.602
Kenya	154	0.474

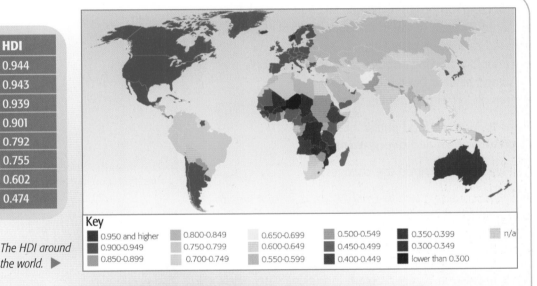

Key

0.950 and higher	0.800-0.849	0.650-0.699	0.500-0.549	0.350-0.399	n/a
0.900-0.949	0.750-0.799	0.600-0.649	0.450-0.499	0.300-0.349
0.850-0.899	0.700-0.749	0.550-0.599	0.400-0.449	lower than 0.300

The top 3 countries

- Norway
- Iceland
- Australia

And the bottom 3

- Burkina Faso
- Sierra Leone
- Niger

The HDI around the world. ▶

The HDI for countries around the world is improving, with two exceptions:

- The new countries of central Asia, e.g. Kazakhstan – worsening education, economies and mortality rates have caused the decline in their HDI.
- Sub-Saharan Africa – HIV/AIDS is the biggest reason for the decline in the HDI in these countries.

Activities

1 Describe the pattern of development shown on the HDI map.
2 Compare the pattern on this map with the map in Unit 9.1. Explain any differences you can see.
3 Differences in development were much less before the 19th century than they are now. Why?

4 Do you think the HDI is a better measure of development than other indicators, such as GDP? Explain your answer, referring to named indicators of development.
5 How do you think the ranking of the countries in the table (2005 HDI factfile) could change in the next century. What reasons could lead to these changes?

The rate of resource use

In this unit you will learn why resource use is growing at a faster and faster rate.

Population growth increases resource use

A resource is anything – natural or man-made – which humans can use. The more people there are, the more resources we need. Between 1980 and 2005, total world population grew from 4.4 billion to 6.4 billion. By 2015, the world's population will be over 7 billion. All 7 billion people will need water and food. Already, trying to feed growing populations has put pressure on soil and water resources.

The photograph on the right was taken in Burkina Faso, a country in West Africa, in the Sahel. Burkina Faso has suffered as a result of:

- a rapidly growing population – and the people use wood as their basic fuel
- rapidly growing numbers of animals.

Trying to increase food output has caused **overcultivation** and **overgrazing**.

A newspaper described the changes:

The landscape is a wreck. Until 20 years ago, it was thick, dry forest teeming with wildlife, and plants and trees that local people used for all aspects of their lives. Now it is dust and bits of scrub.

Water is an even bigger problem in Burkina Faso. The total yearly rainfall has gone down from 500 mm to 400 mm in the north, and from 1400 mm to 1100 mm in the south of the country. What has caused this change in the climate? It's possible that as the trees are cut down, there's less **evapotranspiration** to pump water vapour into the air.

Many scientists believe that the carbon dioxide that comes from our cars and lorries, and from our oil-, coal-, and gas-burning power stations, has helped to cause the **droughts** that have harmed the Sahel region of Africa. The droughts have been the worst the world has ever seen, and have often led to famine.

▲ The effect of overcultivation and overgrazing in Burkina Faso.

▲ These women have to walk for four hours a day to get water – even during a sandstorm.

Economic development increases resource use

In the last 30 years, the population of the UK, in common with most MEDCs, hasn't grown very much. But energy use per person in the UK has gone up from 82 to 195 G-joules. Your granny could tell you why …

The richer a country gets, the more energy it uses – the more we have, the more we seem to want. The more we want, the more we buy. The more we buy, the more resources are used up. Some people call all of this **materialism**.

Materialism is wanting only belongings or comfort, and having no interest in morals. To be called materialist isn't really a compliment!

But LEDCs understandably want to improve the living standards of their populations through economic development. You can see the link between **economic development** and energy use per person if you look at what's happening in China:

When I was your age we didn't have computers ... nor those play stations ... nor these empeethree things – we made our own music. Switch the kettle on love – it's time for Countdown.

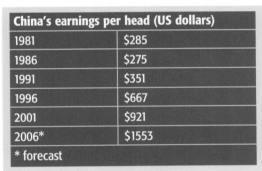

China's earnings per head (US dollars)	
1981	$285
1986	$275
1991	$351
1996	$667
2001	$921
2006*	$1553
* forecast	

Key

- total
- oil
- gas
- other

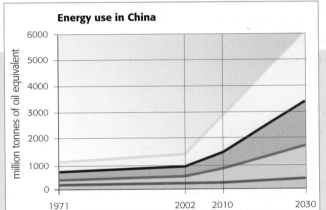

Energy use in China

million tonnes of oil equivalent

1971   2002 2010   2030

Activities

1 'Overgrazing' means there are too many animals on the land. What does 'overcultivation' mean?

2 Between 1950 and 2005, the population of Burkina Faso grew from 4 million to 14 million. Copy out and complete the flow diagram below to show how population increase can damage the environment:

3 a Use the numbers in the table (above left) to draw a bar chart to show China's earnings per head.

b What has happened to China's earnings per head? Use figures in your answer.

c How is your bar graph connected to the graph showing fuel use (above right)? Explain your answer.

4 Describe three ways in which economic development leads to increased resource use.

population increase → more farming → ⟨ _____ ⟩ → more bare land → soil _____

Food

In this unit you'll learn why some people don't have enough to eat.

How much food do we need?

The amount of food we need, or consume, is measured in calories. The **dietary energy supply** (DES for short) is the number of calories each person needs. People living in temperate climates (MEDCs like the UK) need at least 2600 calories a day. People living in tropical climates (many LEDCs) need at least 2300 calories. Why the difference?

◆ There's a greater proportion of adults in MEDCs (they need more than children).

◆ In temperate climates, people need more energy to keep warm.

And what type?

You know about healthy balanced diets. Everyone needs:

◆ protein – like meat, eggs, and milk, for their bodies to grow and repair themselves

◆ carbohydrates – like cereals, potatoes, sugar and fat, for energy

◆ vitamins and minerals – found in all sorts of fruit, vegetables, fish, and meat, to help prevent disease.

But we don't all eat a balanced diet, do we? For many people in LEDCs, their basic diet is based on carbohydrates like rice, wheat and maize, and it lacks protein, vitamins and minerals.

What happens if you don't have enough?

You'll be hungry and you'll suffer from malnutrition if you don't have enough food, or the right kind. You'd only die in extreme conditions, but it would reduce your ability to work, and your resistance to disease. If you're a child, you might not develop properly and you might have:

◆ **marasmus** – caused by not eating enough food. A child would be very thin and wouldn't grow.

◆ **kwashiorkor** – caused by eating too many cereals and not enough protein. A child's body would be swollen, their skin would be very dark and peeling. Their hair would turn orange.

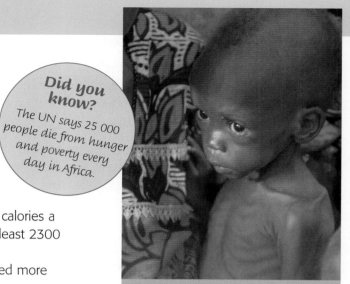

Did you know?
The UN says 25 000 people die from hunger and poverty every day in Africa.

Niger 2005

It wasn't a famine – but it was a crisis. The cause? Not enough food. Or was it? Drought in 2004, was followed by a plague of locusts, then another drought.

People – adults, children, babies – died from **malnutrition**. There was some food from the local harvest, but few people could afford it. So the developed world stepped in with food aid.

Did you know?
Up to half a million children go blind every year because they don't get enough vitamin A.

Did you know?
◆ Lack of vitamin B can cause beri-beri (wasting of the limbs).
◆ Lack of vitamin D can cause rickets (deformities in the bones, especially the legs and spine.

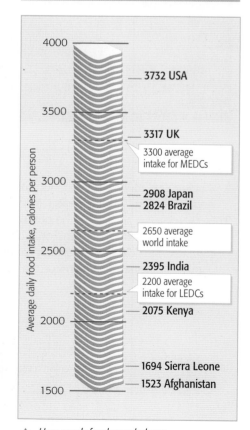

Average daily food intake, calories per person

4000

— 3732 USA

3500

— 3317 UK

3300 average intake for MEDCs

3000

— 2908 Japan
— 2824 Brazil

2650 average world intake

2500

— 2395 India

2200 average intake for LEDCs

— 2075 Kenya

2000

— 1694 Sierra Leone
— 1523 Afghanistan

1500

▲ How much food people have.

Who's suffering?

Look at the map and table. The table shows that the percentage of malnourished people has fallen since 1970 everywhere *except* sub-Saharan Africa. But what it doesn't show is that the actual *number* of people has increased. This is because of the rise in world population.

Region	1970	2000
Sub-Saharan Africa	35	42
Near East and North Africa	23	12
Central America and Caribbean	24	11
South America	17	9
South Asia	34	22
East Asia	35	16
China	46	14
All developing regions	36	19

Percentage of people suffering from malnutrition. ▼ ▶

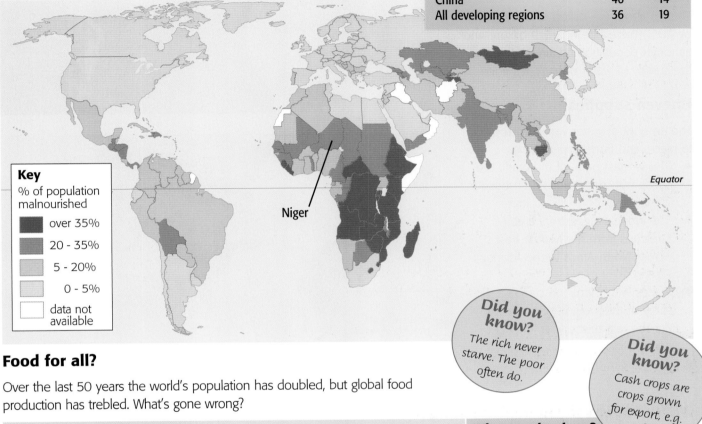

Key

% of population malnourished

- over 35%
- 20 - 35%
- 5 - 20%
- 0 - 5%
- data not available

Niger

Equator

Did you know?
The rich never starve. The poor often do.

Did you know?
Cash crops are crops grown for export, e.g. coffee

Food for all?

Over the last 50 years the world's population has doubled, but global food production has trebled. What's gone wrong?

Why are people still hungry?

- Poverty. People are too poor to buy the food they need.
- Some LEDCs have been encouraged by MEDCs and TNCs to grow cash crops, so fewer crops are grown for local people to eat.
- MEDCs export subsidised crops, which works against farmers in LEDCs.
- Food production is uneven across the world.
- Local physical factors. In some places, the climate means crops might fail; soil erosion has reduced the amount of land available for farming; a lot of good irrigated land has been damaged by salinisation and waterlogging.

What can be done?

- Make farming more sustainable.
- Make trade fairer (see Unit 10.3).
- Provide short-term aid – food.
- Help countries develop so people can afford to buy the food they need – year after year.

Activities

1. What were the causes of the crisis in Niger in 2005?
2. The UK government provides food aid for countries such as Niger. What long-term problems might this cause?
3. Charities raise money to help people such as those in Niger. Do you think people should raise money through charities, or do you think only governments should give aid?
4. 'Poverty and hunger are problems for Africa, not all LEDCs'. Using information from this page and any other sources, explain why you agree or disagree with this statement.

Water – a matter of life and death

In this unit you'll learn about the difference in availability of clean water in MEDCs and LEDCs.

Bring me water

The world's population is growing fast. There's about 6.5 billion of us now, and by 2050 there'll be nearly 9 billion. And although population continues to grow, the supply of water doesn't. It's finite.

Did you know?
You can live for about 2 months without food, but less than a week without water.

Uneven supplies

The amount of water varies from place to place, and from time to time.

- The wettest parts of the world are those with equatorial and monsoon climates.
- The world's biggest dry area stretches from the Middle East across North Africa to the Atlantic Ocean.
- Places with monsoon climates get most of their rain in one season. For the rest of the year, they get barely a drop.
- Rainfall can be unreliable.

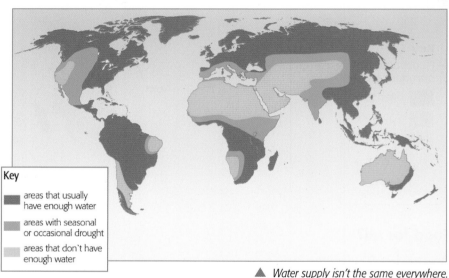

Key
- areas that usually have enough water
- areas with seasonal or occasional drought
- areas that don't have enough water

▲ Water supply isn't the same everywhere.

How clean is our water?

In some parts of the world, water is very clean; in others it's filthy. 1 billion people don't have access to clean piped water.

The map on the right shows the percentage of the world's population that **does** have access to safe (clean) water. Compare it with the map in Unit 9.1. Notice anything?

Does it matter if people don't have clean water? Yes!

- More than 5 million people die from water-borne diseases every year.
- People spend hours every day walking to fetch water. Time they could be spending in school, or working and earning money to improve their lives.

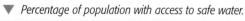

▼ Percentage of population with access to safe water.

Key
- 0-40%
- 41-60%
- 61-80%
- 81-100%
- No data

Water use and abuse

The graph on the right shows some staggering differences in water use around the world.

The UN recommends that people need a minimum of 50 litres a day for drinking, washing, cooking and sanitation. But not everyone has that much.

Now look at the pie charts for individual countries. Compare India and the UK. Bit of a difference isn't there?

And it's going to get worse ...

For countries to develop, they need more water – for irrigation (to produce more and better food), and for industry. And they need cleaner, safer water for people to use.

And, as they develop, they'll use more water as people's lifestyles change. Plus, the world's population is growing. But there's only so much water to go around.

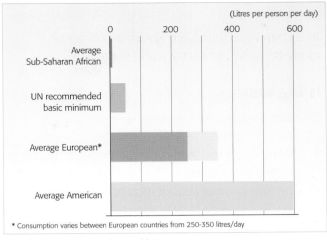

▲ *Water use around the world.*

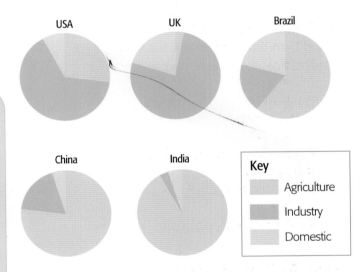

▲ *Water use for individual countries.*

So, what can be done?

Get technical

◆ Change to drip irrigation, which uses less water.
◆ Treat waste water so it can be reused.
◆ Tackle pollution to make more water useable.

Increase supply
◆ Build dams and other large-scale projects.
◆ Use underground supplies.
◆ Build wells and supply pumps – small-scale projects.

Do deals
◆ In 2004, Israel signed a deal with Turkey to ship 50 million cubic metres of water a year for 20 years in return for arms.
◆ In 1999, Egypt, Ethiopia and Sudan agreed a strategy for the sustainable development of the River Nile.

Use less
◆ This might mean using and reusing water more efficiently.

Get the UN to act
◆ The UN launched an International Decade for Action called 'Water for life', in 2005, to try to halve the number of people without access to safe drinking water and basic sanitation by 2015.

Activities

1 Describe the pattern of access to safe water shown by the bottom map opposite.
2 Compare this pattern with the map of global population distribution in Unit 8.1. What problems will this cause?
3 Contrast the ways in which water is used in the countries shown in the pie charts above. Give an example of at least one type of water use from each sector of the graphs.
4 The box on the left shows what can be done about water shortages. For each solution, suggest whether you think it would be more suitable in MEDCs or LEDCs. Explain why.

Water – increasing supply

Did you know?
Most of Egypt gets less than 125 mm of rain a year.

Did you know?
The Nile is the only river in Egypt.

In this unit you'll find out about two different approaches to increasing water supply.

Is big best?

By 1950, Egypt had a water crisis. Why?
- It depended on the River Nile for all its water.
- Urbanisation and industrialisation were increasing and needed more water.
- The Nile was needed for irrigation. And more land needed irrigating to feed the rapidly rising population.

Egypt needed more water and power, and decided to build the High Aswan Dam to provide both. Work started in 1960 and, by 1968, the reservoir, Lake Nasser, was full. Like all big schemes, the High Aswan Dam brought benefits, but there are disadvantages too (see below).

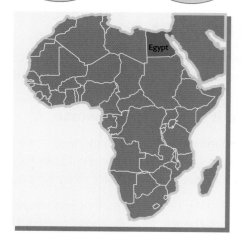

Key

- Irrigated land (also area where most people live)
- Towns with new industries

Egypt

0   300 km

Mediterranean Sea

N

Cairo

EGYPT

River Nile

Aluminium smelting
Nag Hammadi

Sugar refining
Kom Ombo

Fertilisers
Aswan

High Aswan Dam and HEP station

Lake Nasser

LIBYA   SUDAN   Red Sea

Benefits

Agriculture – it increased:
- the amount of irrigated land
- crop yields
- crops grown for export
- food processing industries and cotton textile production

Lake Nasser – provides:
- protection against flooding and famine
- a large reliable supply of water
- fishing, giving food and jobs
- tourism-based jobs

HEP – means:
- electricity for agriculture, industry and villages
- farmers can use electric pumps to get more water from wells

Jobs and the economy
- have both grown fast

Disadvantages

Declining water quality
- water pollution is caused by the use of fertilisers (see below)

Floodplain
- no silt is deposited now
- farmers have to use expensive chemical fertilisers instead
- the shallow water helps to spread the diseases bilharzia and malaria

Lake Nasser
- evaporation causes water loss
- silt is deposited here

Resettlement
- 120 000 people were forced to move home because the new lake covered their villages
- many resettled in Kom Ombo and Cairo

... And now Toshka

This is Egypt's new plan to create habitable land in the desert. Why? The population has soared from 20 to 70 million in the last 20 years. It's predicted to reach 120 million in the next 20. The plan is to create a second Nile valley to:

◆ increase the amount of arable land and so produce more food
◆ create nearly 3 million jobs
◆ attract 16 million people to the planned new towns.

The Mubarak pumping station – which pumps water out of Lake Nasser – is already operating. Toshka will cost $70 billion.

Or is small beautiful?

Imagine having a small, muddy pool as your only source of water. Every day you wait for hours in a long queue. Wait as water slowly seeps through the mud. And wait until enough water has collected to fill your bowl. Then lug it home.

Apoyanga's story

Apoyanga Nash from northern Ghana doesn't have to imagine waiting by that muddy pool. It was what she did, day in, day out, for years.

The muddy water could be lethal. Animals drink from the same pool. When Apoyanga and her children drank the water, it gave them diarrhoea and stomach cramps.

Water Aid, a UK charity, and their partners Rural Aid, helped Apoyanga's community to build a well with a pump to provide clean water.

Apoyanga says 'Now we have the well our lives have improved. We're much healthier. I don't spend so much time collecting water. I've got time to weave baskets to sell so that I can afford to send my children to school.'

Did you know?
Egypt is 95% desert.

Did you know?
A hand-dug well costs about £1200.

You can find stories like Apoyanga's in many countries. Little by little, people's lives can be improved. Small projects like providing wells and pumps to ensure a safe, clean supply of water for a community are often supported by **NGOs**. They are examples of:

◆ **Appropriate technology** – suitable for the people who are using it. It's not expensive and complicated. It's cheap and simple. And allows people to manage things for themselves.

◆ **Sustainable development** – they improve people's standard of living and quality of life without wasting resources or harming the environment.

Did you know?
NGO stands for non-governmental organisation. They include charities like Oxfam, Water Aid etc.

Activities

1 Using information on this page, and other sources if you need to, explain why Egypt relied so heavily on the Nile for its water.

2 What are the benefits and problems caused by the Aswan Dam? To answer this, make a cost-benefit table, like the one here. List the effects of the dam in the columns. Use your completed table to evaluate the overall impact of the dam.

Cost	Benefit

3 Explain why using pumps to provide water in Ghana is an example of 'appropriate technology'.

4 Compare the advantages of the schemes in Egypt and Ghana. Which do you think is the most suitable
  a for the people in an LEDC?
  b for the environment?

In this unit you'll find out what international influence is, and how we can measure it.

What gives a country influence?

Some people want to be boss – but how can they influence others? Being the biggest, strongest or richest can help. And it's the same for countries too. **International influence** is the ability of a country, or group of countries, to control or affect other countries. How might the activities in these photos affect a country's influence?

Can you measure international influence?

Yes. As geographers (that's you and me) we need to look at a range of things, like how wealthy a country is, how many people it has, and how big it is before we can decide what level of influence and power it has.

The Big Five!

1 Wealth We usually measure this as GDP per capita (PPP) – see Unit 9.1. A wealthy country can spend money on things like education, health care and new industry. These can improve people's lives. So, wealthier countries can have more international influence. But remember – wealth is often unevenly distributed.

2 Population Countries with big populations are often thought to have more influence. Lots of people means they can work to improve the economy, increase the country's wealth and provide troops. But, the population needs to be healthy. Some LEDCs (e.g. Bangladesh) have big populations but many people are malnourished. So they can't work as hard, and contribute less to the economy.

3 The **land area** of a country (how big it is) is important because the land (or the sea around it) might contain valuable natural resources (eg coal, iron ore or oil.) There may also be space for new settlements and industry. A big country won't necessarily have more influence if the land doesn't contain natural resources, or if the climate means crops won't grow.

4 The **military strength** of a country can mean the number of people in its armed forces, the power of its weapons, or both. A country with a strong military can defend its borders, and protect its people and resources. It can also help other countries, which may be good for international relations and trade. But some countries spend a lot of money on their military, instead of healthcare and education.

5 **Natural resources** The most important ones are oil, gas, coal, and iron ore. A country with lots of resources can produce electricity and make manufactured goods to increase its wealth. As its wealth increases, so does its international influence.

Did you know?
The British Empire was once referred to as 'the empire on which the sun never sets'. The empire spanned the world, meaning the sun was always shining on at least one of its colonies.

Who is the greatest ?

World Rank	Wealth (GDP)	Population	Resources (Oil, Gas and Iron Ore)	Military Strength (Size of armed forces)	Land Area
1	USA	China	Russia	China	Russia
2	China	India	USA	India	Canada
3	Japan	USA	China	USA	USA
4	India	Indonesia	Saudi Arabia	Russia	China
5	Germany	Brazil	Canada	North Korea	Brazil

How does Scotland compare?

	Scotland	United Kingdom	European Union	USA	Japan
Wealth (GDP per capita, PPP US$)	$25 546	$29 600	$28 477	$40 100	$29 400
Population	5 062 011	59 834 300	457 514 494	298 540 006	127 417 244
Resources Oil (barrels /day) Gas (million cu/m) Iron ore (million tonnes)	1 900 000 280 <1	2 393 000 102 800 <1	3 424 000 239 200 25	7 610 000 539 000 54	120 700 2814 <1
Military Strength (size of armed forces)	Combined UK Military Force	210 000	1 782 920	1 414 000	240 000
Land area (km^2)	78 782	244 820	3 976 372	9 631 418	377 835

Activities

1 What does 'international influence' mean? Explain it in your own words.
2 Complete the spider diagram to show how international influence can be measured. Add an explanation which says how each thing can be a measure of a country's influence.

International influence

Land area is important – the land or sea around a country might contain valuable natural resources.

3 a Draw a bar chart to show the wealth of Scotland, the United Kingdom, the European Union, the USA and Japan.
  b Rank these according to their wealth.

International alliances

In this unit you'll learn about different types of international alliances.

Safety in numbers!

Sometimes countries join together to increase their international influence. This is called an alliance. There are lots of different types of alliance, including:

◆ trading Alliances, e.g. the European Union (EU)
◆ social Alliances, e.g. the United Nations Children's Fund (UNICEF)
◆ defence Alliances, e.g. the North Atlantic Treaty Organisation (NATO)

A trading alliance – the EU

The European Union began as a small trade alliance between six countries (Belgium, France, West Germany, Italy, Luxembourg, and the Netherlands) in 1958. Denmark, Ireland and the UK joined in 1973. The EU now has 27 countries on board. The largest expansion was in 2004, when ten new countries joined. The newest members are Bulgaria and Romania, who joined on 1 January 2007.

In a trade alliance the countries work together to make it easy to buy and sell goods to, and from, one another, and make trading harder for non-member countries by using **quotas** and **tariffs**.

As well as trade, the EU now deals with things like the environment, transport, farming (see Unit 6.6), foreign policy and employment. For example, anyone living in an EU country should be able to work in any other member country, so a French person could work in Scotland.

The EU has an increasing influence in the world.

> **Did you know?**
> Quotas are limits on the amount of goods that can be imported. Tariffs are taxes or customs duties paid on imports.

Map of Europe showing members of the EU.

Key
Members of the EU

A social alliance – UNICEF

In a social alliance, countries work together to develop policies on a social interest that they have in common, e.g. education and religion.

◆ The United Nations (UN) consists of 192 countries – it is one of the largest alliances in the world.

◆ UNICEF was formed by the UN in 1946.

◆ Its original name was United Nations International Children's Emergency Fund.

◆ UNICEF is the world's leading children's organisation and has collected and distributed more research on children than any other organisation.

◆ UNICEF fund-raises world-wide to benefit children.

◆ UNICEF is an inter-governmental organisation so it has access to every country in the world.

A defence alliance – NATO

NATO was originally made up of 12 countries that were mainly the UK and USA's allies after the Second World War. NATO now has 26 members. In a defence alliance, countries promise to help each other if one country is attacked by another outside the alliance.

NATO's main role is to 'safeguard the freedom and security of its member countries by political and military means'.

NATO's agreement states that:

'The Parties agree that an armed attack against one or more of them in Europe or North America shall be considered an attack against them all.'

(Article V of the North Atlantic Treaty)

NATO also helps to end conflicts and assists with peace-keeping activities.

On 12 September 2001, less than 24 hours after the ▶ terrorist attacks on the USA, NATO declared them to be an attack against all NATO member countries.

UNICEF supplies arrive in southern Lebanon

The first convoy of aid supplies for children has reached Tyre in southern Lebanon. The convoy contains emergency supplies for thousands of displaced children affected by the violence between Israel and Hezbollah.

UNICEF estimates that 45% of the displaced people are children.

July 2006

Activities

1 **a** Name three types of international alliances.
  b Explain how these alliances work.
2 **a** Find out which countries belong to NATO.
  b Colour these in on a blank world map, and name them (use an atlas to help you).
  c Describe the pattern shown on your map.

The big picture

This chapter is about development, trade and aid. These are the big ideas behind the chapter:

◆ There's an imbalance in trade. The rich North gets richer, and the poor South gets poorer.

◆ Trade isn't fair – but it can be made better with things like Fair Trade.

◆ Industry is global – companies locate factories all over the world, and there are advantages and disadvantages to this.

◆ Different types of aid have advantages and disadvantages.

◆ Self-help schemes enable people to help themselves.

Your goals for this chapter

By the end of this chapter you should be able to answer these questions:

◆ What is trade?

◆ What trading problems do LEDCs have?

◆ Why isn't trade fair, and how can it be made fairer?

◆ What do these terms mean?

trade balance, trade surplus, trade deficit, tariffs, quotas, free trade, trading blocs, World Trade Organisation, transnational corporations, self-help schemes

◆ List the advantages and disadvantages that TNCs bring to the countries they locate in.

◆ Give one example of a TNC in an LEDC. Why did it locate here? Is its manufacturing sustainable?

◆ Aid can provide short-term emergency relief, or long-term sustainable help. What other types of aid are there, and what advantages and disadvantages do they have?

◆ What else can help LEDCs develop their economy and reduce poverty?

◆ Give two examples of self-help schemes. How do they help people?

And then . . .

When you finish the chapter, come back here and see if you've met your goals!

Did you know?
Developing countries lose $1.3 billion every day due to unfair trade rules.

Did you know?
Developing countries' share of world trade has dropped by 50% since 1981.

Did you know?
Britain makes more from trade than South Asia and sub-Saharan Africa combined.

Did you know?
Developed countries spend $1 billion a day on subsidies to farmers – six times the amount they give in aid to developing countries.

Your chapter starter

Look at the photo on p176.
What sort of ship is this?
What sort of place is it leaving? Where do you think it might be going?
What might it be carrying?
Do ships like this have anything to do with you?

I'd like to apply for the job of ship's cat.

Development and trade

In this unit you'll find out what trade is, and who has the lion's share.

Trouble brewing

As you made your cup of tea this morning, Elizabeth Miheso will have been at work for hours picking tea on a small Kenyan tea estate – for 30p a day.

And as you stirred in the sugar, Ibrahim Shikanda will have been helping his parents harvest the sugar cane that no longer provides them with a living wage.

You're unlikely to meet Elizabeth or Ibrahim. But your life and theirs are linked – by trade.

Did you know?
More than 165 million cups of tea are drunk in the UK every day. And half the tea we drink comes from east Africa.

So, what is trade?

If someone wants something that someone else has, they have to trade for it. Tea, sugar, trainers, mobiles – they're all traded. A country buys goods and services that it either doesn't have enough of, or can get more cheaply from somewhere else. These are **imports**. **Exports** are things which one country sells to another. Take Kenya and Japan. The diagrams on the right show their imports and exports.

The difference between imports and exports is called the **trade balance**.

What most countries want is a **trade surplus**. This should mean the country will become richer and people's standard of living should improve.

If it's the other way round, there'll be a **trade deficit**. A country with a trade deficit will stay poor, get into debt and people's lives won't improve.

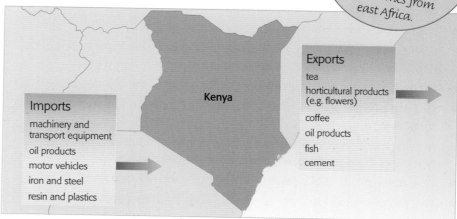

Kenya

Imports
machinery and transport equipment
oil products
motor vehicles
iron and steel
resin and plastics

Exports
tea
horticultural products (e.g. flowers)
coffee
oil products
fish
cement

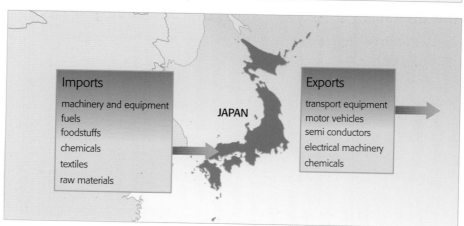

JAPAN

Imports
machinery and equipment
fuels
foodstuffs
chemicals
textiles
raw materials

Exports
transport equipment
motor vehicles
semi conductors
electrical machinery
chemicals

Exports ($) are bigger than imports($) = trade surplus

Imports ($) are bigger than exports ($) = trade deficit

Look at Kenya and Japan again.

Kenya – 2004. Exports = $2.6 billion. Imports = $4.2 billion. You don't need to be a maths genius to see that the sums don't add up. Perhaps that's one of the reasons why Kenya is 154th in the HDI rankings.

Japan – 2004. Exports = $538.8 billion. Imports = $401.8 billion. That's a healthy surplus. And that's what countries want. That's why Japan is high up (11th) in the HDI rankings.

Patterns of trade

Kenya's an LEDC. Japan's an MEDC. Generally:
- MEDCs *export* 'expensive' manufactured goods, and *import* 'cheap' primary products to make into manufactured goods.
- LEDCs *export* 'cheap' primary products (like tea, coffee, flowers, fish) and *import* manufactured goods they can't make (if they can afford them).

Look at the two pie charts.

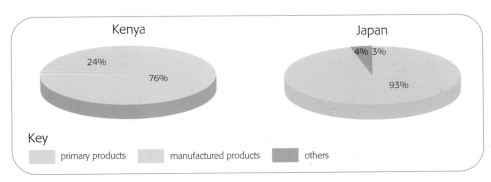

Did you know?
Countries that trade with other countries are **interdependent**.

Exports by type of product.

Have you spotted the pattern? Add to this the fact that most trade – 80% – is between MEDCs, and only 20% is between LEDCs, and things look a bit unbalanced.

One reason why LEDCs trade foodstuffs is that MEDCs can afford to buy them. People in LEDCs can't. Lack of purchasing power in LEDCs is a major reason why people continue to live in poverty.

So, what's the problem?

- Primary products like tea and sugar are sold cheaply, and the price goes up and down. When it goes down, people like Elizabeth Miheso and Ibrahim Shikanda suffer.
- Manufactured goods are sold for more and the price usually stays steady.

There's an imbalance in trade. This results in:
- a trade deficit for many LEDCs, like Kenya – look at those import/export figures again – making it hard for these countries to develop
- a trade surplus for MEDCs – look at Japan's figures again
- a bigger share of world trade for MEDCs, and less for LEDCs
- the rich North getting richer, the poor South getting poorer.

Activities

1 Explain the difference in Japan and Kenya's exports.
2 Why is it unlikely that every country in the world will have a trade surplus?
3 What problems are caused if a country has a trade deficit?
4 Why do you think the prices of primary products, such as tea and sugar, often go up and down? What effects will this have on people in countries exporting these products?
5 Why do you think the 'imbalance in trade' doesn't show any signs of improving, and may even be getting worse?

Trade – problems and partners

In this unit you'll learn about some of the other trading problems LEDCs have, and about trading partners.

Problems for traders

Ibrahim Shikanda (see Unit 10.1) helps his parents grow sugar in Kenya. The cost of fertiliser is rising rapidly and the price of sugar is falling. The poor are getting poorer.

Now scale that up. If a country has only one or two goods to sell, they can end up in real difficulty if:

◆ prices fall – like sugar (and it's the same for tea)
◆ other countries can produce the same thing more cheaply
◆ a crop fails, or a natural raw material runs out
◆ demand falls for their product.

Did you know?

The sugar industry in Kenya supports 3 million people. But factories are closing. When they close people lose their jobs, their healthcare, their schools and even their football teams.

Did you know?

Sugar costs five times as much to produce in Europe as in Africa. But Europe is allowed to subsidise its sugar industry. Europe exports its sugar and increases its share of the global market at the expense of the LEDCs.

Lots of LEDCs, especially those in Africa, rely on just one or two goods, as this map shows. If any of the things in the list above happens, it's seriously bad news for the country concerned. The economy will be affected, and people will suffer.

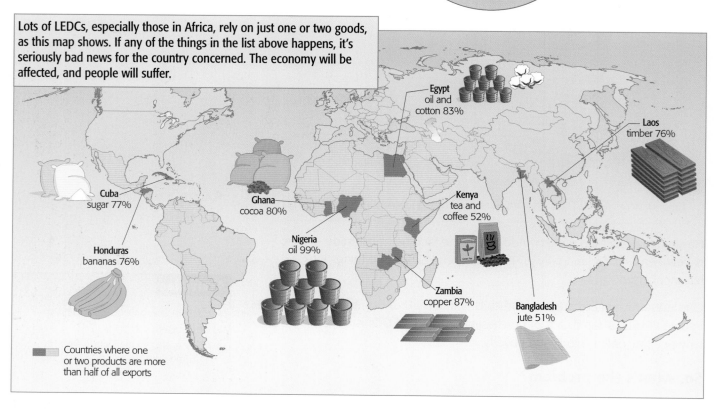

Egypt
oil and
cotton 83%

Laos
timber 76%

Cuba
sugar 77%

Ghana
cocoa 80%

Kenya
tea and
coffee 52%

Honduras
bananas 76%

Nigeria
oil 99%

Zambia
copper 87%

Bangladesh
jute 51%

Countries where one
or two products are more
than half of all exports

Who wins? Who loses?

There are always winners and losers – especially when it comes to trade and development. How does it look to you so far? Look at the text on the right and make your mind up.

MEDCs

1 We can get cheap imports of foodstuffs and raw materials, and export expensive manufactured goods. So we've got a trade surplus.

2 We've got the money to improve the environment if we damage it by mining etc.

3 We can put pressure on the LEDCs.

4 Our imports can come a long way – so we've got high transport costs.

5 And manufacturing causes pollution.

LEDCs

1 MEDCs provide a market for our cheap exports. And producing primary goods provides lots of jobs.

2 We've got a limited range of exports. Our imports cost more than we get for our exports, so we have a trade deficit.

3 Mining, deforestation and over-grazing damage the environment.

4 We might be able to get aid from MEDCs, but it might be tied (see Unit 10.6)

Trading partners

Trade makes the world go around. Ships, planes, lorries and trains are taking goods all over the world from one place to another – day in, day out. So, who trades with who?

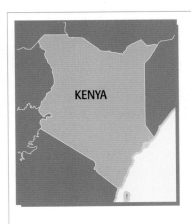

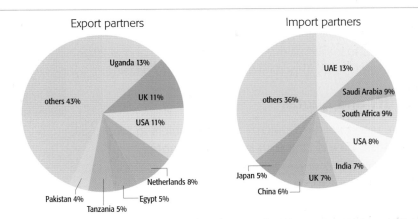

Kenya:

◆ imports 22% of its goods (oil) from the UAE and Saudi Arabia
◆ had to start buying more Japanese goods in the 1990s as Japan became Kenya's largest overseas investor (see bilateral aid in Unit 10.7)
◆ exports things like cement and refined oil to Uganda and Tanzania
◆ exports goods such as cut flowers and vegetables to Europe by air.

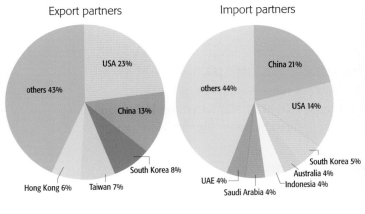

Japan:

◆ has few natural resources and has to import lots of raw materials, food and energy resources
◆ imports most from China (an LEDC)
◆ exports most to the USA (an MEDC).

Activities

1 Explain what problems LEDCs might have if they rely on a small number of export products.
2 Why are the prices of primary products more likely to vary over time than the prices of manufactured goods?
3 Divide the statements in the MEDC and LEDC boxes opposite into social/economic, environmental and political. Which group seems to be the most important? Are there any differences between the MEDC and LEDC examples?
4 Describe and explain the pattern of import and export partners for Kenya and Japan.

Trade – it's not fair

In this unit you'll find out some reasons why trade isn't fair, but that it can be made fairer.

Bananas

Fancy a banana? Trading anything – including bananas – should be easy. Somehow the world has managed to make trade complicated, and at times unfair. But increasing trade is an important way for LEDCs to develop.

Free trade, tariffs and quotas

Most countries have tried to control trade by creating barriers to protect their own jobs and industries. They do this with **tariffs** and **quotas**.

- ◆ Tariffs are taxes or customs duties paid on imports. This is usually done to make the imported goods more expensive.
- ◆ Quotas are limits on the amount of goods that can be imported. They are usually restricted to primary goods, and so work against LEDCs.
- ◆ **Free trade** is when countries don't discourage, or restrict, the movement of goods.

So, how does this affect bananas? The box on the right shows you.

The tariff on Latin America bananas (from countries like Ecuador, Colombia and Brazil) is £126 a tonne.

There is a limit (quota) on the amount of bananas those same countries can export to the EU.

There is no tariff on bananas from African, Caribbean and Pacific countries (mainly former EU colonies) exported to the EU.

Trading blocs

These are countries which have grouped together to improve their trade balance. The UK belongs to the EU, which has grown to 25 countries. When the EU began, it cut duties on goods traded between member countries – making them cheaper.

You need to know that:

- ◆ World trade isn't shared fairly. The EU and the USA have over half the world's trade. Developing countries have less than a quarter.
- ◆ As trading blocs like the EU try to increase trade within the bloc, developing countries lose out – increasing the gap between the rich North and the poor South.

Did you know?
60% of the EU's bananas come from Latin America. 20% come from Africa and the Caribbean. The other 20% come from the EU (mainly from Spanish and French islands).

▼ *Trading blocs.*

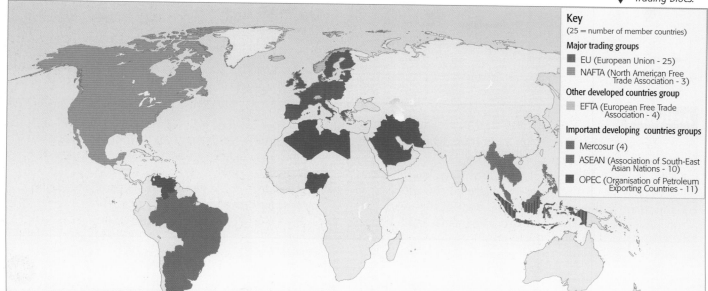

Key
(25 = number of member countries)

Major trading groups
- ■ EU (European Union - 25)
- ■ NAFTA (North American Free Trade Association - 3)

Other developed countries group
- ▨ EFTA (European Free Trade Association - 4)

Important developing countries groups
- ■ Mercosur (4)
- ■ ASEAN (Association of South-East Asian Nations - 10)
- ■ OPEC (Organisation of Petroleum Exporting Countries - 11)

The World Trade Organisation (WTO)

The WTO makes the rules on world trade. It polices free trade agreements, settles trade disputes and organises trade negotiations. So, when countries argue over bananas and beef it's the WTO who sorts it out.

The WTO promotes free trade by persuading countries to get rid of tariffs and other trade barriers.

Some people are for free trade. They say:
- it will help countries' economies to grow and will reduce poverty
- developing countries will earn more money from exports.

Others are against it. They say:
- it means that developing countries will import food that puts their own farmers out of work
- that while developing countries have imported more food, the USA and EU haven't.

At the WTO talks in Hong Kong, in December 2005, little progress was made. Rich countries agreed to end export subsidies to farmers by 2013 (most were being phased out anyway).

Did you know?
148 countries belong to the WTO. China joined in 2001, but Russia still hasn't been allowed in.

▲ *Campaigners at WTO trade talks, 2005.*

Making it fairer

Fair trade is where producers in developing countries get a guaranteed price for their product. This gives them a decent return for their work, even when world prices are low. Take Renson (pictured with his family on the right). He's a banana farmer from Ecuador. He's been able to build a new home for his family since selling bananas to the Fairtrade market. He hopes to be able to give his children the education he missed.

Fairtrade started with coffee, chocolate and tea. There are now over 800 Fairtrade products which support farmers in 49 developing countries.

Did you know?
Global citizenship is the idea that we should all try to improve the quality of life for everyone. Fairtrade is one way of doing this.

Activities

1 Explain why some countries have introduced tariffs and quotas on some products.
2 Would you expect MEDCs or LEDCs to create tariffs and quotas? Which type of imports are most often affected?
3 Why have countries joined together to form trading blocs?
4 'Free trade will never happen. MEDCs are all-powerful, and it's in their own interest to keep things as they are.' What is your opinion of this statement?
5 Why do you think Russia isn't a member of the WTO? Does this matter?
6 Would you buy Fairtrade products, even if they were more expensive?

In this unit you'll find out about transnational corporations.

Chen Ernu's story

I'm 42 years old. I came to Beijing with my husband and our 3 children 10 years ago. We used to be farmers, but got fed up with not being able to grow enough to eat.

I make clothes. Do you know how much I get paid? In your money it's 33p an hour. Not much is it?

The factory's not much fun. I'm expected to work longer and faster than ever. It's a job. I suppose it's better than nothing. But if you people in the UK don't buy enough of our clothes, I could lose my job overnight.

CHINA

Beijing

Britain may be an island, but we're part of a **global market**. Look at your jeans, your mobile – who made them, and where? Probably someone like Chen Ernu, in somewhere like China.

People who make things have to be paid. Wages vary enormously. Look at the wage rates in the table. Would you fancy working for 33p an hour?

Transnational corporations

Some businesses are now so large that they have offices and factories around the world. They're called **transnational corporations** (TNCs for short) or multinational companies. The headquarters and main factory are often in an MEDC, like the USA or Japan. Smaller offices and factories are in LEDCs where workers are cheaper. And, because of that, it is cheaper to make things there.

TNCs can be huge. Some of the biggest make more money in one year than some countries do. Some of the first businesses to become TNCs were car manufacturers. They found that by locating in different countries, they could:

- make their cars more cheaply (workers were paid less and raw materials might cost less)
- be nearer to large markets (places with big populations).

But it's not just car manufacturers that are TNCs as the table on the next page shows.

Country	Average wage rates per hour (manufacturing) 2003
USA	£12.09
UK	£10.92
Japan	£10.64
Spain	£7.72
Korea	£5.54
China	£0.33

Did you know?
Half the women who work in garment factories in Bangladesh don't have a contract – so no job security.

Did you know?
Because our fashions change so quickly, workers in garment factories in LEDCs have to work harder.

Revenue for 10 TNCs, 2000			
TNC	Type of business	Based in	Revenue ($ billions)
Wal-Mart	supermarkets	USA	244
BP	Oil/petrol	UK	233
Exxon Mobil	Oil/petrol	USA	180
Toyota	cars	Japan	168
Nestle	foods	Switzerland	49
Microsoft	software	USA	32
Coca-Cola	Soft drinks	USA	21
McDonald's	Fast food	USA	17
Gap	clothing	USA	15
Nike	Sports goods	USA	11

Total GDP for 8 countries, 2000	
Country	GDP (or total wealth produced) ($ billions)
USA	10 980
India	3022
UK	1664
Bangladesh	259
Nigeria	111
Tunisia	68
Ghana	44
Jamaica	10

Are TNCs good or bad?

It depends who you are. Some people are for TNCs, some are against them.

They help to develop mineral wealth and improve energy production.

The money we earn goes into the local economy.

They invest in big projects.

They can improve education and our work skills.

They improve roads, airports.

They give us jobs.

Most of the profits go abroad.

Few of the managers are local people.

Sometimes we're badly paid.

They can cause pollution.

Minerals are exported.

TNCs might pull out with little warning.

The things we make are no use to us, or they're too expensive.

Activities

1 Why are most TNCs based in MEDCs?
2 Explain why many TNCs manufacture their products in LEDCs.
3 a What are the costs and benefits for a country of having a branch of a TNC located there.
  b Overall, do you think TNCs bring more benefits or problems?
4 Look at the example of Toyota, a Japanese TNC located in the UK (see Unit 7.2).
  a Do you think the UK benefits from having a Toyota factory in Derbyshire?
  b Are the arguments 'for and against' the same as for an LEDC? If not, why are they different?
5 What is your opinion of the 'increasing trend towards globalisation'? Is it right that some TNCs earn more than some countries?

Did you know?

Globalisation means the way companies, ideas and lifestyles spread around the world. TNCs create world markets for their products.

Global industry - Ford in India

In this unit you'll learn about one TNC in India.

In the last unit we looked at TNCs. The Ford Motor Company is just one example of a TNC which has located factories in different parts of the world.

Ford factfile

- The Ford Motor Company is the world's second largest car manufacturer.
- Ford employs over 300 000 people worldwide.
- Ford makes Jaguars, Land Rovers, Aston Martins and other ranges of cars. It also makes lots of trucks.
- The Ford Motor Company was started by Henry Ford in Detroit in 1903, with 10 employees. Hardly the global company it is today.

By the late 1990s, Ford was:
- manufacturing, or assembling, cars worldwide
- locating new factories in LEDCs
- making different parts, for different models, in different countries
- facing competition from other manufacturers.

Did you know?
- Ford sold over 7 million vehicles in 2001.
- Over half a million cars were sold in India in 2001.

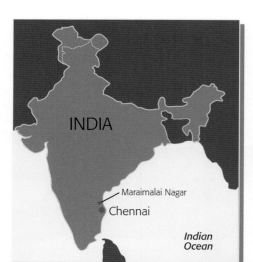

Ford India

In 1995 Ford went into partnership with Mahindra & Mahindra Limited in India. They opened an integrated high-tech manufacturing plant at Maraimalai Nagar, 45 km north of Chennai, in 1999. The site is huge. It covers 140 hectares. It can make up to 100 000 vehicles a year.

Ford India:
- employs about 1800 people at the plant at Maraimalai Nagar
- has 94 Indian suppliers
- has 33 dealerships in India.

Did you know?
The 100 000th Ford Ikon rolled out from Ford's Indian plant in April 2005.

The launch of the Ford Endeavour Special ▶ Edition in September 2005. This vehicle was specially designed for Asian markets.

Ford chose India because:

◆ it has a huge population – over 1 billion people (so there's a big market for cars)

◆ it may be an LEDC, but it has a high-earning middle class

◆ labour costs are much cheaper than in MEDCs.

What about people and the environment?

◆ Ford India pays its workers more than other workers in similar industries in India.

◆ All workers are offered training.

◆ Almost three-quarters of the goods and services that Ford India buys, come from India. And over 70% of these come from the Chennai area.

◆ Ford India contributes to development projects. Like a health centre for people around Maraimalai Nagar, and disaster relief for victims of earthquakes and floods.

◆ Ford India is working towards the sustainable use of resources, such as water and energy, in its production processes. (There is a shortage of water around Chennai.)

◆ Ford India treats all the waste water from its plant. It is then reused. Other waste products are sold and recycled. And its cars are designed to be more environmentally friendly too, both during use and at the end of their lives. 85% of the materials used in the cars can be recycled or dismantled.

Did you know?

India had the world's 12th highest GDP in 2003 (and it was growing faster than the UK's).

Activities

1 Explain why Ford decided to locate in India.

2 a Write down your opinion about each of Statements A–C.

   A 'Ford wants to make money, and the Indian market is huge. That's all they care about.'

   B 'The benefits to the local economy have been tremendous. Even people not directly involved in the industry have benefited from things like a new health centre and help with the recent flooding – all from Ford's money.'

   C 'Ford does not benefit India – it benefits the middle classes who can afford to buy new cars.'

   b Overall, do you think Ford has benefited the Indian economy?

3 How far do you think that Ford has tried to make its car manufacturing in India sustainable? Explain your answer.

Aid – closing the gap?

In this unit you'll learn about different types of aid and why it's needed.

Food aid for Niger

Food shortages in Niger reached crisis point. An urgent appeal by the Disasters Emergency Committee raised an impressive £5.4 million on its first night. Food aid was sent to Niger.

Niger's prime minister agreed with the UN's plans to stop large-scale food aid. He said it needed to stop so that Niger didn't rely on aid.

The UN said that cutting food aid would allow food prices in Niger to come down to normal levels. They had risen dramatically during months of desperate food shortages.

September 2005

Urgent appeal for Zimbabwe

The situation was dire, and getting worse. 4.8 million people in Zimbabwe needed help. If the rains failed again they'd be staring famine in the face.

Practical Action helps people like those in Zimbabwe to help themselves. By sharing techniques with farmers such as building earth dams – contour ridges and furrows to trap water for crops – they can make the difference between food and famine, life and death.

They know the techniques work. When the harvest comes in families have enough food to last a year. Practical Action says 'If there's one thing we have learnt about famines in Africa it is this: listen to the early warnings and respond quickly'.

November 2005

The examples above are just two types of aid. Food aid to help in an emergency, and long-term sustainable aid – helping people to help themselves to prevent an emergency happening. There are other types, as this diagram shows (see also Unit 10.7).

2 International organisations (multilateral)
From organisations like the World Health Organisation (WHO) and International Monetary Fund (IMF).

1 Government (bilateral)
Given from one country to another. Often 'tied' – which means the receiving country has to buy goods from the donor country.

AID

3 Voluntary
These are NGOs like Oxfam and Comic Relief.

Aid can be:

◆ **Short term / emergency** – to cope with the immediate problems of hazards such as earthquakes.

◆ **Long term / sustainable** – organisations like Practical Action help people to help themselves.

Why is aid needed?

◆ There's an imbalance in trade. LEDCs don't have a fair share.

◆ There are differences in levels of development. LEDCs need to develop to improve people's quality of life and standard of living.

◆ To recover from natural hazards like floods, drought, earthquakes and hurricanes, and hazards of our own making, like wars.

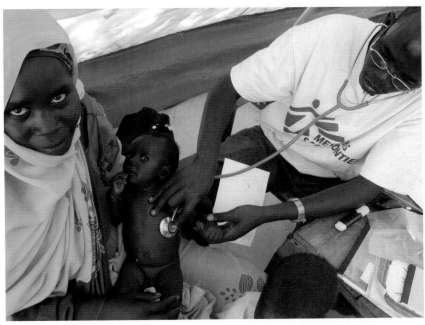

▲ *Refugees like these in Sudan are given medical help.*

What exactly is aid?

Aid is when one country, or organisation, gives resources to another country. It comes in different shapes and sizes:

◆ Money – it might be grants or loans which have to be paid back.

◆ Goods, food, machinery, technology.

◆ People with special skills like engineers, teachers etc.

Aid should help countries to develop their economies and services, and so improve people's lives.

Did you know?
The **donor** is the country giving the aid. The **recipient** is the country receiving the aid.

How much do we give?

MEDCs like the USA, UK and Japan are in the top 15 countries when it comes to quality of life. The UN set a target that MEDCs should give 0.7% of their income in aid to LEDCs. The table shows what these three MEDCs gave in 1990 and 2003.

Hardly generous was it? The USA's and Japan's percentage went down! Only the UK's went up, and that's still only half the UN's target.

HDI rank	Country	1990	2003
10	USA	0.21%	0.15%
11	Japan	0.31%	0.20%
15	UK	0.27%	0.34%

Aid given as a percentage of a country's income

Activities

1 When do you think it is best to give
  a short-term aid like food?
  b long-term aid?
  Give at least one example in each case.

2 Niger and Zimbabwe are both African countries receiving aid. How are the two examples similar, and how are they different?

3 **a** What is 'tied' aid?
  b What problems might tied aid cause for countries receiving it?

4 Do you think it's right that MEDCs such as the UK should give 0.7% of their wealth to poorer nations as aid? Do you think they should give more than this, or less? Justify your opinion.

Aid – is it all good news?

In this unit you'll need to think about whether aid is the best way to help LEDCs develop.

The good and the bad

Different types of aid have advantages and disadvantages. Here are some.

KEY

Advantages

Disadvantages

1 Government (bilateral)

- ◆ 'Tied' means the LEDC has to buy goods from the donor.
- ◆ Money is given for specific projects, like big dams, which don't benefit poor people.
- ◆ If the LEDC can't repay the money, they get further into debt, and rely more on the donor.
- ◆ Can provide grants for students to study in MEDCs.

2 International organisations (multilateral)

- ◆ Not meant to be tied but unlikely to be given to countries with unfavourable economic and political systems.
- ◆ Encourages farming and industry – but products are exported to MEDCs.
- ◆ LEDCs depend on aid and get into debt.
- ◆ Helps LEDCs develop new crops, raw materials and industry.

▲ *Ghana got loans from the World Bank, the UK and the USA to build the Akosombo dam in the 1960s. Ghana wanted water for irrigation, and electricity to help the country develop. As part of the deal, an American company called Valco got the right to produce aluminium in Ghana using cheap electricity from the dam.*

AID

3 Voluntary

- ◆ Not tied.
- ◆ Helps with emergencies.
- ◆ Encourages low-cost, self-help schemes.
- ◆ Benefits poor people.
- ◆ Money available depends on how much people give.

4 Short term/emergency

- ◆ Not tied.
- ◆ Provides help when needed.
- ◆ Goes to people and places who need it most.

5 Long term/sustainable

- ◆ Not tied.
- ◆ Provides people with new skills.
- ◆ Helps develop farming, small industries and schools.
- ◆ LEDCs don't get into debt.

Presents £51— £150

counting sheep

A gift of two sheep – a ewe and a ram – quickly multiplies, giving poor families in Senegal a way out of poverty. With her lambs, Mbayang Diop is now able to nourish her children with milk, and use fresh manure to fertilise her crops of millet, peanuts and green beans.

CODE V05 A007 A couple of sheep **£80**

▲ *Many charities offer people in MEDCs like the UK imaginative ways to help others.*

Aid – what could be better?

Aid has a part to play in helping LEDCs develop in terms of their economy and reducing poverty. But there are other things which would help.

Aid

- ◆ MEDCs should give more aid (0.7% of a country's income) and set a definite timetable for it to happen.
- ◆ MEDCs should make their aid more effective.

Did you know?
Leaders from around the world pledged to halve the number of hungry people in the world by 2015. So far they're failing.

Do they (our world leaders) know how the aid they give can be made more effective? ▶

Other things

- ◆ Cancel *all* debt of the world's poorest countries.
- ◆ Focus less on emergencies and more on chronic problems, for example by providing water storage tanks, and tools so families can plough and irrigate their land and feed themselves.
- ◆ LEDCs need to develop sound economic policies. These, not aid, lifted millions of people in Asia out of poverty.
- ◆ MEDCs should stop exporting subsidised crops which damage poor rural communities around the world.
- ◆ Reduce tariffs in MEDCs for crops and foodstuffs from LEDCs.

Food aid to Kenya in the 1990s killed local food production and increased dependency on aid. ▶

Activities

1 Summarise what you have learnt about aid. What are the main benefits of each type of aid?

2 Parts of the UK (and other European countries) receive money from the EU because they are relatively poor. Do you think this is aid? Should the UK receive such help, or should it all go to the world's poorest countries?

3 The world's poorest countries owe huge amounts of money to MEDCs in interest payments on loans. Do you think these payments should be cancelled to help these countries? Justify your opinion.

4 'Trade, not aid, is what is needed to help LEDCs develop.' What do you think of this statement?

Self-help schemes

In this unit you'll learn about schemes in LEDCs which help people to help themselves.

What is self-help?

Many LEDCs work with aid agencies, like Oxfam, to introduce self-help schemes. These are where local people take part in activities to help themselves and their communities. The schemes tend to be small-scale and use simple technology.

Magic stones

In 1979 Oxfam encouraged local farmers in Burkina Faso to build **diguettes**, or stone lines, along the contours of the ground on gently sloping farmland. These hold back the rain so it soaks into the ground, and trap soil (soil conservation). Gradually the soil behind the diguettes increases in depth. This means that farmers can grow more crops and have a better life.

Awa Bundani, from Siguin Voussé explains why the diguettes are important to her community. 'Last year the rains were good. But in some years they stop and the crops die. Then we go hungry. Since we built the diguettes the land produces more. Now we get twice as many groundnuts. We sell the extra and use the money to buy tools to work on the diguettes and build houses.'

Did you know?
The building of diguettes has been so successful that they are often called magic stones.

Afforestation

Afforestation is planting trees in areas that haven't been forested before.

32 000 trees have been planted in Haremfema Utuba, in eastern Ethiopia. Before the trees were planted, women and children walked up to 25 km a day to collect wood. Now, thanks to fast-growing trees such as eucalyptus, life has improved:
◆ People have better access to wood for building and fuel.
◆ The trees help bind the soil, reduce run-off after the rains and raise the water table. When the leaves rot they form humus and make the soil more fertile.
◆ The trees act as wind breaks to protect crops, provide shade and can produce food such as nuts and fruit.
◆ Because they no longer have to help collect wood, children can go to school.

Education and training

Practical Action is a British charity. It works with people in LEDCs helping to provide practical answers to poverty, and sustainable solutions. One of the projects it's involved with is the Jua Kali engineering workshops in Kenya. The project aims to train local people and increase production from its workshops so that more jobs are created and people can earn more money.

Practical Action ensures that the equipment, tools, information, skills and organisation needed to make the workshops run well are in place.

The workshops use scrap metal. They are supported by the Kenyan government, as well as Practical Action. Schemes like this are **sustainable** – they can continue for years without using up resources, or harming the environment.

Other schemes include training local people as farming advisers, and giving others basic medical training. This allows them to treat simple illnesses and refer more complicated cases to hospital. They are often called **barefoot doctors**.

Education also holds the key to self-help schemes in MEDCs, e.g. campaigns to stop people smoking.

Did you know?
Sustainable development means improving people's lives without wasting resources or harming the environment.

Recycling goats

Sounds silly? Not really. Organisations like Christian Aid and Oxfam provide ways for families in LEDCs to buy goats. Goats provide manure which helps plants grow. This means families can grow more food and may be able to sell some. Goats also produce nutritious milk.

When the goat has kids (baby goats) some are given, or sold, to other local families so they can also benefit. Families use the extra money to buy medicines, send their children to school or build a house, and so improve their lives. All from just one goat!

It's not just goats that can be recycled. Almost anything that multiplies – seeds, bees, cows, even ducks can be recycled!

Activities

1 a What are self-help schemes?
   b What is sustainable development? Give at least one example in each case.
2 a What other examples of self-help schemes can you think of that would make a big difference in LEDCs?
   b Explain how they could improve people's lives.
3 Write 'self-help schemes' in the middle of your page. Create a mind map around it with as many ideas and links as you can.
4 Schemes like the Jua Kali workshops are examples of 'appropriate technology'. What does this mean (see Unit 9.6)?

The big picture

This chapter is all about enquiry skills – gathering and processing techniques – and how to use them. These are the big ideas behind the chapter:

◆ Enquiry skills are important in geography – they are worth 60% of your marks for Standard Grade.

◆ Gathering techniques are to do with how you find out information – for example by using questionnaires, carrying out surveys, doing fieldwork and so on.

◆ Processing techniques are to do with what you do with your information – for example producing different types of graphs, maps, and tables.

◆ You can use lots of technology to help with fieldwork – the internet, mobile phones, PDAs, and laptops.

Your goals

By the time you have learnt all these skills you should be able to answer these questions:

◆ Give the advantages and disadvantages of different types of questionnaires.

◆ When would you use a questionnaire and when would you use an interview to find out information?

◆ What will an environmental quality survey tell you? Can you give three examples of when you would use an environmental quality survey?

◆ What is the difference between a field sketch and a sketch map?

◆ What would you measure if you were doing river fieldwork? And how?

◆ Can you draw and label a river cross-section?

◆ Give at least six ways that you could use technology to help with your fieldwork.

◆ Give five examples of processing techniques, explain what they are good for, and give examples of their use.

And then …

When you have learnt all these skills, come back here and see if you have met your goals!

> **Did you know?**
> The dictionary definition of enquiry is 'an act of asking for or seeking information.'

> **Did you know?**
> Geographers carry out enquiries into many different things, all over the world.

> **Did you know?**
> The Dead Sea is so salty almost nothing can survive in it – just tiny quantities of bacteria and fungi.

Your chapter starter

Look at the photo on page 194.

What do you think this person is doing?

What might he be studying?

Where do you think he is?

He's helping with enquiries

11.1 Questionnaires and interviews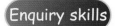

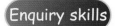

Asking the right questions

Questionnaires and interviews are important tools in geography fieldwork; however they are only as good as the questions that are asked. Developing the right questions can take a lot of thought, time and consultation, but the questionnaire or interview will be of little value if you don't get the questions right.

A word about sensitive information

Be very careful when asking people sensitive information. If this type of information is important to your project, try to think of other ways of obtaining it. For example, instead of asking, 'How much is your house worth?', Go to an estate agent or an on-line solicitor and look at the prices of other houses in the area.

Questionnaires

There are several different types of questionnaire, including face-to-face, postal and on-line. Whatever type of questionnaire you use, here are a few golden rules to ensure success:

- Keep your questionnaire short and easy to complete quickly (normally not more than ten questions).
- Keep your questions simple (don't use complicated terminology).
- Multiple-choice questions are easier to analyse but don't provide as much depth.
- Make sure that you find out where people have come from – a postcode is good for this.
- Consider finding out or noting other core information about the person you are questioning (for example, their sex, age range, etc.).
- Make a note of the time and location where you completed the questionnaire.
- Choosing the location, time and who you approach are important considerations to bear in mind when conducting questionnaires.

An example of a questionnaire is shown on the right.

A study of shopping habits at a local shopping centre

Location _____ Time _____

1. Please could you tell me your postcode? _____
   (*This will be used later to calculate the distance the person has travelled.*)

2. Which age bracket do you fall into?
   a Under 16 ☐ **b** 16 – 21 ☐ **c** 22 – 40 ☐
   d 41 – 65 ☐ **e** over 65 ☐

3. On average, how often do you come to this shopping centre?
   a more than once a week ☐ **b** once a week ☐
   c once every 2 weeks ☐ **d** once every 3 to 4 weeks ☐ **e** less than once a month ☐

4. How many shops will you visit while you are here?
   a just one ☐ **b** 2 or 3 ☐ **c** 4 or 5 ☐
   d 6 to 10 ☐ **e** more than 10 ☐

5. On average, how much do you think you will spend here today?
   a nothing (just window shopping) ☐
   b under £20 ☐ **c** £21 – £50 ☐
   d £51 – £100 ☐ **e** over £100 ☐

6. How did you get here today?
   a walk or cycle ☐ **b** bus ☐ **c** train ☐
   d car ☐ **e** coach ☐

7. Could you quickly tell me one good thing and one bad thing about this shopping centre?

   Good thing: _____

   Bad thing: _____

Thank you for your time and help with my geography project.

Enquiry skills

Advantages and disadvantages

The table below summarizes the advantages and disadvantages of different types of questionnaire.

	Advantages	Disadvantages
Face-to-face	• It normally guarantees a response from participants. • You have the option to ask extra questions – to clarify a response.	• It's time-consuming for you to question people individually. • There is a possible threat to your personal safety (you really need to have two people working together).
Postal	• It's less time-consuming for you, because you can send out a lot of questionnaires in a short space of time.	• It's costly. You need to provide a stamped, addressed envelope for the return of each questionnaire – on top of the initial postage costs. • There is no guarantee of getting the questionnaires back.
On-line	• It's less time-consuming for you, because you can e-mail out a lot of questionnaires in a short space of time. • It's cheap. Sites like survey monkey (www.surveymonkey .com) provide free questionnaire tools for educational use.	• It's difficult to distribute the questionnaires in the first place, because you have to obtain the e-mail addresses. • There is no guarantee of getting any responses back.

Interviews

Unlike questionnaires, interviews are an opportunity to ask more in-depth questions about a topic or issue. Again, you should prepare a set of questions in advance, but you could also allow the interviewee to digress from the point or expand on some of their answers.

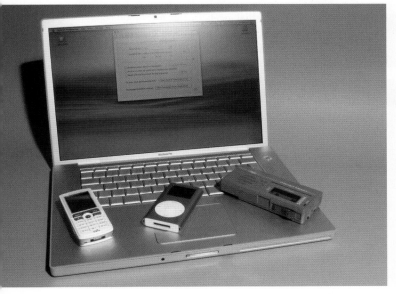

▲ When conducting an interview, it's difficult to write everything down. A small tape recorder, an MP3 player with a voice recorder, a laptop, or your mobile phone may be useful to record the interview in order to play it back and analyse the information at a later date.

Interviews versus questionnaires

Sometimes it is difficult to know when to use a questionnaire and when to use an interview. As a general rule, questionnaires should be used to gauge public opinion, and interviews should be used to gain a specific viewpoint. For example, you might complete 100 questionnaires asking village residents what they think of a proposal to build a new supermarket. You might then interview a representative of the main planning company responsible for the development, to allow them to respond to the opinions you obtained.

Activities

1 Briefly summarize when you would use questionnaires and when you would use interviews.
2 You have been asked to do a geography project on the function of a village. Come up with between 5 and 10 questions which you could ask local residents.
3 You need to collect some data on visitor numbers to the Glasgow Science Centre. What type of questionnaire would you use and why?
4 When would you use a postal questionnaire and when would you use an on-line questionnaire?
5 Using www.surveymonkey.com come up with a list of questions to ask the rest of your class on the topic of school travel.
6 You have been given a chance to interview a countryside ranger about visitor impact in a local nature reserve. What questions would you ask the ranger and why?

In this unit you'll learn about environmental quality surveys and traffic surveys.

Environmental quality surveys

An environmental quality survey is a way of assessing the environmental quality of a place or location. It's useful because it generates a number or percentage score, which can then be compared with other possible locations. The higher the number, the better the location is considered to be. There are no real rules about what should be in your environmental quality survey, as long as you are consistent with your observations.

Here are two examples of environmental quality surveys.

A The quality of an industrial site

This example has allowed for the assessment of a potential industrial site to gauge its quality. The higher the final score, the better suited this area is to become an industrial location. This technique could be used by investors to find the best possible site for the location of new industry.

Disadvantages	POINTS					Advantages
	1	2	3	4	5	
high rent/rates						low rent/rates
access is very difficult						excellent roads adjoining
unpleasant surroundings						pleasant surroundings
no room for expansion						good room for expansion
no car park						large car park
many storeys						single storey
poor land – drainage/slope						flat land
very old building						new building
building in bad condition						building in good condition
SUB-TOTALS						**TOTAL POINTS**

INDUSTRIAL SITE QUALITY INDEX

B Water pollution

WATER POLLUTION VISUAL SURVEY INDEX						
Polluted	**POINTS**					**Clean**
	1	2	3	4	5	
very murky water						clear water
stones covered with scum						stones clean and bare
choked with weed						no water weed
much grey sewage algae						no grey sewage algae
much scum or froth or oil						no scum or froth or oil
much rubbish						no rubbish
much sewage						no sewage
SUB-TOTALS						**TOTAL POINTS**

In this example, the higher the score recorded, the cleaner the stretch of river. If a low score is recorded, it indicates that the observer found the river to be dirty or polluted.

Traffic surveys

Traffic surveys are useful because they allow us to find out about the routes that vehicles use, and how these routes are used by different types of traffic.

Traffic counts are useful if you want to find out how many vehicles or types of vehicle pass a specific point on a road at different times of day. Traffic counts are normally recorded on a tally chart like the one on the right.

The location where you conduct your traffic count is important. It's also important that you are clearly visible and safe from passing cars.

You have to think carefully about what time(s) of day to conduct your traffic count, as this may affect your results. Some of the best traffic counts show the changes in traffic flow throughout a day, e.g. between 8 am and 8 pm you might survey the traffic for 15 minutes each hour.

This technique could be used to assess whether new roads are necessary in an area, and also to establish whether busy roads are dangerous to local people and whether they require traffic calming measures (speed bumps or crossings) to minimize the problem.

Location: *Main Street Roundabout*				
Time	0800-0815		0900-0915	
Type of vehicle	No.	total	No.	total
car	𝍷𝍷𝍷𝍷𝍷𝍷𝍷𝍷𝍷𝍷 II	52	𝍷𝍷𝍷𝍷𝍷𝍷𝍷 II	37
van	𝍷𝍷𝍷 III	18	𝍷 IIII	9
light lorry	𝍷𝍷 I	11	𝍷 I	6
HGV lorry	𝍷	5	III	3
bus	II	2	II	2
motorbike/scooter	𝍷 II	7	III	3
pedal cycle	𝍷𝍷	10	III	3
Grand Total		105		63

Field sketching and photography

In this unit you'll learn about the role of field sketching and photography in geography fieldwork.

What is a field sketch?

A field sketch of a place is a quick drawing of what the place looks like. Field sketches help to remind you about what your study area was like when you get back to the classroom to write up your fieldwork report. They don't need to be works of art — as long as they create a visual image in your mind, they will do the job. Good labelling (annotation) is an adequate replacement for poor artistic talent!

Below is an example of a field sketch, with a photograph showing the area it illustrates.

This photograph shows part of Warkworth in ▶ *Northumberland. It is a historic settlement which built up on the inside of a meander for defence purposes. Facing you is the remains of a Norman Castle.*

This is a field sketch of the same place. ▶

All field sketches and sketch maps should:
- have a title, North arrow and key;
- be surrounded with a border frame (use a ruler);
- include labels and annotations (notes) where extra information is needed;
- have simple lines and just enough detail to give a rough idea of a place — there is no need to show every building, tree or rock;
- include a date showing when the drawing was made.

Sketch maps are not to scale. You can add a note to say this.

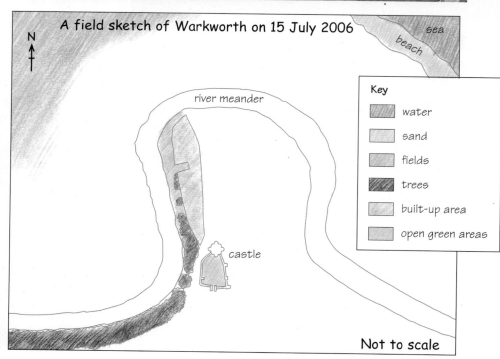

A field sketch of Warkworth on 15 July 2006

N

sea
beach

river meander

Key
- water
- sand
- fields
- trees
- built-up area
- open green areas

castle

Not to scale

What is a sketch map?

A sketch map is like a field sketch but its job is to help others find a place or feature, or to re-create a journey.

The street map below shows part of an area of Liverpool. The streets are drawn to scale. The sketch map below it shows a journey from a house to the local post office. It's not drawn to scale, but has enough detail to be helpful.

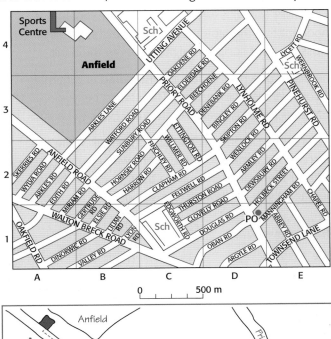

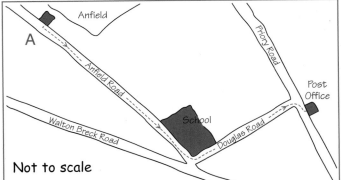

Photography

Drawing a field sketch and drawing a sketch map can take a long time. Most geographers now use photographs instead of field sketches.

Digital photography has nearly replaced traditional photography in geography fieldwork. Although the cost of a cheap digital camera may be more expensive than a traditional camera, the cost of developing pictures is less and you can easily delete poor-quality photographs.

Digital photographs can also be easily imported onto your computer for processing. They can be touched up, cropped and annotated. Then they can be cut and pasted directly into your fieldwork project to produce a really professional-looking piece of work.

Fieldwork top tip

If you don't have a digital camera, you could try using your mobile phone (see page 203). Alternatively, you could buy a cheap disposable camera for under £10 (some of them are even waterproof).

To take you further – using GPS

Handheld GPS (Global Positioning Systems) have come down in price in the last few years. You might even have one in your school. A GPS links with satellites to give an exact grid reference of your location. Most GPS will also record your track (the route that you walk). This means that when you plug your GPS into your computer, it will automatically draw a sketch map for you from one place to another. You can even overlay your track into free map programmes like Google Maps to draw a professional-looking map overlay – how about that!

Activities

1 Draw a field sketch for a suitable photo from this book. Don't forget a key.
2 Compare the street map and the sketch map above.
   a Write down three differences between them.
   b Why was the school marked on the sketch map?
3 Look again at the street map. House A is on Anfield Road in square A3.
   a Work out an easy route from house A to the school in Wernbrook Road (E4)
   b Now draw a sketch map of the route. Show just enough detail to be helpful.

4 Below is a route from house A to house B.
   Go out of the front door and turn left.
   Take the seventh street on the left, then first right, then first left.
   Next take the first right, then second left.
   The house you are going to is the second house from the end, on the right-hand side.
   a Which street is house B in?
   b Which direction is it from house A?
   c About how far is the distance between the two houses?
   d Draw a sketch map to show the route.

River fieldwork   Enquiry skills

In this unit you'll find out about river fieldwork

Water, water everywhere

River fieldwork can be great fun but it can also be really dangerous. Choosing the best site to carry out your fieldwork is the most important consideration. You must find a site that has easy access, is shallow enough to get into the water, has safe banks, and has no rapids or whitewater.

Channel characteristics

Most river investigations compare and contrast the channel characteristics of a river, or rivers. Channel characteristics include the width, depth and the speed of a section of river. This data can be used to calculate the cross-sectional area, wetted perimeter and river discharge.

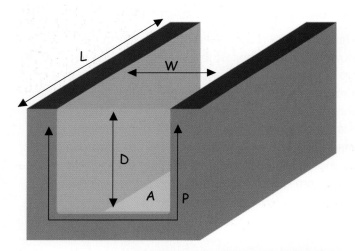

Key

L = Length
W = Width
D = Depth
A = Cross sectional area (D x W)
P - Wetted perimeter

Width and depth

Width and depth are measured in centimetres (cm) using a tape measure or metre ruler. When measuring the width of the river (just the water and not the channel!) it is important that the tape measure is stretched straight across the river surface at right angles to the bank.

The depth of a river should be measured at a number of points across the channel. This should be done systematically (e.g. every 20 cm from bank to bank).

The final measurements that should be taken are the height of the bank above the river's water level and the width of the river channel from bank to bank. This will then allow you to draw a cross-section.

Name of river/stream	River Avon	
Site	1	
Location/grid reference	near Blue Bridge/125545	
Width (water surface)		542 cm
Width (bank-to-bank)		595 cm
Height of banks above water level	Bank A	72 cm
	Bank B	67 cm
Depth measurements taken every		50 cm
Depth (across stream, from bank A to bank B)		1 88 cm
		2 103 cm
		3 115 cm
		4 127 cm
		5 135 cm
		6 142 cm
		7 176 cm
		8 182 cm
		9 133 cm
		10 90 cm

Cross-sections

Cross-sections should be drawn on graph paper, or by using a graphing package such as Microsoft Excel.

Decide what scale you are going to use, and then draw in the width of the river on your graph paper. Now mark on the height of the banks above the river's surface and the width from bank to bank. Finally, you can mark on the riverbed by marking on the depth measurements and joining the dots to complete your cross-section.

Depending on the scale you have used, it should now be possible to calculate the **cross-sectional area** of the river channel by counting up the squares that are covered by the river on the graph paper. The **wetted perimeter** of the river can also be calculated by measuring the amount of contact that the water has with the bank and bed of the river. The greater the contact, the greater the friction.

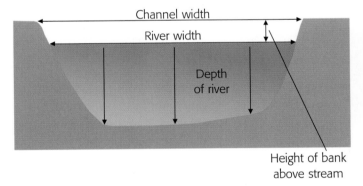

River speed

River speed (velocity) is measured in metres per second (m/s). It can be measured by using a flow meter or a floating object and stopwatch.

Flow meters are great, but expensive. If you are lucky enough to have one, it's worth measuring the speed of the river at each point where you measure the river's depth. This means that you will be able to investigate any relationship between river speed and river depth.

Flow meters are simple to use – you place the propeller in the water and read the speed on the recording box. Make sure that you stand downstream of the propeller, or you will affect the results.

If you don't have a flow meter, you can still calculate the river's speed by using a floating object and a stopwatch (use the one on your mobile phone). Measure ten metres along the bank and time how long it takes the object to travel the ten metres downstream. Repeat the exercise at least five times to calculate an average. Use the equation: speed = distance / time to work out the velocity.

Top tip

An orange or half-filled plastic bottle works best when working out the speed of a river. This is because these objects float mostly in the water instead of on the surface and are, therefore, not affected by the wind.

To take you further: discharge

Once you have collected the speed and cross-sectional area data, it is possible to calculate a river's discharge. This is the amount of water flowing down a river at any one time. It is calculated using the formula:
discharge = velocity x area.

Activities

1 Use the information below to draw the cross-section for this section of river and calculate the average depth, average speed, wetted perimeter, cross-sectional area and discharge.

- ◆ Width of the channel from bank to bank = 200 cm
- ◆ Width of the water surface from bank to bank = 180 cm
- ◆ Height of the bank above the water surface:
  right bank = 45 cm and left bank = 22 cm

Depth and speed data:

	Left bank ⬅				➡ Right bank	
Site	1	2	3	4	5	6
Depth (cm)	8	21	39	42	32	16
Speed (m/s)	1.2	1.9	2.5	2.6	2.1	1.6

2 Study the above data and your cross-section.
  a Is there a relationship (a pattern) between speed and depth?
  b Why does the water seem to be flowing faster on the right-hand side of the river?

New technologies for fieldwork enquiry

In this unit you'll find out how you can use new technologies, such as the Internet, blogging and mobile phones, to improve your fieldwork.

Using the Internet

Everyone uses the Internet to help with geography homework, but quite often people forget about using the Internet to help them with geography fieldwork. Here are some ideas for using the Internet to improve your fieldwork project:

- **Find out about the place you are visiting**. You could use a search engine (e.g. Google or Yahoo) to find out about a place.

- **Find out what the weather is going to be like**. Visit the Met Office or BBC Weather web sites for up-to-date weather information. These web sites are also useful for finding out what the weather has been like recently, because this information may affect your data collection (e.g. if it's been raining for 5 days in the Highlands, will this be a good time to do a river investigation?).

- **Get a map or aerial photograph of the place that you are going to be visiting**. Web sites like Ordnance Survey (get-a-map) and Google Maps can provide you with base maps that you can use in your projects. Google Maps, Google Earth and Windows Live Local can also provide you with high-resolution aerial photographs of parts of the UK.

Tips for searching the Internet
- Use the advanced search field.
- Search with a phrase, e.g. type in "geography fieldwork" rather than geography fieldwork.
- Be specific, e.g. "river fieldwork" Scotland Highlands.
- Use alternative search words (use an on-line thesaurus to help you do this), e.g. instead of 'river fieldwork' search for 'stream fieldwork' or 'creek fieldwork'.
- Insert a plus or minus sign. This trick usually works in most search engines. Put a plus sign (+) in front of a word that must be found in the search window. For example, Urban fieldwork + Edinburgh will help you narrow the search for urban fieldwork to Edinburgh only.

Useful web links
BBC Weather: http://www.bbc.co.uk/weather/
Google Maps: http://maps.google.com/
Met Office: http://www.metoffice.gov.uk/
Ordnance Survey: www.ordnancesurvey.gov.uk
Technorati: www.technorati.com
Wikipedia: http://en.wikipedia.org
Windows Live Local: http://local.live.com

Blogging

A blog (from web log) is an on-line journal that anyone can set up. Any blog entries are professionally published to the Internet to create a web page. When you publish a web blog there is an option for other web users to leave comments on your entry. You do not need to know any complicated code to publish a blog, if you can send an e-mail you can blog!

Blogs can be used in two ways:

- You could set up your own fieldwork blog to record your fieldwork investigation from the planning to the evaluation stage. Your teacher, members of your class and other web users can comment on your blog entries to provide you with feedback and other ideas. You can even up-date your blog directly to the Internet using a modern mobile phone (this is called moblogging!).

- You can search other people's web logs and leave comments asking for some help with your project. The best blog search tool to use is Technorati. This is a powerful search engine that only searches blogs.

PDAs and laptops

Like mobile phones, PDAs (Personal Desktop Assistants) and laptops can also be useful when carrying out fieldwork. They often have more functionality and processing power than mobile phones, but on the other hand they're more expensive and not as robust.

Calendar and alarm: Put your fieldwork deadline dates into your phone's calendar. Set the alarm to remind you when you are going to complete each part of your enquiry. You can also use your phone calendar to help remind you of other things, such as the time of interviews, high-tide times and the bus timetable (to get you to your fieldwork venue in the first place).

Mobile phones

Most people have mobile phones these days, and it's important to take a mobile phone with you for safety reasons when carrying out fieldwork. Mobile phones can be used in other ways too.

Text message: Record your fieldwork notes and data as a text message (that will save carrying around one of those old-fashioned fieldwork notebooks). Some phones have Microsoft Office Mobile on them, so that data can be input directly into a Word or Excel file.

Voice recorder: Use your phone's voice recorder (if it has one) to record interviews. This uses less phone memory than a video. You could also use it to record your own notes (a bit like an old-fashioned dictaphone).

Video: Some mobile phones have video cameras built in. When conducting an interview, ask if you can video any responses to questions. This will save you scribbling down loads of notes.

Photograph: Lots of mobile phones have cameras on them (some of them really good cameras). Use your phone to take photos of your fieldwork site, to help remind you of where you've been. Add text notes to your photographs to remind you of the orientation and venue. Your phone will store the date and time for you.

Activities

1 Imagine that you're going to carry out an environmental quality survey (see pages 198-199) in the Loch Lomond National Park. Part of your project write up should include some background information on the national park, including visitor numbers and information about visitor attractions. Use the Internet search tips opposite to research the park and write two clear and concise paragraphs introducing it. Do not just 'cut and paste'!

2 Now imagine that you are going to carry out the fieldwork project over the next three days. Use the Internet to find out what the weather will be like in this area of Scotland and write a kit list of everything that you will need to take with you to prepare for any changes in the weather.

3 Draw a concept map of how you could use your mobile phone to make geography fieldwork easier. The first part has been done for you.

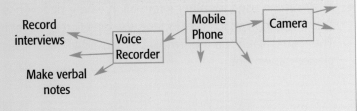

Processing techniques

In this unit you'll find out more about the different processing techniques used in geography.

Pie charts

◆ Pie charts are good for showing percentages and proportions.
◆ They are also easy to compare if you have more than one.
◆ They can be enhanced by colour.
◆ Pie charts can be drawn in different sizes to show an overall total as well as segments.

Line graphs / multiple line graphs

◆ They are good for showing changes and trends over time.
◆ Multiple line graphs show how similar or different things are over time, and allow comparisons to be made.

Scatter graphs

◆ Scatter graphs are good for showing a link or correlation between two sets of data. The scatter diagram on the right shows the relationship between settlement size and the number of services provided in a selection of different settlements.
◆ A 'best fit line' can be drawn to show the link more clearly.

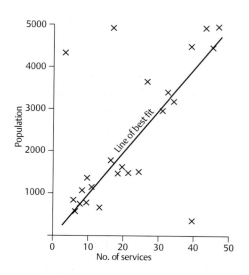

Bar graphs

◆ They are good for comparing different amounts.
◆ Highs and lows can be clearly identified.
◆ They are good for comparing more than one set of information.

Land use maps and overlay maps

◆ They are good for showing changes in land use over time.
◆ Two sets of information can be put on the same map using acetate or tracing paper.
◆ Relief, height and land use can all be compared.
◆ The falling price of GIS (Geographical Information System) computer software has made digital mapping accessible to all geographers.

Rose diagrams

◆ They are usually used for wind direction (wind rose); they show the frequency of wind, usually over a month, and are used to work out the prevailing wind.
◆ They can be used for other information where direction is important (e.g. the direction in which corries face, the direction of travel from the CBD). The rose diagram on the right is being used to show the direction of glacier movement.

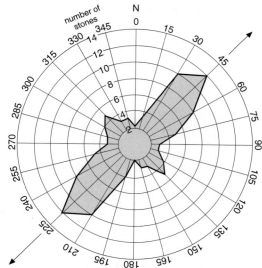

Long axes of pebbles showing a NE–SW direction of movement

Annotated field sketches or digital photographs

◆ Field sketches and digital photographs give a clear picture of an area. When annotations (labels) are added, the main features can be highlighted and conclusions drawn about the area.

◆ It's possible to write notes on maps and graphs in order to highlight information and patterns.

◆ Photos can be used to compare different urban areas. They can also be used to highlight changes in an area (see pages 95 and 99), or changes in the characteristics of a river.

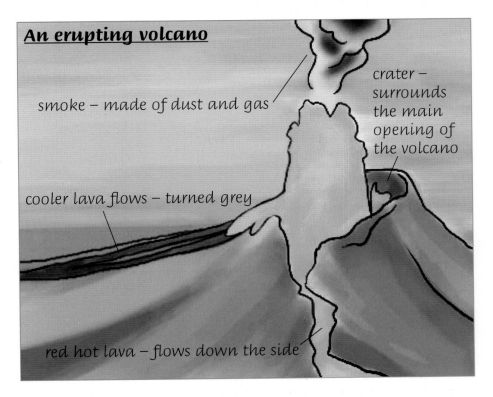

An erupting volcano

smoke – made of dust and gas

crater – surrounds the main opening of the volcano

cooler lava flows – turned grey

red hot lava – flows down the side

Presentation skills

All graphs should have a title and any axis should be clearly labelled. Different colours can be used to highlight the different sections of the graph and to increase the overall presentation.

Most geographers these days use a computer to process their results. Data can be added quickly into spreadsheets and professional-looking graphs can be created in minutes.

Activities

1 Make a larger copy of the table below and complete the missing sections.

Processing technique	Justification	Example of use
Pie chart		
Line graph	Good for showing changes over time	
Bar graph		Bar graph showing the amount of precipitation in mm in an area for each month of the year
Overlay map		
Scatter graph	Good for comparing two values and seeing if there is a link between the two variables	
Rose diagram		
Annotated field sketch		Sketching a waterfall and labelling the hard rock, soft rock, gorge, ledge and plunge pool

2 Write a list of advantages and disadvantages of using a computer to process data.

Ordnance Survey symbols

ROADS AND PATHS

M1 or A6(M) — Motorway
A35 — Dual carriageway
A31(T) or A35 — Trunk or main road
B3074 — Secondary road
— Narrow road with passing places
— Road under construction
— Road generally more than 4 m wide
— Road generally less than 4 m wide
— Other road, drive or track, fenced and unfenced
— Gradient: steeper than 1 in 5; 1 in 7 to 1 in 5
Ferry — Ferry; Ferry P – passenger only
— Path

PUBLIC RIGHTS OF WAY

(Not applicable to Scotland)

1:25 000	1:50 000	
-----------	-----------	Footpath
-+-+-+-+-	----------	Road used as a public footpath
+++++++	----------	Bridleway
-+-+-+-+-	-+-+-+-+-	Byway open to all traffic

RAILWAYS

— Multiple track
— Single track
— Narrow gauge/Light rapid transit system
— Road over; road under; level crossing
— Cutting; tunnel; embankment
— Station, open to passengers; siding

BOUNDARIES

-+-+-+- National
-+-+-+- District
—·—·—·— County, Unitary Authority, Metropolitan District or London Borough
National Park

HEIGHTS/ROCK FEATURES

—60— Contour lines
·144 Spot height to the nearest metre above sea level

outcrop cliff scree

ABBREVIATIONS

P	Post office	PC	Public convenience (rural areas)
PH	Public house	TH	Town Hall, Guildhall or equivalent
MS	Milestone	Sch	School
MP	Milepost	Coll	College
CH	Clubhouse	Mus	Museum
CG	Coastguard	Cemy	Cemetery
Fm	Farm		

ANTIQUITIES

VILLA Roman
Castle Non-Roman
✗ Battlefield (with date)
✶ Tumulus

LAND FEATURES

Buildings
Public building
Bus or coach station
Place of Worship — with tower
— with spire, minaret or dome
— without such additions
° Chimney or tower
Glass structure
Ⓗ Heliport
△ Triangulation pillar
Mast
Wind pump / wind generator
Windmill
+ Graticule intersection
Cutting, embankment
Quarry
Spoil heap, refuse tip or dump
Coniferous wood
Non-coniferous wood
Mixed wood
Orchard
Park or ornamental ground
Forestry Commission access land
National Trust – always open
National Trust, limited access, observe local signs
National Trust for Scotland

TOURIST INFORMATION

P Parking
V Visitor centre
ℹ Information centre
Telephone
Camp site/ Caravan site
Golf course or links
Viewpoint
PC Public convenience
Picnic site
Pub/s
Cathedral/Abbey
Museum
Castle/fort
Building of historic interest
English Heritage
Garden
Nature reserve
Water activities
Fishing
☆ Other tourist feature

WATER FEATURES

Map of the British Isles

Key

- - - - - - international boundary
———— national boundary
〜〜〜 river
lake
▲ highest point in the UK

towns
■ largest cities
● large cities and towns

Land height
measured in metres above sea level

- more than 1000 m
- 500 – 1000 m
- 200 – 500 m
- 100 – 200 m
- less than 100 m
- land below sea level

Scale
1 : 4 500 000

One centimetre on the map represents 45 kilometres on the ground.

0   45   90   135   180 km

Shetland Islands

Orkney Islands

Cape Wrath

Outer Hebrides

Lewis

Skye

NORTHWEST HIGHLANDS

Mull

Great Glen
Loch Ness
River Spey
CAIRNGORMS
River Dee
Aberdeen

1344m ▲
Ben Nevis

GRAMPIAN MOUNTAINS
R. Tay
Dundee

Loch Lomond
SCOTLAND

Islay
Glasgow
River Clyde
Edinburgh
Firth of Forth
Firth of Clyde

NORTHERN IRELAND

ANTRIM MOUNTAINS
River Bann
Lough Neagh
Belfast

River Erne

SOUTHERN UPLANDS
R. Tweed
CHEVIOT HILLS

UNITED KINGDOM

North Channel

Isle of Man

Newcastle upon Tyne
River Tyne
Sunderland
Stockton-on-Tees
Middlesbrough

North Sea

REPUBLIC OF IRELAND

Lough Corrib

River Shannon

R. Boyne

R. Liffey
Dublin

WICKLOW MOUNTAINS

Barrow River

River Suir

River Blackwater

Cork

NORTH ATLANTIC OCEAN

St George's Channel

Irish Sea

Anglesey

LAKE DISTRICT
River Eden
PENNINES
River Tees
NORTH YORK MOORS
River Ouse

Blackpool
Preston
Bradford
Leeds
Kingston-upon-Hull
Huddersfield
River Aire
Bolton
Manchester
Stockport
Sheffield
River Humber
Liverpool
Warrington
River Mersey

ENGLAND

R. Dee
Stoke-on-Trent
Derby
Nottingham
R. Trent
The Wash

CAMBRIAN MOUNTAINS

Cardigan Bay

Telford
Wolverhampton
Dudley
Walsall
Birmingham
Solihull
Coventry
Leicester
Northampton
THE FENS
Peterborough
R. Wensum
Norwich

WALES

River Teifi

River Tywi
BRECON BEACONS
River Usk
R. Wye
R. Severn
River Avon
COTSWOLD HILLS
R. Great Ouse
Milton Keynes
R. Stour
Ipswich
CHILTERN HILLS
Luton
Basildon
Southend-on-Sea

Swansea
Cardiff
Newport
R. Thames
Reading
London

Bristol Channel
Bristol
SALISBURY PLAIN
NORTH DOWNS
Strait of Dover

NORTH ATLANTIC OCEAN

EXMOOR
R. Exe
Southampton
Bournemouth
Poole
Portsmouth
Isle of Wight
SOUTH DOWNS
Brighton

DARTMOOR
Plymouth
Torbay

Isles of Scilly
Land's End

English Channel

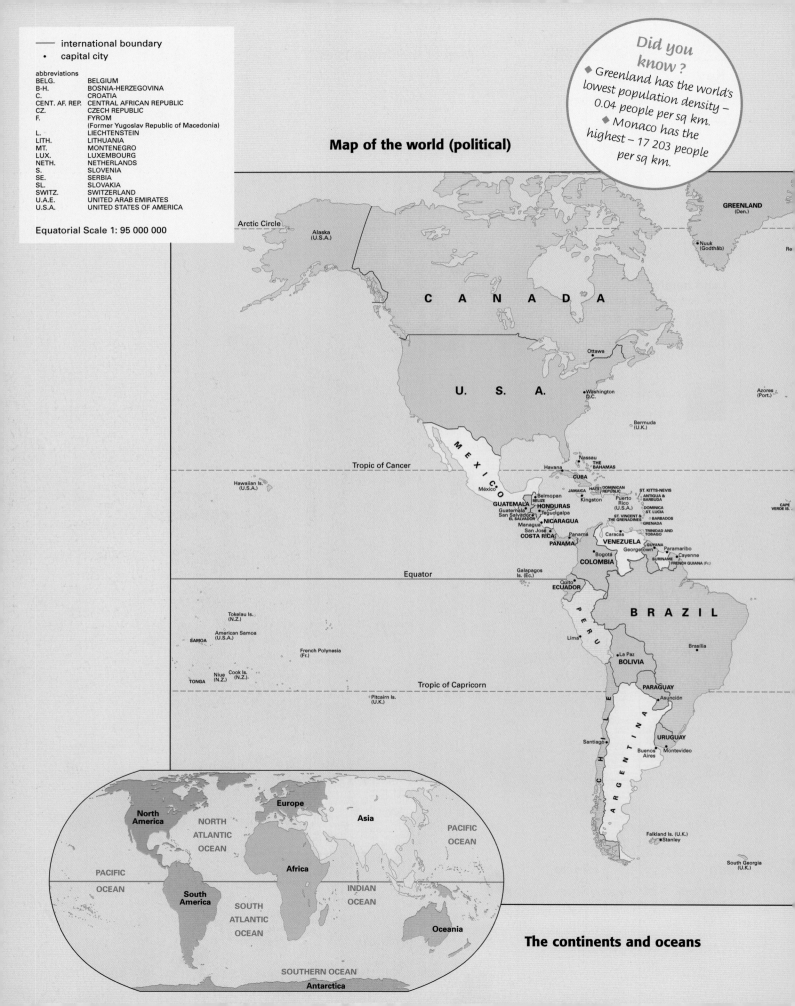

Map of the world (political)

The continents and oceans

Population of the world's continents		The world's top five languages	
◆ Asia	3.92 billion		(speakers)
◆ Africa	0.90 billion	◆ Chinese (Mandarin)	over 1 billion
◆ Europe	0.72 billion	◆ English	512 million
◆ N America	0.48 billion	◆ Hindi	498 million
◆ S America	0.35 billion	◆ Spanish	391 million
◆ Oceania	0.03 billion	◆ Arabic	245 milion

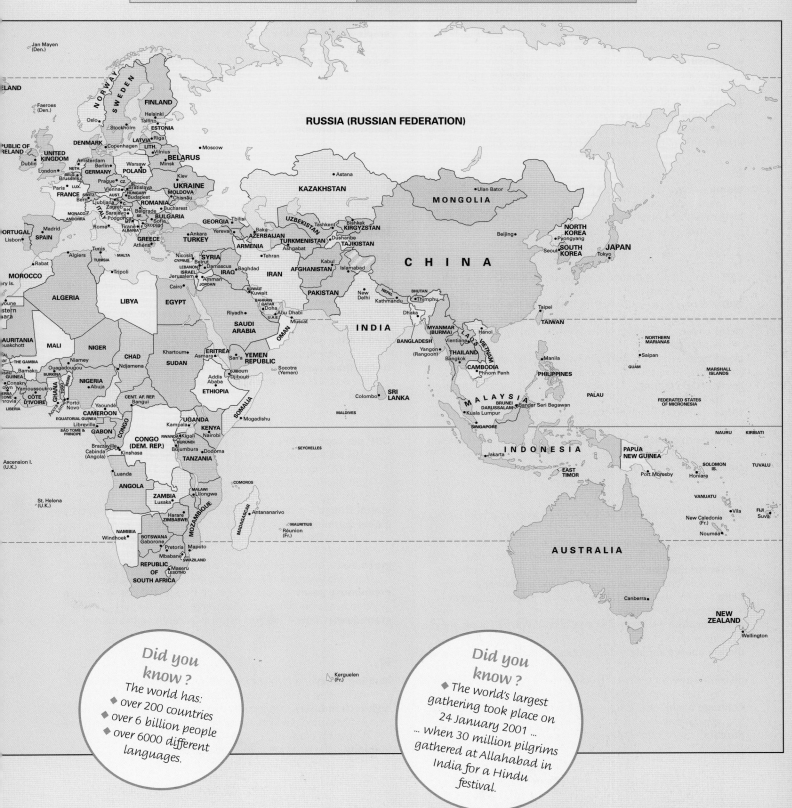

Did you know?
The world has:
◆ over 200 countries
◆ over 6 billion people
◆ over 6000 different languages.

Did you know?
◆ The world's largest gathering took place on 24 January 2001 … … when 30 million pilgrims gathered at Allahabad in India for a Hindu festival.

Glossary

A

abrasion – the scratching and scraping of a river bed and banks by the stones and sand in the river

agribusiness – large-scale capital-intensive farming

agri-environment scheme – schemes which combine farming with looking after, and improving, the environment, such as Tir Gofal in Wales and Environmental Stewardship in England

air pressure – the weight of air pressing down on the Earth's surface. Low pressure means warm air is rising, so rain is on the way. (The rising air cools and its water vapour condenses.)

altitude – the height of the land above sea level

appropriate technology – meets the needs of local people and the environment they live in

arête – a sharp ridge between two corries (see corrie)

B

biome – a very large ecosystem. The rainforests are one biome. Hot deserts are another

birth rate – the number of live births in a country in a year, per 1000 people

C

CAP – Common Agricultural Policy set up by the EU and which subsidised farmers

CBD – central business district. It's the area at the centre of a town or city where you find the main shops and offices

cloud cover – how much of the sky is hidden by cloud. It is given in eighths (oktas).

cloud type – there are five main types of cloud: stratus, cumulus, nimbus, cumulonimbus and cirrus

commercial farming – outputs from the farm are sold to make a profit

corrie – a circular, armchair-shaped hollow cut into rock by ice during glaciation

counter-urbanisation – the movement of people out of cities to smaller towns and villages

crevasse – a vertical or wedge-shaped crack in a glacier

D

death rate – the number of deaths in a country in a year, per 1000 people

deforestation – clearing forest for another use. For example cutting down rainforest to make way for a motorway or cattle ranches

deindustrialisation – the decline in manufacturing (secondary) industry, and the growth in tertiary and quaternary industry

delta – a flat area at the mouth of a river, made of sediment deposited by the river

desertification – when soil in a savanna region gets worn out, dusty and useless

dietary energy supply – the number of calories per person available each day

distributaries – if sediment blocks a river it has to divide into small channels called distributaries

drainage basin – the land around a river, from which water drains into the river

drumlin – a smooth hill shaped by glaciers

E

economic migrants – people who move voluntarily for jobs and higher wages

ecosystem – a unit made up of living things and their non-living environment. For example a pond, a forest, a desert

employment structure – what % of workers are in the primary, secondary and tertiary sectors of the economy

esker – a long ridge of material deposited from streams flowing under glaciers

estuary – the mouth of a large river, which is affected by the tides. As the tide rises, sea water flows up into the estuary and mixes with the river water

extensive farming – has smaller inputs of labour, money or technology than intensive farming. Extensive farms are usually larger than intensive farms

F

factors – things which affect where industry, agriculture, settlements etc will locate

feedback – things are put back into the system – like profits which may be reinvested

fertility rate – the number of children, on average, a woman will have in her lifetime

floodplain – flat land around a river that gets flooded when the river overflows

footloose – an industry which is not tied to raw materials and so can choose where to locate

free trade – when goods and services can flow freely from country to country, without any taxes

freeze-thaw weathering – the weathering (breakdown) of rock by the action of water getting into cracks in the rock, freezing and thawing

G

GDP per capita (PPP) – GDP is gross domestic product. It is the total value of the goods and services produced in a country in a year. GDP per capita means the GDP divided by the population. PPP means purchasing power parity. GDP is adjusted because a dollar buys more in some countries than others

glacial trough – a steep-sided U-shaped valley caused by glaciers

global warming – the way temperatures around the world are rising. Scientists think we have made this happen by burning too much fossil fuel

green belt – an area of open land around a city, which is protected from development. This is to stop the city spreading further

greenhouse gases – gases like carbon dioxide and methane that trap heat around the Earth, leading to global warming

groundwater flow – the flow of groundwater through saturated rock or soil

H

hanging valley – a high-level tributary valley with a sharp fall to the main valley; a feature of glacial erosion

high-tech industry – an industry that develops and produces new and advanced products. For example new kinds of mobile phones or medical drugs

humidity – the % of water vapour in the air

I

impermeable – doesn't let water through

infant mortality – the number of babies out of every 1000 born alive, who die before their first birthday

infiltration – the soaking of rainwater into the ground

inputs – things that go into a system. They can be physical, or human and economic.

intensive farming – has large inputs of labour, money or technology to produce high outputs. Farms are usually quite small

interception – the capture of rainwater by leaves. Some evaporates again and the rest trickles to the ground

interlocking spurs – hills that stick out on alternate sides of a V-shaped valley like the teeth of a zip

irrigation – artificial watering of land and crops

K

kame – a mound or heap of material dropped from a glacier

L

latitude – distance north or south of the equator, expressed in degrees and minutes (for example, 51° 5′ North). Lines of latitude are imaginary circles drawn round the Earth parallel to the equator

levees – embankments built up on either side of a river channel

life expectancy – how many years a new baby can expect to live, on average. Life expectancy is higher for females than for males

M

materialism – wanting only belongings or comfort, and having no interest in morals

meander – a bend in a river

Mediterranean climate – a climate type that has hot dry summers and warm wet winters, named after the climate conditions found around the Mediterranean Sea

melt-water – the water produced when snow or ice melts. Glacial melt-water is produced by melting at the surface of the glacier and by pressure at the base of the glacier

misfit stream – a small stream in the bottom of glacial trough

moraine – material carried by a glacier

mouth – the end point of a river, where it enters the sea or a lake

N

natural increase – the birth rate minus the death rate for a place. It is always given as a % of the total population

NGO – non-governmental organisation. NGOs work to make life better, especially for the poor. Oxfam, the Red Cross and Greenpeace are all NGOs

O

ocean current – the movement of warm or cold ocean water, to a depth of about 100 metres. Cold ocean currents start in polar regions, warm ocean currents start in tropical waters

outputs – things that come out of the system (products)

oxbow lake – a lake formed when a loop in a river is cut off by floods

P

percolation – the movement of water downwards through rock

plucking – when ice freezes on to rock, moves, and so plucks the rock away

population density – the average number of people per square kilometre

population growth rate – the number of people added to a population each year due to natural increase and net migration. It is given as a %

porous – lets water soak through

precipitation – water falling from the sky. It could fall as rain, hail, sleet or snow

prevailing wind – the one that blows most often; for the British Isles it's the south-west wind (blowing from the south-west)

primary industry – people extract raw materials from the land or sea. For example farming, fishing and mining

processes – things that happen in the middle of the system to turn inputs into outputs

pyramidal peak – the peak formed when three or more corries form round a mountain (see corrie)

Q

quaternary industry – people are employed in industries providing information and expert help. For example IT consultants and researchers

quota – a limit on the amount of goods produced or purchased

R

refugee – a person who is forced to flee from danger (for example war or an earthquake) and seek refuge in another country

river channel – the bed and sides of a river form a river channel

river terraces – areas of flatter land above the floodplain

rural-urban fringe – the area where a town or city meets the countryside

S

secondary industry – people make, or manufacture, things. For example turning iron ore into steel, making cars and building houses

self-help scheme – a project or activity that helps people to help themselves; this term is often used about small-scale development schemes in LEDCs

set-aside land – land which isn't used for growing crops or keeping animals on; farmers are paid for this

source – the starting point of a river

sphere of influence – area around a settlement (or shop, or other service) where its effect is felt. London has a very large sphere of influence

SPS – Single Payment System, part of the CAP reform. Farmers now get one single payment a year instead of several different subsidy payments

striation – scratches in rock caused by abrasion in a glacier

subsistence farming – where farmers grow food to feed their families, rather than to sell

sunshine – in the study of weather and climate, sunshine is measured in hours

surface run-off – rainwater that runs across the surface of the ground and drains into the river

sustainable – can be carried on without doing any harm (to people, or other living things, or the environment)

sustainable development – development that will not lower our quality of life or harm the environment

sustainable management – meeting the needs of people now and in the future, and limiting harm to the environment

system – has inputs, processes and outputs. Industry and agriculture can be described as systems

T

tariff – a tax that a country places on goods being imported or exported

temperature – how hot or cold something is, usually measured in degrees Centigrade

tertiary industry – people are employed in providing a service. For example the health service (doctors, nurses, dentists) and education (teachers)

through-flow – the flow of rainwater sideways through the soil, towards the river

till – jumbled, unsorted material dropped by glaciers

trade balance – the difference between the value of imports and exports of a country

trade deficit – a country spends more on imports than it earns from exports

trade surplus – a country earns more money from exports than it spends on imports

trading bloc – a group of countries that have joined together to improve trade

TNC (transnational corporation) – a company with branches in many countries

tributary – a smaller river flowing into a larger river

truncated spurs – where a glacier has eroded and cut off interlocking spurs

tundra – the cold, treeless plains of northern Canada, Alaska, northern Europe and northern Russia

U

urban model – a simplified diagram of the way land is used in a city

urban redevelopment – clearance and rebuilding of old inner city areas

urban renewal – improving (without knocking down and clearing) old inner city areas

urban zones – areas of different land use in an urban area

urbanisation – an increase in the percentage of people living in towns and cities

U-shaped valley – see glacial trough

V

visibility – the greatest distance you can see, in kilometres or metres. On a foggy day it could be just 1 or 2 metres

V-shaped valley – a valley shaped like the letter V, carved out by a river

W

waterfall – where a river or stream flows over a steep drop

watershed – an imaginary line separating one drainage basin from the next

wind direction – the direction the wind blows from

wind strength (speed) – how fast the wind blows

World Trade Organisation – a body set up to help trade between countries

Index